Ageing Population Risks

Special Issue Editor
Pavel Shevchenko

MDPI • Basel • Beijing • Wuhan • Barcelona • Belgrade

Special Issue Editor
Pavel Shevchenko
Macquarie University
Australia

Editorial Office
MDPI
St. Alban-Anlage 66
Basel, Switzerland

This edition is a reprint of the Special Issue published online in the open access journal *Risks* (ISSN 2227-9091) from 2016–2018 (available at: http://www.mdpi.com/journal/risks/special_issues/ageing_population).

For citation purposes, cite each article independently as indicated on the article page online and as indicated below:

Lastname, F.M.; Lastname, F.M. Article title. *Journal Name* **Year**, *Article number*, page range.

First Editon 2018

ISBN 978-3-03842-824-4 (Pbk)
ISBN 978-3-03842-823-7 (PDF)

Table of Contents

About the Special Issue Editor

Pavel Shevchenko is a Professor of Applied Finance and Actuarial Studies at Macquarie University since 2016. He is also a Director of the Risk Analytics Lab and Co-Director of the Centre for Financial Risk at Macquarie University since 2017. Prior to joining Macquarie University, Prof Shevchenko worked at CSIRO Australia (1999–2016), holding a position of Senior Principal Research Scientist (2012–2016). Since 1999, Prof Shevchenko has worked in the area of financial risk, leading research and industry commercial projects on: modelling of operational and credit risks; longevity and mortality, retirement income products; option pricing; insurance; modelling commodities and foreign exchange; and the development of relevant numerical methods and software. He received a MSc from the Moscow Institute of Physics and Technology (1994) and a PhD from The University of New South Wales (1999). Prof Shevchenko publication records include three monographs, over 60 journal papers and over 80 technical reports.

risks MDPI

Editorial

Special Issue "Ageing Population Risks"

Pavel V. Shevchenko

Department of Applied Finance and Actuarial Studies, Macquarie University, Sydney, NSW 2109, Australia; pavel.shevchenko@mq.edu.au; Tel.: +61-2-9850-8492

Received: 27 February 2018; Accepted: 1 March 2018; Published: 5 March 2018

An ageing population is a major challenge for every country in the world arising from the declining fertility rate and increasing life expectancy. A longevity risk (the adverse outcome of people living longer than expected) exacerbated by declining equity returns coupled with the record low interest rate environments has significant implications for societies and manifests as a systematic risk for providers of retirement income products. The aim of this special issue is to highlight advances in quantitative modelling of risks related to ageing population problems. We received an enthusiastic response to the call for research papers and are proud of the special issue now being published. This special issue contains seven research papers.

One paper by Marcos Escobar, Mikhail Krayzler, Franz Ramsauer, David Saunders, and Rudi Zagst (Escobar et al. 2016) presents the pricing of variable annuities with guaranteed minimum repayments at maturity and in the case of policyholder death using a closed form approximation. All important risk factors (risky investment asset, interest rate, mortality intensity, and policyholder surrender behaviour) are modelled under an affine linear stochastic framework. The presented pricing framework can be easily implemented, which is important for applications in practice.

There are four papers studying and developing advanced stochastic mortality models.

The paper by Syazreen Shair, Sachi Purcal, and Nick Parr (Shair et al. 2017) evaluates the forecasting accuracy of two recently-developed coherent mortality models (the Poisson common factor and the product-ratio functional models) designed to forecast the mortality of two or more subpopulations simultaneously. The models are applied to age-gender-specific mortality data for Australia and Malaysia and age-gender-ethnicity-specific data for Malaysia, and the results show that coherent models are consistently more accurate than independent models for forecasting sub-populations' mortality.

The paper by Yuan Gao and Han Lin Shang (Gao and Shang 2017) develops a model for the forecasting of mortality rates in multiple populations that combines mortality forecasting and functional data analysis. The model relies on functional principal component analysis for dimension reduction and a vector error correction model to jointly forecast mortality rates in multiple populations. The usefulness of this model is demonstrated through a series of simulation studies and applications to the age-and sex-specific mortality rates in Switzerland and the Czech Republic.

The paper by Jonas Hirz, Uwe Schmock, and Pavel Shevchenko (Hirz et al. 2017) introduces an additive stochastic mortality model which allows joint modelling and forecasting of underlying death causes. The model takes its roots from the extended version of the credit risk model CreditRisk+ that allows exact risk aggregation via an efficient numerically stable Panjer recursion algorithm and provides numerous applications in credit, life insurance, and annuity portfolios to derive profit and loss distributions. Many examples, including an application to partial internal models under Solvency II, using Austrian and Australian data are shown.

The paper by Dorota Toczydlowska, Gareth Peters, Man Chung Fung, and Pavel Shevchenko (Toczydlowska et al. 2017) develops a multi-factor extension of the family of Lee-Carter stochastic mortality models to include exogenous observable demographic features that can be used as additional factors to improve model fit and forecasting accuracy. They develop a dimension reduction robust feature extraction framework amenable to different structures of demographic data. A detailed case study on the Human Mortality Database demographic data from European countries is performed, where the extracted features are used to better explain the term structure of mortality in the UK over time for male and female populations.

Two papers consider optimal decisions in retirement under the expected utility maximisation models solved as optimal stochastic control problems.

The paper by Jinhui Zhang, Sachi Purcal, and Jiaqin Wei (Zhang et al. 2017) considers the financial planning for a retiree wishing to enter a retirement village. The date of entry is determined by the retiree's utility and bequest maximisation problem within the context of uncertain future health states. In addition, the retiree must choose optimal consumption, investment, bequest, and purchase of insurance products prior to full annuitisation on entry to the retirement village.

The paper by Johan Andréasson and Pavel Shevchenko (Andréasson and Shevchenko 2017) considers the impact of recent changes to the Australian means-tested Age Pension policies. They examine the implications of the new changes in regard to the optimal decisions of a retiree for consumption, investment, and housing. The policy changes are considered under a utility-maximising lifecycle model solved as an optimal stochastic control problem.

All papers appearing in this special issue went through a refereeing process subject to the usual high standards of *Risks*. We would like to thank all of the authors for their excellent contributions and all of the referees for thorough and timely reviews. We hope that this special issue will help to stimulate advanced quantitative modelling, both theoretical and applied in the area of ageing population problems.

Conflicts of Interest: The author declares no conflicts of interest.

References

Andréasson, Johan, and Pavel Shevchenko. 2017. Assessment of Policy Changes to Means-Tested Age Pension Using the Expected Utility Model: Implication for Decisions in Retirement. *Risks* 5: 47. [CrossRef]

Escobar, Marcos, Mikhail Krayzler, Franz Ramsauer, David Saunders, and Rudi Zagst. 2016. Incorporation of Stochastic Policyholder Behavior in Analytical Pricing of GMABs and GMDBs. *Risks* 4: 41. [CrossRef]

Gao, Yuan, and Han Lin Shang. 2017. Multivariate Functional Time Series Forecasting: Application to Age-Specific Mortality Rates. *Risks* 5: 21. [CrossRef]

Hirz, Jonas, Uwe Schmock, and Pavel V. Shevchenko. 2017. Actuarial Applications and Estimation of Extended CreditRisk+. *Risks* 5: 23. [CrossRef]

Shair, Syazreen, Sachi Purcal, and Nick Parr. 2017. Evaluating Extensions to Coherent Mortality Forecasting Models. *Risks* 5: 16. [CrossRef]

Toczydlowska, Dorota, Gareth W. Peters, Man Chung Fung, and Pavel V. Shevchenko. 2017. Stochastic Period and Cohort Effect State-Space Mortality Models Incorporating Demographic Factors via Probabilistic Robust Principal Components. *Risks* 5: 42. [CrossRef]

Zhang, Jinhui, Sachi Purcal, and Jiaqin Wei. 2017. Optimal Time to Enter a Retirement Village. *Risks* 5: 20. [CrossRef] risks

MDPI

Article

Incorporation of Stochastic Policyholder Behavior in Analytical Pricing of GMABs and GMDBs

Marcos Escobar [1], Mikhail Krayzler [2], Franz Ramsauer [3,*], David Saunders [4] and Rudi Zagst [3]

1 Department of Statistical and Actuarial Sciences, Western University, 1151 Richmond Street, London, ON N6A 5B7, Canada; marcos.escobar@uwo.ca
2 risklab GmbH, Allianz Global Investors, Seidlstraße 24-24a, 80335 Munich, Germany; mikhail.krayzler@allianzgi.com
3 Chair of Mathematical Finance, Technical University of Munich, Parkring 11, 85748 Garching-Hochbrück, Germany; zagst@tum.de
4 Department of Statistics and Actuarial Science, University of Waterloo, 200 University Avenue West, Waterloo, ON N2L 3G1, Canada; dsaunders@uwaterloo.ca
* Correspondence: franz.ramsauer@tum.de; Tel.: +49-89-289-17417; Fax: +49-89-289-17407

Academic Editor: Pavel Shevchenko
Received: 5 September 2016; Accepted: 1 November 2016; Published: 8 November 2016

Abstract: Variable annuities represent certain unit-linked life insurance products offering different types of protection commonly referred to as guaranteed minimum benefits (GMXBs). They are designed for the increasing demand of the customers for private pension provision. In this paper we analytically price variable annuities with guaranteed minimum repayments at maturity and in case of the insured's death. If the contract is prematurely surrendered, the policyholder is entitled to the current value of the fund account reduced by the prevailing surrender fee. The financial market and the mortality model are affine linear. For the surrender model, a Cox process is deployed whose intensity is given by a deterministic function (s-curve) with stochastic inputs from the financial market. So, the policyholders' surrender behavior depends on the performance of the financial market and is stochastic. The presented pricing scheme incorporates the stochastic surrender behavior of the policyholders and is only based on suitable closed-form approximations.

Keywords: variable annuities; surrender behavior; closed-form approximation; pricing; affine linear model

1. Introduction

Variable annuity (VA) contracts represent a *"wide range of life insurance products, whose benefits can be protected against investment and mortality risks by selecting one or more guarantees"* Bacinello *et al.* (2011). Since VAs are usually unit-linked, they allow policyholders to participate in rising stock prices while their guarantees offer protection against the reverse trend. For further reading on VAs and implicit options embedded in general life insurance products, see Ledlie *et al.* (2008); Gatzert (2010); Shevchenko and Luo (2016). In contrast to the policyholders, for VA providers the GMXBs that are offered may cause severe financial and actuarial risks: First, the minimum benefits could expire in-the-money, i.e., worth more than the corresponding position in stocks. Second, there might be a difference between the expected and the realized mortality rates.

Furthermore, VA providers are also exposed to behavioral risk, which in this context is often referred to as surrender or lapse risk. This is the risk that the policyholders cancel their contracts in a manner different from the assumptions made by the VA provider. Longevity risk can be modeled independently from financial risk, whereas surrender risk substantially depends on the evolution of the financial markets. For example, increasing interest rates might lead to increasing cancellation rates, as alternative investment products with a higher guaranteed rate or at a cheaper price will appear.

Modeling policyholder risk should deserve special attention, as "it has influence on the pricing of the options and guarantees within the contracts, on solvency capital requirements, and hedging effectiveness" Knoller *et al.* (2015). High losses have been reported by VA carriers due to changes in surrender assumptions (Mountain Life reported an increase in the value of its liabilities by USD 48 bn due to a reduction of assumed surrender rates[1]). Policyholder risk is not hedgeable, might lead to severe liquidity problems, and, therefore, needs to be analyzed and priced carefully. In this paper we focus on this type of risk; we do not claim to find the precise relationship between surrender rates and economic factors (internal or external), but rather show how the well-known patterns can be included in the pricing framework suggested by Krayzler *et al.* (2016). Furthermore, as opposed to the work of Krayzler *et al.* (2016), the market price of mortality risk is explicitly taken into account.

In the last decade, several empirical studies appeared analyzing the main drivers of policy cancellations. From the perspective of a classical life insurance business, two major hypotheses can be differentiated: the *interest-rate hypothesis* and the *emergency fund hypothesis*. The first one, advanced by, e.g., Tsai *et al.* (2002); Kuo *et al.* (2003) (especially in the long run), assumes that an increase in interest rates leads to an increase in surrender rates. This is explainable by the fact that higher interest rates generally lead to higher annuity rates within other similar decumulation products and, hence, policyholders have an incentive to cancel their existing VA and enter a new one. In the VA business, high interest rates lead to either higher guaranteed benefits for the same guarantee price or to the same guaranteed benefits but for lower prices. The second hypothesis, empirically supported, e.g., by Outreville (1990), assumes that policyholders might need to terminate their life or pension insurances due to a personal financial distress. To model this dependency, most of the papers use macroeconomic risk factors assuming that the general state of the economy serves as a proxy for personal financial circumstances. Some of the papers support both hypotheses, see, e.g., Kim (2005) for an analysis of the Korean case or Jiang (2010) for the U.S. life insurance market.

As variable annuities depend on the performance of financial markets, apart from the interest-rate and the emergency fund hypotheses driving policyholder behavior within traditional life insurance business, the so-called *moneyness hypothesis* has been the focus of several recent studies. This concept relies on the fact that the value of the guarantee (approximated by the moneyness defined as the ratio of the surrender to the guaranteed value) should have a substantial impact on policyholders' decisions. That is, the better the performance of a fund underlying the VA product, the higher the moneyness of the contract and, consequently, the lower the economic value of the guarantee. Therefore, there is a significant incentive for the insured person to cancel the contract and potentially enter a new one with a higher guaranteed value. Empirical evidence for this hypothesis is given, for example, in Knoller *et al.* (2015); Kiesenbauer (2012). The former paper also tests and supports interest-rate and emergency fund hypotheses in the context of variable annuities. According to the company surveys conducted by Knoller *et al.* (2015); Kent and Ed (2008) as well as shown in some examples of Tsai *et al.* (2002), policyholders do not always act rationally. They cancel their products even when it is not economically rational[2] and also do not surrender their guarantees deep out of the money.

Additionally, there is abundant literature on the incorporation of lapse behavior in pricing models. We provide here just a short overview of the main papers in that area and refer interested readers to Eling and Kiesenbauer (2012) for a broad classification of lapse rate models. According to their work, one can differentiate between three major groups of papers depending on the assumptions made on the policyholder rationality.

First, pure dynamic surrender models assume optimal cancellation for risk-neutral investors (Bacinello 2003 2005; Milevsky and Salisbury 2006; Chen *et al.* 2008; Kling *et al.* 2011). These

1 Source: White Mountain Insurance Group Report 2010. In this case the expected number of policyholders entitled to the final payoff increases and therefore, the present value of liabilities rises as well.

2 This is more or less a general assessment. Cancellation could be rational and utility-maximizing for specific policyholders, however, these personal reasons for cancellation are not included in the model.

authors interpret the surrender option as an American option and provide numerical solutions for optimal stopping problems to determine its price. The second group of papers assumes optimal dynamic lapsation for rational and risk-averse investors (Moore 2009; Moenig and Bauer 2015). The authors assume that policyholders maximize their expected utility, which is modeled via a constant relative risk aversion (CRRA) function. The third group of papers eschews the assumption of optimal policyholder behavior and rather tries to incorporate the above mentioned empirical evidence in dynamic lapse modeling. Examples of these papers include Ledlie *et al.* (2008); Albizzati and Geman (1994); Mudavanhu and Zhuo (2002); Kolkiewicz and Tan (2006); De Giovanni (2010); Loisel and Milhaud (2011).

Our work also belongs to the third group of papers. The contributions to the literature are as follows. First, instead of the stand-alone consideration of different stylized facts, we explicitly incorporate the moneyness and interest-rate hypotheses in our hybrid pricing framework at the same time; Second, we include the emergency fund hypothesis in the model; Finally, we derive analytical approximations for the selected guarantees under financial, actuarial, and behavioral risks. In this paper we concentrate on Guaranteed Minimum Accumulation, Death, and Surrender Benefits. Extension of the suggested approach for the pricing of other variable annuity products constitutes one of the directions of future research.

The remainder of the paper is structured as follows: The second section describes the stochastic models for the financial market, the insureds' mortality, and the policyholders' surrender behavior. The third section specifies the considered type of VAs and derives the closed-form approximations. The fourth section shows how the models of the second section can be calibrated using actively traded products and historical mortality tables. The fifth section presents an example of the pricing scheme. The sixth section discusses extensions to the surrender model. The seventh section provides conclusions and possible directions for future research.

2. Stochastic Models

2.1. Financial Market Model

Let $(\Omega, \mathcal{F}, \mathbb{F}, \mathbb{Q})$ be a filtered probability space with risk-neutral pricing measure $\mathbb{Q}$ and filtration $\mathbb{F} := (\mathcal{F}_t)_{t\geq 0}$ satisfying the usual conditions, i.e., the filtration is right-continuous and $\mathcal{F}_0$ is saturated. Furthermore, let the instantaneous interest-rate process $r := (r(t))_{t\geq 0}$ and the stock price process $S := (S(t))_{t\geq 0}$ be given by the Hull-White extended Vasicek model Hull and White (1994) and a generalized geometric Brownian motion with stochastic drift r. For any point in time $t \geq 0$ the stochastic process $Y := (Y(t))_{t\geq 0}$ defined by $Y(t) := \ln(S(t)/S(0))$ represents the accumulated log-return up to t. If the constant $\rho_{Sr} \in [-1; 1]$ denotes the correlation between the Brownian motions of the processes r and S, we end up with the following risk-neutral financial market:

$$
\begin{aligned}
\mathrm{d}r(t) &= (\theta_r(t) - a_r r(t))\,\mathrm{d}t + \sigma_r \mathrm{d}W_r^{\mathbb{Q}}(t),\\
\mathrm{d}Y(t) &= \left(r(t) - \frac{1}{2}\sigma_S^2(t)\right)\mathrm{d}t + \sigma_S(t)\,\mathrm{d}W_S^{\mathbb{Q}}(t),\\
r(0) &= r_0,\; Y(0) = 0,\; \mathrm{d}W_S^{\mathbb{Q}}(t)\,\mathrm{d}W_r^{\mathbb{Q}}(t) = \rho_{Sr}\mathrm{d}t.
\end{aligned}
\tag{1}
$$

To derive the closed-form approximation in Section 3.2 a_r and σ_r are assumed to be non-negative constants, while $\theta_r(t), t \geq 0$, and $\sigma_S(t), t \geq 0$, are supposed to be deterministic functions in time. However, future research might focus on extensions such that $\theta_r(t)$ or $\sigma_S(t)$ can be stochastic processes. $W_r^{\mathbb{Q}}(t)$ and $W_S^{\mathbb{Q}}(t)$ represent standard $\mathbb{Q}$-Brownian motions.

2.2. Mortality Model

Historical data normally confirm the assumption of an exponential relation between age and one-year death probabilities. For instance, see the plot on the left in Figure 1 illustrating the United

Kingdom (U.K.) mortality tables (principal projection, men, 1951–2011)[3] published by the Office for National Statistics. Furthermore, life expectancy is increasing. If we focus on how the U.K. one-year death probability for a fixed age has evolved over time (see the plot on the right in Figure 1), the decline underpins this assertion. But, the second plot of Figure 1 also indicates that there are random fluctuations partially resisting an enduring downturn. To take into account all findings we apply the mortality model described in Krayzler *et al.* (2016) which is based on Dahl (2004); Dahl and Møller (2006). We assume an upper limit in age T^* (e.g., 125 years) and model under the real-world measure $\mathbb{P}$ the remaining lifetime $\tau^m(x)$ of an insured aged x years in the form of the first jump of a Cox process $(N^m(x+t))_{t\geq 0}$ characterized by a $\mathbb{F}$-measurable intensity $\lambda_t^m(x+t), t\geq 0$ (Biffis 2005):

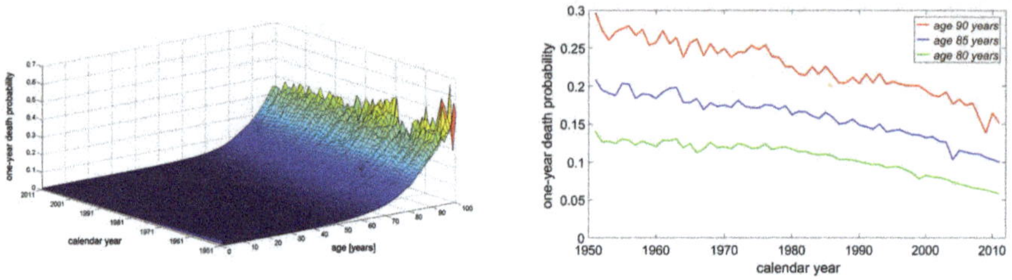

(a) (b)

Figure 1. U.K. Mortality Tables (**a**) and One-Year Death Probabilities (**b**) of Men (1951–2011).

$$\tau^m(x) := \min\left(T^* - x, \inf\{t \geq 0 : N^m(x+t) > 0\}\right).$$

The index m refers to *mortality*. Furthermore, we define:

$$\mathbb{H}^m := (\mathcal{H}_t^m)_{t\in[0,T^*-x]}, \; \mathcal{H}_t^m := \sigma\left(\mathbb{1}_{\{\tau^m(x)\leq u\}} : u \leq t\right).$$

Hence, $\mathbb{H}^m$ captures whether the insured is still alive or has already died up to a certain point in time.

Let the initial mortality intensity $\lambda_0^m(x+t)$ be given by the static Gompertz model and let an Ornstein-Uhlenbeck process $\xi := (\xi(t))_{t\geq 0}$ describe the evolution of the $\mathbb{P}$-dynamics of the mortality improvement ratio. Then, we get for the mortality model under $\mathbb{P}$:

$$\begin{aligned}
\lambda_t^m(x+t) &= \lambda_0^m(x+t)\cdot\xi(t),\\
\lambda_0^m(x+t) &= \frac{1}{b}\exp\left(\frac{x+t-z}{b}\right),\\
\mathrm{d}\xi(t) &= \kappa\left(\exp(-\gamma t) - \xi(t)\right)\mathrm{d}t + \sigma_\xi \mathrm{d}W_\xi^{\mathbb{P}}(t).
\end{aligned}$$

The constants z, κ and σ_ξ are non-negative, b is positive and $\gamma \in \mathbb{R}$. A positive γ indicates that people are growing older on average, whereas a negative γ implies the opposite. For $\gamma = 0$ the mortality improvement ratio is fluctuating close to 1 and hence, there are no trends. In this paper the mortality improvement ratio ξ does not depend on the age x of an insured, since it is supposed to reflect a general improvement in mortality. The correlations between $W_\xi^{\mathbb{P}}(t)$ and the $\mathbb{P}$-Brownian motions of the financial market, are assumed to be zero implying the independence of the

---

[3] For the underlying data set see http://www.ons.gov.uk/ons/rel/lifetables/historic-and-projected-mortality-data-from-the-uk-life-tables/2010-based/rft-qx-principal.xls

insurance and the financial processes. Subsequent measure changes are designed such that this feature is preserved. Using Itô's Lemma we obtain the $\mathbb{P}$-dynamics of the overall mortality intensity:

$$\mathrm{d}\lambda_t^m(x+t) = \left(c_1 \exp(c_2 t) - c_3 \lambda_t^m(x+t)\right)\mathrm{d}t + c_4 \exp(c_5 t)\,\mathrm{d}W_\xi^{\mathbb{P}}(t), \tag{2}$$

with

$$c_1 := \frac{\kappa}{b}\exp\left(\frac{x-z}{b}\right),\ c_2 := \frac{1}{b} - \gamma,\ c_3 := \kappa - \frac{1}{b},\ c_4 := \frac{\sigma_\xi}{b}\exp\left(\frac{x-z}{b}\right),\ c_5 := \frac{1}{b}.$$

Mortality has been modeled under the real-world measure $\mathbb{P}$ so far. However, risk-neutral pricing techniques require probabilities with respect to the risk-neutral measure $\mathbb{Q}$ of the financial market. A lack of transparency, the relatively small number of (variable) annuity providers (supply) compared to the multitude of policyholders (demand) and the informational asymmetry between both parties cause us to reject the assumption of an efficient market for mortality risk (Harrison 2012). Except for extremely competitive business segments, VA providers should be able to implicitly charge an additional premium for taking longevity and other actuarial risks. On the assumption that all actuarial risks are already taken into account in the form of the mortality tables entering the calibration of the real-world mortality model in (2), the work in Krayzler *et al.* (2016) assumes that the $\mathbb{P}-$ and $\mathbb{Q}-$survival probabilities coincide. Since this assumption is quite strong, we work with a market price of mortality risk that is permitted to be zero to gain flexibility. Whenever the existence of the market price of mortality risk is difficult to accept as valid, the risk premium can be set to zero to end up in the setting of Krayzler *et al.* (2016). If there are good reasons for the existence of a mortality risk premium, which has not yet been covered by the mortality tables themselves, our approach allows its estimation. Furthermore, we are able to analyze how a mortality risk premium affects the $\mathbb{Q}$-survival probabilities (sensitivity tests). To keep our mortality model analytically tractable, in particular, to preserve the independence of the insurance and the financial market, we consider a constant market price of mortality risk γ_m. However, alternative risk premium models like in Biffis *et al.* (2010) should be part of future research. In our setting, the Radon-Nikodym density defined by:

$$\left.\frac{\mathrm{d}\mathbb{Q}}{\mathrm{d}\mathbb{P}}\right|_{\mathcal{F}_t \vee \mathcal{H}_t^m} = \exp\left(-\gamma_m W_\xi^{\mathbb{P}}(t) - \frac{1}{2}\gamma_m^2 t\right),$$

$$W_\xi^{\mathbb{Q}}(t) = W_\xi^{\mathbb{P}}(t) + \gamma_m t,$$

and the Girsanov theorem provide[4]:

$$\mathrm{d}\lambda_t^m(x+t) = \left(c_1 \exp(c_2 t) - c_3 \lambda_t^m(x+t) - c_4 \gamma_m \exp(c_5 t)\right)\mathrm{d}t + c_4 \exp(c_5 t)\,\mathrm{d}W_\xi^{\mathbb{Q}}(t). \tag{3}$$

2.3. Surrender Model

At first, we describe the characteristics of the considered VAs. Thereby, we especially focus on the surrender benefit to model the policyholders' surrender behavior properly. Let $I > 0$ be the initial premium which the policyholder has to pay at once at the beginning when entering into the VA contract with maturity T. Since I is fully invested in a fund or stock, $A(t) := I\exp(Y(t)), t \in [0, T]$, gives the evolution of the fund account value over time. The contract includes a guaranteed minimum accumulation benefit (GMAB). If $\delta \geq 0$ denotes the preliminary agreed (annual) roll-up rate, $G(t) := I\exp(\delta t)$ specifies how the (implicit) value of the guarantee moves over time. The GMAB is

4 In the suggested modeling approach the mortality intensity can become negative with positive probability. This probability can be calculated analytically, see Appendix A.2. However, in practical applications, like for the parameters used in our example (see Section 4), this probability is negligible (less than 10^{-5}).

executable at maturity only. This means that only at maturity the policyholder is allowed to choose between the fund account value and the guarantee. In case of early surrender his right of refund is restricted to the current fund account value reduced by the compulsory surrender fee. From the perspective of the policyholders, the charged surrender fee and the forbidden execution of the GMAB option before maturity reduce the incentives for early surrender. For VA providers the combination of both serves as a perfect hedge, since the repayment to the policyholder is less (in the presence of surrender fees) or equal to the fund account value (when the fee is zero). In case of early surrender let $f : [0,T] \to \mathbb{R}_0^+$ be a non-increasing function of time such that the surrender benefit at t is equal to: $I \exp(Y(t) - f(t))$. If f is properly chosen, we are able to overcome the problem that an insurance company could be unable *"to fully recover its initial expenses"* (Kuo *et al.* 2003) due to (early) surrender. For all $t \in [0,T]$, let $R(t,T)$ be the annual, continuously compounded long-term interest rate at t for the period $[t,T]$. Let $P(t,T)$ be the price of a default-free zero-coupon bond at time t with maturity T. Then, we have that:

$$R(t,T) = -\frac{1}{T-t} \ln(P(t,T)).$$

Apart from their actuarial characteristics VAs are capital market products. This is why it might happen that policyholders behave similar to investors pursuing a long-term investment strategy. If early surrender takes place at time t, the policyholder would be able to reinvest the surrender benefit at $R(t,T)$ for the remaining time to maturity. In this case, the final payoff at maturity would be given by:

$$I \exp(Y(t) - f(t) + R(t,T)(T-t)).$$

In the absence of early surrender, the repayment at maturity is at least $G(T)$, serving as a benchmark for the above long-term strategy. If the stochastic process $D := (D(t))_{t \geq 0}$ is equal to the logarithm of the ratio of both final payoffs, we have that:

$$D(t) = Y(t) - f(t) - \delta T + R(t,T)(T-t).$$

Similar to the mortality model, let the time τ^s until the early surrender option is exercised be equal to the time until the first jump of a Cox process $(N^s(t))_{t \geq 0}$ with intensity $\lambda^s(t)$ defined by:

$$\lambda^s(t) = \beta \max[\min[D(t), \alpha], 0] + C, \tag{4}$$

where the constants α, β and C are non-negative. The index s in case of λ^s denotes *surrender* to distinguish it from the mortality intensity λ^m. The lower limit C covers all policyholders who are willing or obliged to surrender their contracts, for example due to a desire for current consumption or debt, even though it is not rational from the perspective of maximizing policy value. The minimum of $D(t)$ and α allows the construction of an upper limit representing all policyholders never willing to exercise the early surrender option. Due to the chosen construction the surrender intensity cannot become negative. Hence, the surrender probabilities always lie inside the range $[0,1]$. Since the capped (upper limit) and floored (lower limit) linear relation results in a curve having an "s" shape, we will call it *s-curve* in the sequel. Aside from the analytical tractability, the surrender intensity in (4) offers some advantages regarding the findings derived from the empirical studies.

On the one hand, the higher the long-term interest rate $R(t,T)$, the higher the decision criterion $D(t)$ and hence, the higher the surrender intensity $\lambda^s(t)$. This means that an increase in the interest rates results in increased surrender probabilities which is in accordance with the *interest-rates hypothesis.* On the other hand, an outperforming fund in the form of a large $Y(t)$ also increases $D(t)$ and thus, the surrender intensity. In this case some profit taking by the policyholders is taken into account as well. In practice, surrender fees often decrease with time to make sure that the contract is kept for a while. By contrast, the more time passes the more the guaranteed minimum benefit gains in importance. When the value of the guarantee increases, the early surrender option should be rarely exercised (at least from a rational point of view). As the surrender intensity in (4) is able to incorporate the impact of the surrender fees and the implicit value of the guarantee at maturity, at any point in time it balances the factors increasing the surrender probabilites with the ones doing the opposite such that it is finally driven by the net impact of both trends.

As before, we define:

$$\mathbb{H}^s := (\mathcal{H}_t^s)_{t\in[0,T^*-x]}, \; \mathcal{H}_t^s := \sigma\left(\mathbb{1}_{\{\tau^s\leq u\}} : u \leq t\right),$$

indicating whether the early surrender option has been exercised up to a certain point in time.

Because of its definition in (4) the surrender intensity $\lambda^s(t), t \geq 0$, is a deterministic function of stochastic inputs from the financial market and so, is $\mathbb{F}$-measurable. Any information on the financial market, mortality and contract surrender up to a certain point in time is covered by the filtration $\mathbb{G}$ with:

$$\mathbb{G} := \mathbb{F} \vee \mathbb{H}^m \vee \mathbb{H}^s.$$

Let $(r_t, Y_t, \lambda_t^m(x+t))'$ be the underlying state process. For any $t \in [0,T]$ Proposition 3.1 in Lando (1998) allows us to replace the filtration $\mathcal{G}_t$ by the filtration $\mathcal{F}_t$ together with indicator functions using τ^s and $\tau^m(x)$ when we determine the present values of $\mathcal{F}_T$-measurable final repayments $X_T\mathbb{1}_{\{\tau>T\}}$ in the absence of default, i.e., no early death or premature contract surrender. Moreover, Proposition 3.1 in Lando (1998) enables this exchange when we price $\mathcal{F}_u$-adapted streams of payments $X_u\mathbb{1}_{\{\tau>u\}}$ up to default or $\mathcal{F}_u$-adapted recovery payments X_u at the time of default $\tau = u$. In particular, we have that:

$$\begin{aligned}&\mathbb{E}_{\mathbb{Q}}\left[\exp\left(-\int_t^T r(u)\,du\right)\mathbb{1}_{\{\tau^s>T\}}\mathbb{1}_{\{\tau^m(x)>T\}}|\mathcal{G}_t\right]\\ &= \mathbb{1}_{\{\tau^s>t\}}\mathbb{1}_{\{\tau^m(x)>t\}}\mathbb{E}_{\mathbb{Q}}\left[\exp\left(-\int_t^T (r(u)+\lambda_u^m(x+u)+\lambda^s(u))\,du\right)|\mathcal{F}_t\right].\end{aligned}$$

3. Products and Approximations

We begin by specifying the type of VAs to be considered. Unfortunately, there is no unique understanding in the literature of what is meant by guaranteed minimum accumulation benefits (GMABs), surrender benefits (SBs) or guaranteed minimum death benefits (GMDBs). Therefore, we introduce the definitions we are working with, since they are crucial for the later product pricing and the derivation of the closed-form approximation.

3.1. Product Definitions and Characteristics

As before, $A(t) := I\exp(Y(t))$ and $G(t) := I\exp(\delta t), t \in [0,T]$, define the (implied) value of the fund and the guarantee. Let $\mathbf{t} := (t_1, \ldots, t_K)'$ with $0 < t_1 < \ldots < t_K < T$ be the dates on which premature surrender is possible. Since $t_K < T$, the early surrender option has to be exercised before maturity, otherwise, the contract will anyway expire at T. In this paper the GMAB provides a payoff and hence, financial protection at T only, i.e., the choice between $A(t)$ and $G(t)$ is restricted to $t = T$. This is the reason why $G(t)$ gives for all $t < T$ the implied value of the GMAB. To make sure that a policyholder is always entitled to a single constituent of the overall VA contract the financial protection of the GMAB is valid as long as the insured is still alive (i.e., $\{\tau^m(x) > T\}$) and early surrender has not taken place (i.e., $\{\tau^s > T\}$). If we summarize the preceding restrictions, we get for the payoff of the GMAB at time $t \in [0,T]$:

$$\text{GMAB}(t,T) = \mathbb{1}_{\{t=T\}}\mathbb{1}_{\{\tau^m(x)>T\}}\mathbb{1}_{\{\tau^s>T\}} \cdot \max[A(T), G(T)]. \tag{5}$$

In case of surrender at time $t_i, 1 \leq i \leq K$, the SB is given by: $I \exp\left(Y\left(t_i\right) - f\left(t_i\right)\right)$ such that there is no guarantee involved. Since the surrender fees are usually stipulated in the VA contract in a determenistic (state-independent) way, the assumption that f is deterministic is not overly restrictive. Assuming that f is decreasing reduces the incentives for early surrender, but it is not required for the subsequent mathematical derivations. Again, to ensure that a policyholder's right of refund is always restricted to a single constituent of the overall VA contract the early surrender option can be exercised only once, if the insured is still alive (i.e., $\{\tau^s < \tau^m(x)\}$) and if this is indicated within the preceding notice period (i.e., $\{t_{i-1} < \tau^s \leq t_i\}$). Assuming $t_0 := 0$, the payoff of the SB at time $t_i, 1 \leq i \leq K$, is given by:

$$\text{SB}\left(t_i, T\right) = \mathbb{1}_{\{t_{i-1} < \tau^s \leq t_i\}} \mathbb{1}_{\{\tau^s < \tau^m(x)\}} \cdot I \cdot \exp\left(Y\left(t_i\right) - f\left(t_i\right)\right). \tag{6}$$

The third feature is a GMDB offering protection when the insured dies before contract expiration. Although an insured can die at any point in time (continuous death event), let $\bar{\mathbf{t}} := (\bar{t}_1, \ldots, \bar{t}_N)'$ with $0 < \bar{t}_1 < \ldots < \bar{t}_N = T$ be the dates the death benefit is paid (discrete repayment dates). In general, the termination dates of the SB and the repayment dates of the GMDB may be different. For simplicity, the roll-up rates of the GMDB and the GMAB are assumed to be equal. In this case, the same roll-up rate is used in the surrender intensity process and in the GMDB guarantee. For the GMDB, there are no fees such that the repayment at $\bar{t}_i, 1 \leq i \leq N$, is equal to $\max\left[A\left(\bar{t}_i\right), I \exp\left(\delta \bar{t}_i\right)\right]$. To avoid double claims of the policyholder, the GMDB provides a payoff before T only once, if the early surrender option has not been exercised so far (i.e., $\{\tau^m(x) < \tau^s\}$). We define $\bar{t}_0 := 0$. If the insured dies within the period $\{\bar{t}_{i-1} < \tau^m(x) \leq \bar{t}_i\}$, the payoff of the GMDB at repayment date $\bar{t}_i, 1 \leq i \leq N$ is given by:

$$\text{GMDB}\left(\bar{t}_i, T\right) = \mathbb{1}_{\{\bar{t}_{i-1} < \tau^m(x) \leq \bar{t}_i\}} \mathbb{1}_{\{\tau^m(x) < \tau^s\}} \cdot \max\left[A\left(\bar{t}_i\right), I \exp\left(\delta \bar{t}_i\right)\right]. \tag{7}$$

The above GMABs, SBs and GMDBs are designed such that a policyholder is not able to have two claims at the same time. Therefore, the payoff at time $t \in [0, T]$ of the overall VA is given by:

$$\text{VA}\left(t, T\right) = \text{GMAB}\left(t, T\right) + \text{SB}\left(t, T\right) + \text{GMDB}\left(t, T\right) \tag{8}$$

3.2. Product Pricing and Required Approximations

We assume an arbitrage-free market, and so, the price of the overall VA at time $t = 0$, i.e., $\text{p}^{\text{VA}}(0)$, has to be equal to the sum of the corresponding prices of its constituents.

$$\text{p}^{\text{VA}}(0) = \text{p}^{\text{GMAB}}(0) + \text{p}^{\text{SB}}(0) + \text{p}^{\text{GMDB}}(0). \tag{9}$$

For any point in time (5)–(8) provide the payoffs of the overall VA contract and its components. To end up with the prices in (9) all payments received during the contract period $[0, T]$ have to be discounted.

By virtue of risk-neutral pricing, the present value of the GMAB (conditioning on $\mathcal{G}_0$ has been omitted as no further information is provided) is given by:

$$\begin{aligned} \text{p}^{\text{GMAB}}(0) &= \mathbb{E}_{\mathbb{Q}}\left[\exp\left(-\int_0^T r(u)\,\mathrm{d}u\right)\text{GMAB}\left(T, T\right)\right] \\ &= \mathbb{Q}\left(\tau^m(x) > T\right) \cdot G(T) \cdot P(0, T) \cdot \left(E_1\left[\lambda^s\right] + E_2\left[\lambda^s\right]\right), \end{aligned} \tag{10}$$

with

$$\begin{aligned}
\mathbb{Q}\left(\tau^m(x) > T\right) &= \mathbb{E}_{\mathbb{Q}}\left[\exp\left(-\int_0^T \lambda_u^m(x+u)\,\mathrm{d}u\right)\right], \\
P(0,T) &= \mathbb{E}_{\mathbb{Q}}\left[\exp\left(-\int_t^T r(u)\,\mathrm{d}u\right)\right], \\
E_1\left[\lambda^s\right] &= \mathbb{E}_{\mathbb{Q}^T}\left[\exp\left(-\int_0^{t_K} \lambda^s(u)\,\mathrm{d}u\right)\right], \\
E_2\left[\lambda^s\right] &= \mathbb{E}_{\mathbb{Q}^T}\left[\exp\left(-\int_0^{t_K} \lambda^s(u)\,\mathrm{d}u\right)\left(\exp\left(Y(T)-\delta T\right)-1\right)^+\right].
\end{aligned} \tag{11}$$

Using (10) the price of the GMAB can be converted into a product of already known factors, except the one in the form of $(E_1[\lambda^s] + E_2[\lambda^s])$ which will be explained in detail later on. The first factor reflects the risk-neutral probability that the insured does not die early. The second factor displays the guaranteed, final payoff. The third factor is given by the price of a default-free zero-coupon bond with maturity T. Hence, the product of factors 2 and 3 provides the present value of the guarantee of the GMAB. The expressions for $E_1[\lambda^s]$ and $E_2[\lambda^s]$ employ the forward measure $\mathbb{Q}^T$ defined through the Radon-Nikodym derivative:

$$\left.\frac{d\mathbb{Q}^T}{d\mathbb{Q}}\right|_{\mathcal{G}_0} = \frac{P(T,T)/P(0,T)}{B(T)/B(0)}, \tag{12}$$

with

$$B(t) := \exp\left(\int_0^t r(u)\,\mathrm{d}u\right),\; B(0) = 1.$$

$E_1[\lambda^s]$ represents the forward probability that no surrender takes place before T (the last possible termination date is t_K), i.e., that the early surrender option is never exercised. Therefore, the first summand in (10) can be interpreted as the surrender and mortality risk adjusted present value of the guarantee $G(T)$. Since $E_2[\lambda^s]$ shows similarities to a European call option, the second summand in (10) can be considered as the surrender and mortality risk adjusted value of a European call option with maturity T written on the fund account value with strike $G(T)$. Hence, it covers the surplus of the fund compared to the guarantee, if the contract is kept in force until maturity.

Owing to their nonlinearity in λ^s, closed-form expressions for $E_1[\lambda^s]$ and $E_2[\lambda^s]$ are not available, and we resort to analytical approximations. If we replace λ^s by its definition in (4) and apply rectangular integration, we get for the first term:

$$\begin{aligned}
E_1\left[\lambda^s\right] &= \exp\left(-C\cdot t_K\right)\cdot\mathbb{E}_{\mathbb{Q}^T}\left[\exp\left(-\beta\int_0^{t_K}\max\left[\min\left[D(u),\alpha\right],0\right]\mathrm{d}u\right)\right] \\
&\approx \exp\left(-C\cdot t_K\right)\cdot\mathbb{E}_{\mathbb{Q}^T}\left[\exp\left(-\beta\sum_{i=1}^{K}\Delta t_i\max\left[\min\left[D(t_i),\alpha\right],0\right]\right)\right],
\end{aligned}$$

with $\Delta t_i := t_i - t_{i-1}, 1 \leq i \leq K$. Here, we would like to highlight that the integral is not approximated through an arbitrarily fine grid decreasing the approximation error at the expense of the enhanced numerical effort. The grid points are defined by $\mathbf{t}$. A rational policyholder exactly exercises the surrender option at one of the termination dates, but not in the meantime, as, e.g., the fund performance may dramatically worsen until his surrender decision takes effect. Therefore, the changes in λ^s between t_{i-1} and t_i are of minor importance so that the surrender intensity at a termination date multiplied by the time period from the last observation serves as a proper approximation for the integrated surrender intensity.

Next, we use that it holds for all $1 \leq i \leq K$:

$$\max\left[\min\left[D\left(t_i\right),\alpha\right],0\right] = D\left(t_i\right)\cdot \mathbb{1}_{\{0<D(t_i)<\alpha\}} + \alpha \cdot \mathbb{1}_{\{D(t_i)\geq\alpha\}}.$$

Thereafter, we take into account that the exponential function represents an absolutely convergent power series which implies that a changed order of summation preserves the limit. If $x_1,\ldots,x_n$ are arbitrary real numbers, the reordering of the exponential function we are working with is given by:

$$\begin{aligned}\exp\left(\sum_{i=1}^n x_i\right) &= \sum_{k=0}^\infty \frac{\left(\sum_{i=1}^n x_i\right)^k}{k!}\\ &= 1+\sum_{i=1}^n\left(\exp\left(x_i\right)-1\right)+\sum_{\substack{i,j=1\\ i<j}}^n x_i x_j + \mathbf{O}\left(\text{mixed terms of order} \geq 3\right),\end{aligned} \tag{13}$$

where $\mathbf{O}\left(\cdot\right)$ denotes the Landau notation. To illustrate the quality of this approximation Figure 2 displays the approximation error for[5] $n = 2$, $-0.15 < x_i < 0$, $\quad i = 1,2$. We can observe that in all cases the approximation error is below $3 \cdot 10^{-3}$.

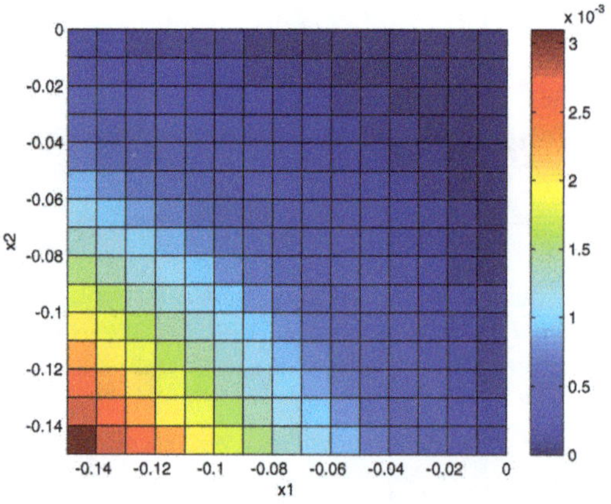

Figure 2. Approximation Error for Equation (13).

Finally, we focus on a reduced number of summands of the reordered power series. For this purpose, we omit all mixed terms of order ≥ 3 and some of the mixed terms of order 2 and get:

$$E_1\left[\lambda^s\right] \approx \exp\left(-C\cdot t_K\right)\cdot\left(S_{11}^{\mathbb{Q}^T}\left(D,\alpha,\beta,\mathbf{t}\right)+S_{12}^{\mathbb{Q}^T}\left(D,\alpha,\beta,\mathbf{t}\right)\right), \tag{14}$$

with:

$$\begin{aligned}S_{11}^{\mathbb{Q}^T}\left(D,\alpha,\beta,\mathbf{t}\right): &= 1+\sum_{i=1}^K \mathbb{E}_{\mathbb{Q}^T}\left[\left(\exp\left(-\beta\Delta t_i D\left(t_i\right)\right)-1\right)\mathbb{1}_{\{0<D(t_i)<\alpha\}}\right]\\ &+\sum_{i=1}^K \mathbb{E}_{\mathbb{Q}^T}\left[\left(\exp\left(-\beta\Delta t_i\alpha\right)-1\right)\mathbb{1}_{\{D(t_i)\geq\alpha\}}\right],\end{aligned} \tag{15}$$

[5] This will be the range for the corresponding expressions in our numerical case studies.

$$
\begin{aligned}
S_{12}^{\mathbb{Q}^T}(D,\alpha,\beta,\mathbf{t}) : &= \sum_{\substack{i,j=1\\ i<j}}^{K} \beta^2 \Delta t_i \Delta t_j \mathbb{E}_{\mathbb{Q}^T}\left[D(t_i)\,D(t_j)\,\mathbb{1}_{\{0<D(t_i)<\alpha\}}\mathbb{1}_{\{0<D(t_j)<\alpha\}}\right] \\
&+ \sum_{\substack{i,j=1\\ i<j}}^{K} \beta^2\alpha^2 \Delta t_i \Delta t_j \mathbb{Q}^T\left(D(t_i)\geq\alpha, D(t_j)\geq\alpha\right).
\end{aligned} \tag{16}
$$

For the ease of exposition, we define $\tilde{Y}(t) := Y(t) - \delta t$ for all $t \in [0,T]$. If we apply the same methods as before, but omit all mixed terms of order ≥ 2, we get for $E_2[\lambda^s]$:

$$
E_2[\lambda^s] \approx \exp(-C\cdot t_K)\cdot S_2^{\mathbb{Q}^T}\left(D,\tilde{Y},\alpha,\beta,\mathbf{t}\right), \tag{17}
$$

with

$$
\begin{aligned}
S_2^{\mathbb{Q}^T}(D,\tilde{Y},\alpha,\beta,\mathbf{t}) &:= \mathbb{E}_{\mathbb{Q}^T}\left[\exp(\tilde{Y}(T))\,\mathbb{1}_{\{\tilde{Y}(T)\geq 0\}}\right] - \mathbb{Q}^T(\tilde{Y}(T)\geq 0) \\
&+ \sum_{i=1}^{K}\mathbb{E}_{\mathbb{Q}^T}\left[(\exp(-\beta\Delta t_i D(t_i))-1)(\exp(\tilde{Y}(T))-1)\,\mathbb{1}_{\{0<D(t_i)<\alpha\}}\mathbb{1}_{\{\tilde{Y}(T)\geq 0\}}\right] \\
&+ \sum_{i=1}^{K}\mathbb{E}_{\mathbb{Q}^T}\left[(\exp(-\beta\alpha\Delta t_i)-1)(\exp(\tilde{Y}(T))-1)\,\mathbb{1}_{\{D(t_i)\geq\alpha\}}\mathbb{1}_{\{\tilde{Y}(T)\geq 0\}}\right].
\end{aligned} \tag{18}
$$

If we define for all $1 \leq i \leq K$:

$$
\begin{aligned}
h_1(\beta,D,t_i) : &= -\beta\Delta t_i \mathbb{E}_{\mathbb{Q}^T}[D(t_i)] + \tfrac{1}{2}\beta^2\Delta t_i^2 \mathbb{V}\mathrm{ar}_{\mathbb{Q}^T}[D(t_i)], \\
h_2(\alpha,\beta,D,t_i) : &= \frac{\mathbb{E}_{\mathbb{Q}^T}[D(t_i)]-\alpha}{\sqrt{\mathbb{V}\mathrm{ar}_{\mathbb{Q}^T}[D(t_i)]}} - \beta\Delta t_i\sqrt{\mathbb{V}\mathrm{ar}_{\mathbb{Q}^T}[D(t_i)]},
\end{aligned} \tag{19}
$$

we get for $S_{11}^{\mathbb{Q}^T}(D,\alpha,\beta,\mathbf{t})$:

$$
\begin{aligned}
S_{11}^{\mathbb{Q}^T}(D,\alpha,\beta,\mathbf{t}) = 1 &+ \sum_{i=1}^{K}\exp(h_1(\beta,D,t_i))\,\Phi(h_2(0,\beta,D,t_i)) - \sum_{i=1}^{K}\exp(h_1(\beta,D,t_i))\,\Phi(h_2(\alpha,\beta,D,t_i)) \\
&+ \sum_{i=1}^{K}\exp(-\beta\alpha\Delta t_i)\,\Phi(h_2(\alpha,0,D,t_i)) - \sum_{i=1}^{K}\Phi(h_2(0,0,D,t_i)),
\end{aligned} \tag{20}
$$

where $\Phi(\cdot)$ denotes the cumulative distribution function (CDF) of the standard Gaussian $\mathcal{N}(0,1)$. The detailed proof is shown in Appendix C.1.

For all $i,j \in \{1,\ldots,K\}$ with $i<j$ we define:

$$
\begin{aligned}
\mu(i,j) : &= \begin{pmatrix} \mathbb{E}_{\mathbb{Q}^T}[D(t_i)] \\ \mathbb{E}_{\mathbb{Q}^T}[D(t_j)] \end{pmatrix}, \\
\Sigma(i,j) : &= \begin{pmatrix} \mathbb{V}\mathrm{ar}_{\mathbb{Q}^T}[D(t_i)] & \mathbb{C}\mathrm{ov}_{\mathbb{Q}^T}[D(t_i),D(t_j)] \\ \mathbb{C}\mathrm{ov}_{\mathbb{Q}^T}[D(t_i),D(t_j)] & \mathbb{V}\mathrm{ar}_{\mathbb{Q}^T}[D(t_j)] \end{pmatrix}.
\end{aligned} \tag{21}
$$

After the indicator set in (16) has been split, we have:

$$
\begin{aligned}
S_{12}^{\mathbb{Q}^T}(D,\alpha,\beta,\mathbf{t}) : &= \sum_{\substack{i,j=1\\ i<j}}^{K}\beta^2\Delta t_i\Delta t_j\mathbb{E}_{\mathbb{Q}^T}\left[D(t_i)\,D(t_j)\,\mathbb{1}_{\{0<D(t_i),0<D(t_j)\}}\right] \\
&- \sum_{\substack{i,j=1\\ i<j}}^{K}\beta^2\Delta t_i\Delta t_j\mathbb{E}_{\mathbb{Q}^T}\left[D(t_i)\,D(t_j)\,\mathbb{1}_{\{0<D(t_i),\alpha\leq D(t_j)\}}\right] \\
&- \sum_{\substack{i,j=1\\ i<j}}^{K}\beta^2\Delta t_i\Delta t_j\mathbb{E}_{\mathbb{Q}^T}\left[D(t_i)\,D(t_j)\,\mathbb{1}_{\{\alpha\leq D(t_i),0<D(t_j)\}}\right] \\
&+ \sum_{\substack{i,j=1\\ i<j}}^{K}\beta^2\Delta t_i\Delta t_j\mathbb{E}_{\mathbb{Q}^T}\left[D(t_i)\,D(t_j)\,\mathbb{1}_{\{\alpha\leq D(t_i),\alpha\leq D(t_j)\}}\right] \\
&+ \sum_{\substack{i,j=1\\ i<j}}^{K}\alpha^2\beta^2\Delta t_i\Delta t_j M\left((0,0)',\mu(i,j),\Sigma(i,j),(\alpha,\alpha)',I_2\right).
\end{aligned} \tag{22}
$$

where I_2 is the two-dimensional identity matrix. The expectations of the product of the truncated random variables $D(t_i)$ and $D(t_j)$ are provided in Appendix B.4. The expression $M(\cdot)$ is explained in Appendix B.2.

For all $1 \leq i \leq K$ we set:

$$\begin{aligned} \mu(i): &= \begin{pmatrix} \mathbb{E}_{\mathbb{Q}^T}\left[D(t_i)\right] \\ \mathbb{E}_{\mathbb{Q}^T}\left[\tilde{Y}(T)\right] \end{pmatrix}, \\ \Sigma(i): &= \begin{pmatrix} \mathbb{V}\mathrm{ar}_{\mathbb{Q}^T}\left[D(t_i)\right] & \mathbb{C}\mathrm{ov}_{\mathbb{Q}^T}\left[D(t_i), \tilde{Y}(T)\right] \\ \mathbb{C}\mathrm{ov}_{\mathbb{Q}^T}\left[\tilde{Y}(T), D(t_i)\right] & \mathbb{V}\mathrm{ar}_{\mathbb{Q}^T}\left[\tilde{Y}(T)\right] \end{pmatrix}. \end{aligned} \tag{23}$$

Then, $S_2^{\mathbb{Q}^T}\left(D, \tilde{Y}, \alpha, \beta, \mathbf{t}\right)$ can be converted into:

$$\begin{aligned} S_2^{\mathbb{Q}^T}\left(D, \tilde{Y}, \alpha, \beta, \mathbf{t}\right) &= \exp\left(\mathbb{E}_{\mathbb{Q}^T}\left[\tilde{Y}(T)\right] + \tfrac{1}{2}\mathbb{V}\mathrm{ar}_{\mathbb{Q}^T}\left[\tilde{Y}(T)\right]\right)\Phi\left(\frac{\mathbb{E}_{\mathbb{Q}^T}\left[\tilde{Y}(T)\right] + \mathbb{V}\mathrm{ar}_{\mathbb{Q}^T}\left[\tilde{Y}(T)\right]}{\sqrt{\mathbb{V}\mathrm{ar}_{\mathbb{Q}^T}\left[\tilde{Y}(T)\right]}}\right) \\ &+ \textstyle\sum_{i=1}^{K} M\left((-\beta\Delta t_i, 1)', \mu(i), \Sigma(i), (0,0)', I_2\right) \\ &- \textstyle\sum_{i=1}^{K} M\left((-\beta\Delta t_i, 1)', \mu(i), \Sigma(i), (\alpha,0)', I_2\right) \\ &- \textstyle\sum_{i=1}^{K} M\left((-\beta\Delta t_i, 0)', \mu(i), \Sigma(i), (0,0)', I_2\right) \\ &+ \textstyle\sum_{i=1}^{K} M\left((-\beta\Delta t_i, 0)', \mu(i), \Sigma(i), (\alpha,0)', I_2\right) \\ &- \textstyle\sum_{i=1}^{K} M\left((0,1)', \mu(i), \Sigma(i), (0,0)', I_2\right) \\ &+ \textstyle\sum_{i=1}^{K} \exp\left(-\beta\alpha\Delta t_i\right) M\left((0,1)', \mu(i), \Sigma(i), (\alpha,0)', I_2\right) \\ &+ \textstyle\sum_{i=1}^{K} M\left((0,0)', \mu(i), \Sigma(i), (0,0)', I_2\right) \\ &- \textstyle\sum_{i=1}^{K} \exp\left(-\beta\alpha\Delta t_i\right) M\left((0,0)', \mu(i), \Sigma(i), (\alpha,0)', I_2\right) - \Phi\left(\frac{\mathbb{E}_{\mathbb{Q}^T}\left[\tilde{Y}(T)\right]}{\sqrt{\mathbb{V}\mathrm{ar}_{\mathbb{Q}^T}\left[\tilde{Y}(T)\right]}}\right). \end{aligned} \tag{24}$$

For the expression $M(\cdot)$ see Appendix B.2. A detailed proof is shown in Appendix C.2.

Finally, $S_{11}^{\mathbb{Q}^T}\left(D, \alpha, \beta, \mathbf{t}\right), S_{12}^{\mathbb{Q}^T}\left(D, \alpha, \beta, \mathbf{t}\right)$ and $S_2^{\mathbb{Q}^T}\left(D, \tilde{Y}, \alpha, \beta, \mathbf{t}\right)$ only require the moments and covariances in Appendix A.1 and thus, GMABs can be priced based on closed-form approximations. Besides the CDF of the standard Gaussian and the exponential function, only sums, products and quotients are involved. Hence, there are no integrals left causing further numerical effort. The number of summands depends on $\mathbf{t}$ implying that the decomposition of the grid may be orientated towards practical needs. For $T = 15$ and a semiannual surrender option we have 29 termination dates, which is easy to handle. The main drawback of our approach is the effort we have to put into its implementation. If we price GMABs using Monte Carlo Simulation (MC), the time and effort we have to spend on implementation may be smaller than in our case. However, to ensure that the provided prices are reliable, many trajectories have to be generated taking time and computational power. For instance, in Case 1 of Table 7 we simulate 500,000 paths for this purpose. By contrast, as soon as the approximation is implemented it takes significantly less time to get comparable prices. Since the implementation has to be done only once at the beginning, whereas performing the MCs can happen serveral times each day, our approach can be justified.

For the present value of the surrender benefit we have that:

$$\begin{aligned}
\mathrm{p}^{\mathrm{SB}}(0) &= \mathbb{E}_{\mathbb{Q}}\left[\exp\left(-\int_0^{\tau^s} r(u)\,du\right)\ \mathrm{SB}(\tau^s,T)\right]\\
&= \sum_{i=1}^{K}\mathbb{E}_{\mathbb{Q}}\left[I\exp\left(-\int_0^{t_i} r(u)\,du + Y(t_i) - f(t_i)\right)\mathbb{1}_{\{t_i<\tau^m(x)\}}\mathbb{1}_{\{t_{i-1}<\tau^s\le t_i\}}\right]\\
&= I\sum_{i=1}^{K}\exp(-f(t_i))\cdot\mathbb{Q}(\tau^m(x)>t_i)\cdot\mathbb{E}_{\mathbb{Q}}\left[\exp\left(-\int_0^{t_i} r(u)\,du + Y(t_i)\right)\mathbb{1}_{\{t_{i-1}<\tau^s\le t_i\}}\right],\\
&= I\sum_{i=1}^{K}\exp(-f(t_i))\cdot\mathbb{Q}(\tau^m(x)>t_i)\cdot\mathbb{Q}^{S(t_i)}(t_{i-1}<\tau^s\le t_i).
\end{aligned} \tag{25}$$

In the second line we use the fact that the surrender benefit is only repaid at certain points in time while the third line arises from the independence of the financial market and mortality. Eventually, for all periods $[0,t_i]$ with $1\le i\le K$ we replace the risk-neutral measure $\mathbb{Q}$ with the respective equity measure $\mathbb{Q}^{S(t_i)}$, whose Radon-Nikodym derivative obeys for $t<t_i$:

$$\left.\frac{d\mathbb{Q}^{S(t_i)}}{d\mathbb{Q}}\right|_{\mathcal{G}_t} = \frac{S(t_i)/S(t)}{B(t_i)/B(t)}. \tag{26}$$

Therefore, at any termination date t_i the surrender benefit in (25) is equal to the present value of the expected fund performance reduced by the prevailing surrender fee, if the insured is still alive $(\tau^m(x)>t_i)$ and if the surrender option has been exercised within the preceding surrender period $(t_{i-1}<\tau^s\le t_i)$. Again, we neglect all mixed terms of order ≥ 2, and so, obtain for the probability that no early surrender occurs before time t_i, $\mathbb{Q}^{S(t_i)}(\tau^s>t_i)$, for $\tilde{\mathbf{t}}_{\mathbf{i}} := \{t_1,\ldots,t_i\}$:

$$\begin{aligned}
\mathbb{Q}^{S(t_i)}(\tau^s>t_i) &= \mathbb{E}_{\mathbb{Q}^{S(t_i)}}\left[\exp\left(-\int_0^{t_i}\lambda^s(u)\,du\right)\right]\\
&\approx \exp(-C\cdot t_i)\cdot S_{11}^{\mathbb{Q}^{S(t_i)}}(D,\alpha,\beta,\tilde{\mathbf{t}}_{\mathbf{i}}).
\end{aligned} \tag{27}$$

The moments of the decision criterion D under the equity measure $\mathbb{Q}^{S(t_i)}$ are provided in Appendix A.1.

Eventually, we get for the present value of the GMDB:

$$\begin{aligned}
\mathrm{p}^{\mathrm{GMDB}}(0) &= \mathbb{E}_{\mathbb{Q}}\left[\exp\left(-\int_0^{\tau^m(x)} r(u)\,du\right)\mathrm{GMDB}(\tau^m(x),T)\right]\\
&= \sum_{i=1}^{N}\mathbb{E}_{\mathbb{Q}}\left[\exp\left(-\int_0^{\bar{t}_i} r(u)\,du\right)\mathbb{1}_{\{\bar{t}_i<\tau^s\}}\cdot\max\left[A(\bar{t}_i),I\exp(\delta\bar{t}_i)\right]\right]\mathbb{Q}(\bar{t}_{i-1}<\tau^m(x)\le\bar{t}_i)\\
&= \sum_{i=1}^{N}\frac{\mathrm{GMAB}(0,\bar{t}_i)\cdot\mathbb{Q}(\bar{t}_{i-1}<\tau^m(x)\le\bar{t}_i)}{\mathbb{Q}(\tau^m(x)>\bar{t}_i)}.
\end{aligned} \tag{28}$$

Using (28) a GMDB serves as a portfolio consisting of N (the number of repayment dates of the death benefit) mortality adjusted GMAB contracts with maturities $\bar{\mathbf{t}}$. If we use the closed-form approximation for the GMAB in (10), we get rid of the denominator $\mathbb{Q}(\tau^m(x)>t_i)$. As soon as a closed-form solution for GMABs is derived, (28) provides an analytic solution for GMDBs. Because of (11) there are no unknown terms in (28). Another important consequence of (28) is the flexibility inherent in the presented approach, as it supports the reuse of existing expressions and hence, allows for encapsulation when it comes to its implementation.

4. Model Calibration

In the sequel, we will calibrate the stochastic models in Section 2 using actively traded financial products and historical mortality tables. Due to a lack of real data, the calibration of the surrender model relies on hypothetical data. However, those insurance companies that have access to sufficient surrender data can easily perform all steps with their inputs. The idea behind this section is to show

how the underlying models can be properly calibrated. We do not claim that this is the one and only way. When actively traded financial products enter the calibration, for instance, they can be used when corresponding trading strategies are set up or hedged. Hence, a link between the estimated models and future actions regarding risk and asset management can be established.

4.1. Financial Market Model

For any $0 \leq t \leq T$ let $P(t,T)$ be the value of a default-free zero-coupon bond at time t with maturity T in (11). Then, it holds in Duffie *et al.* (2000) that:

$$P(t,T) = \exp\left(A_r^{\mathbb{Q}}(t,T) + B_r^{\mathbb{Q}}(t,T)\, r(t)\right), \tag{29}$$

with

$$A_r^{\mathbb{Q}}(t,T) = \int_t^T \theta_r(s)\, B_r^{\mathbb{Q}}(s,T)\, ds + \frac{1}{2}\sigma_r^2 \int_t^T B_r^{\mathbb{Q}}(s,T)^2\, ds,$$
$$B_r^{\mathbb{Q}}(t,T) = \frac{1}{a_r}\left[\exp\left(a_r(t-T)\right) - 1\right].$$

Let $f(0,T)$ denote the instantaneous forward rate of $P(0,T)$ at time $t=0$, i.e.,

$$f(0,T) = -\frac{\partial}{\partial T}\ln\left(P(0,T)\right).$$

By taking the partial derivative with respect to T (two times) of the logarithm of both sides of (29) the Leibniz's rule in Flanders (1973) provides for the function $\theta_r(t), t \geq 0$:

$$\theta_r(t) = \frac{\partial}{\partial t} f(0,t) + a_r f(0,t) + \frac{\sigma_r^2}{2a_r}\left[1 - \exp(-2a_r t)\right].$$

Inserting this in (29) we get:

$$A_r^{\mathbb{Q}}(t,T) = \frac{\sigma_r^2}{4a_r^3}\left[\exp(-2a_r T) - 1 - \exp(2a_r(t-T)) + \exp(-2a_r t)\right] + \ln\left(\frac{P(0,T)}{P(0,t)}\right)$$
$$+ \frac{\sigma_r^2}{2a_r^3}\left[\exp(a_r(t-T)) - \exp(-a_r(t+T))\right] + f(0,t)\,\frac{1-\exp(a_r(t-T))}{a_r}.$$

The calibration of $\theta_r(t), t \geq 0$, relies on the zero-coupon bond prices in Figure 3 which are derived from Reuters quotes of 6 month EURIBOR interest-rate swaps (downloaded on 16 January 2013). For missing interest-rate swaps with maturity less than one year suitable EURIBOR spot rates are chosen. We follow Sections 5.5.1–5.5.4 in Zagst (2002) to obtain the discount curve in Figure 3. As Reuters provides quotes of caps and floors written on the 6 month EURIBOR, for the estimation of a_r and σ_r the mid price at-the-money (ATM) Black volatilities of Table 1 are used. First, these ATM Black volatilities have to be converted into market prices, see Sections 5.8.2–5.8.3 in Zagst (2002). Then, the prices of caps and floors are related to portfolios consisting of options written on default-free zero-coupon bonds as in Sections 5.6.1–5.6.2 in Zagst (2002). Finally, we minimize the squared difference between the theoretical cap prices provided by the Hull-White model as a function of the unknown parameters a_r and σ_r and the market prices derived from the Black volatilities under the conditions $a_r \geq 0$ and $\sigma_r \geq 0$. The resulting optimal parameters are given in Table 2.

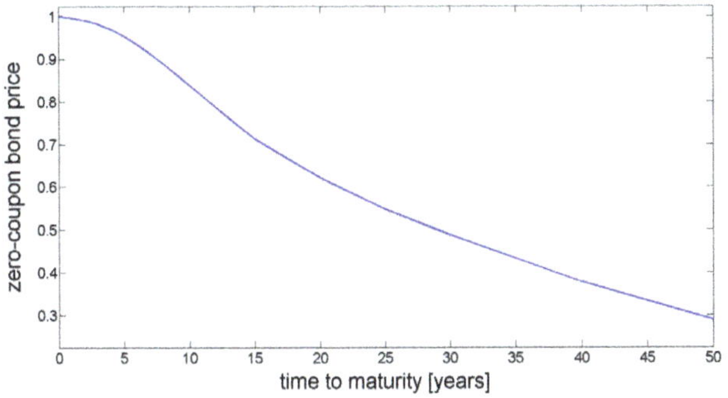

Figure 3. Discount Curve on 16 January 2013.

Table 1. 6 Month EURIBOR Mid Price ATM Volatilities [%].

Maturity	2Y	3Y	4Y	5Y	6Y	7Y	8Y	9Y	10Y
Volatility	99.7	66.1	61.2	55.4	50.0	45.3	41.6	38.5	36.1

Based on (1) let $Option\,(t,T,S,K,\psi)$ be the value at time $t < T$ of a European call ($\psi = 1$) or put ($\psi = -1$) option with strike K, maturity T and underlying S. Then, it holds:

$$Option\,(t,T,S,K,\psi) = \psi S\,(t)\,\Phi\,(\psi h_S) - \psi K P\,(t,T)\,\Phi\,(\psi h_T)\,,$$

with

$$h_S := \frac{\ln\left(\frac{S(t)}{K}\right) - Y\,(t) + \mathbb{E}_{\mathbb{Q}^{S(T)}}\left[Y\,(T)\,|\mathcal{G}_t\right]}{\sqrt{\mathbb{V}\mathrm{ar}_{\mathbb{Q}^{S(T)}}\left[Y\,(T)\,|\mathcal{G}_t\right]}},$$

$$h_T := \frac{\ln\left(\frac{S(t)}{K}\right) - Y\,(t) + \mathbb{E}_{\mathbb{Q}^{T}}\left[Y\,(T)\,|\mathcal{G}_t\right]}{\sqrt{\mathbb{V}\mathrm{ar}_{\mathbb{Q}^{T}}\left[Y\,(T)\,|\mathcal{G}_t\right]}}.$$

The index $\mathbb{Q}^T$ denotes the forward measure in (12), whereas $\mathbb{Q}^{S(T)}$ denotes the equity measure in (26).

The risky asset in (1) shall be given by the German stock index DAX. We use European options written on the DAX, i.e., ODAX quotes, published by the EUREX on 16 January 2013 for the calibration of S and hence, Y. Because of the limited number of data we assume that all options with the same maturity $T_i, 1 \leq i \leq n$, are characterized by the same volatility $\sigma_S\,(T_i)$ and that the deterministic function $\sigma_S\,(t)\,, t \geq 0$, is piecewise constant, i.e., $\sigma_S\,(t) = \sigma_S^i\ \forall\ t \in (T_{i-1}, T_i]$ for all $1 \leq i \leq n$ with $T_0 := 0$. For $t = 0$ the preceding option pricing formula can be transformed to:

$$Option\,(0,T_i,S,K,\psi) = \psi S\,(0)\,\Phi\,(\psi d_1\,(T_i)) - \psi K P\,(0,T_i)\,\Phi\,(\psi d_2\,(T_i))\,,$$

where $\forall\ i \in \{1,\ldots,n\}$ we get for $d_1\,(T_i)$ and $d_2\,(T_i)$:

$$d_1\,(T_i) = \frac{\ln\left(\frac{S(0)}{K \cdot P(0,T_i)}\right) + \frac{1}{2}V\,(Y\,(T_i))}{\sqrt{V\,(Y\,(T_i))}},$$

$$d_2\,(T_i) = d_1\,(T_i) - \sqrt{V\,(Y\,(T_i))}.$$

For all $i \in \{1, \ldots, n\}$ it holds for $V(Y(T_i))$ that:

$$V(Y(T_i)) = \frac{\sigma_r^2}{a_r^3}\left[a_r T_i - \frac{3}{2} + 2\exp(-a_r T_i) - \frac{1}{2}\exp(-2a_r T_i)\right] + \sum_{k=1}^{i}\left(\sigma_S^k\right)^2 (T_k - T_{k-1})$$
$$+ 2\rho_{Sr}\frac{\sigma_r}{a_r}\sum_{k=1}^{i}\sigma_S^k\left[(T_k - T_{k-1}) + \frac{1}{a_r}\left(\exp(a_r(T_{k-1} - T_i)) - \exp(a_r(T_k - T_i))\right)\right].$$

For reasons of simplicity, we use the historical correlation between the (simple) daily DAX returns and the 6 month EURIBOR rates as an approximation for ρ_{Sr}. However, more sophisticated models for ρ_{Sr} could be part of future research. Tables 2 and 3 summarize the derived calibration results of the financial market model.

Table 2. Parameters of the Financial Market Model.

a_r	σ_r	ρ_{Sr}
0.0799	0.0079	−0.0403

Table 3. Estimated Standard Deviations for DAX Index.

T_i	01/18/2013	02/15/2013	03/15/2013	06/21/2013	09/20/2013	12/20/2013
$\sigma_S(T_i)$	0.1368	0.1232	0.1557	0.1712	0.1898	0.1993
T_i	06/20/2014	12/19/2014	06/19/2015	12/18/2015	12/16/2016	12/15/2017
$\sigma_S(T_i)$	0.2179	0.2146	0.2367	0.2624	0.2432	0.2237

4.2. Mortality Model

In Sections 2.2 and 3.2 we do not discuss the real-world and risk-neutral survival probabilities in detail, as the respective $\mathbb{P}$- and $\mathbb{Q}$-survival probabilities are heavily affected by the model for the mortality risk premium. This is the reason why both should be part of this calibration section.

Assume $0 \le t \le T$. Then, Duffie *et al.* (2000) provide the $\mathbb{P}$-survival probability based on (2):

$$\mathbb{P}(\tau^m(x) > T|\mathcal{G}_t) = \mathbb{E}_{\mathbb{P}}\left[\exp\left(-\int_t^T \lambda_s^m(x+s)\,ds\right)|\mathcal{G}_t\right]$$
$$= \exp\left(A_x^{\mathbb{P}}(t,T) + B_x^{\mathbb{P}}(t,T)\lambda_t^m(x+t)\right),$$

with

$$A_x^{\mathbb{P}}(t,T) = \frac{c_1\exp(c_2T)}{c_3(c_2+c_3)}\left[1-\exp((c_2+c_3)(t-T))\right] + \frac{1}{4}\left(\frac{c_4}{c_3}\right)^2\frac{\exp(2c_5T)}{c_5}\left[1-\exp(2c_5(t-T))\right]$$
$$-\left(\frac{c_4}{c_3}\right)^2\frac{\exp(2c_5T)}{2c_5+c_3}\left[1-\exp((2c_5+c_3)(t-T))\right] - \frac{c_1\exp(c_2T)}{c_2c_3}\left[1-\exp(c_2(t-T))\right]$$
$$+\frac{1}{4}\left(\frac{c_4}{c_3}\right)^2\frac{\exp(2c_5T)}{c_3+c_5}\left[1-\exp(2(c_3+c_5)(t-T))\right],$$
$$B_x^{\mathbb{P}}(t,T) = \frac{1}{c_3}\left[\exp(c_3(t-T)) - 1\right].$$

Using Duffie *et al.* (2000) the $\mathbb{Q}$-survival probability based on (3) is given by:

$$\mathbb{Q}(\tau^m(x) > T|\mathcal{G}_t) = \mathbb{E}_{\mathbb{Q}}\left[\exp\left(-\int_t^T \lambda_s^m(x+s)\,ds\right)|\mathcal{G}_t\right]$$

$$= \exp\left(A_x^{\mathbb{Q}}(t,T) + B_x^{\mathbb{Q}}(t,T)\,\lambda_t^m(x+t)\right),$$

with

$$\begin{aligned} A_x^{\mathbb{Q}}(t,T) &= A_x^{\mathbb{P}}(t,T) + \frac{c_4}{c_3c_5}\gamma_m\left(\exp(c_5T) - \exp(c_5t)\right) - \frac{c_4}{c_3(c_3+c_5)}\gamma_m \exp(c_5T) \\ &+ \frac{c_4}{c_3(c_3+c_5)}\exp(-c_3T)\,\gamma_m \exp\left((c_5+c_3)\,t\right), \\ B_x^{\mathbb{Q}}(t,T) &= \frac{1}{c_3}\left[\exp\left(c_3(t-T)\right) - 1\right]. \end{aligned}$$

For a fixed age x, and $0 \le t \le T$, let $\mathrm{M}_x(t,T)$ be defined by:

$$\begin{aligned} \mathrm{M}_x(t,T) &= \ln\left(\frac{\mathbb{Q}\left(\tau^m(x) > T|\mathcal{G}_t\right)}{\mathbb{P}\left(\tau^m(x) > T|\mathcal{G}_t\right)}\right) \\ &= \frac{c_4}{c_3c_5}\gamma_m\left(\exp(c_5T) - \exp(c_5t)\right) - \frac{c_4}{c_3(c_3+c_5)}\gamma_m \exp(c_5T) \\ &+ \frac{c_4}{c_3(c_3+c_5)}\exp(-c_3T)\,\gamma_m \exp\left((c_5+c_3)\,t\right). \end{aligned} \tag{30}$$

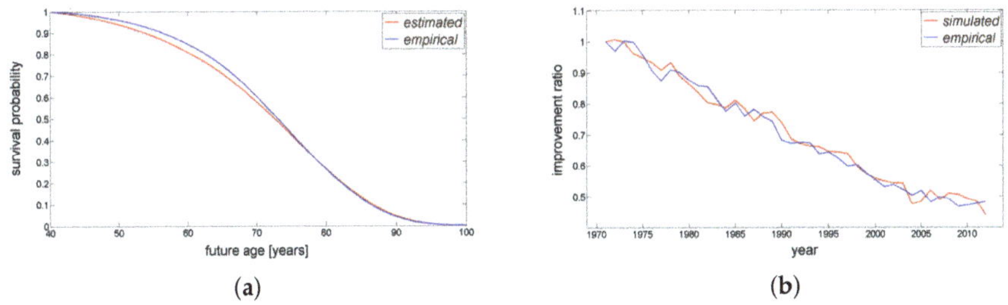

Figure 4. Gompertz Model (**a**) and Improvement Ratio (**b**) for Men Aged 40 Years in 1971.

Figure 4 displays the calibration results for the real-world measure $\mathbb{P}$ which are derived from U.K. mortality data. On the left we show the empirical survival probabilities (blue) and their analogs based on the estimated, static Gompertz model (red). The decreasing blue line on the right indicates that mortality for the given group is generally improving. The mortality improvement ratio ξ is modeled as an Ornstein-Uhlenbeck process, this is why the red line on the right-hand side illustrates an arbitrary trajectory. As there is no liquid market for actively traded annuities (especially not for variable ones), the estimation of the mortality risk premium γ_m has to rely on primary market prices. For this purpose, the annual averages of level annuity rates (equipped with a five-year guarantee, offered to men aged 65 years in the U.K.) provided by Cannon and Tonks (2004) serve as an approximation and are displayed in the left plot of Figure 6. To enter a level annuity contract a policyholder has to pay a lump sum at the beginning. Thereafter, he is entitled to a constant (annual) repayment for his remaining lifetime. Consequently, there are no adjustments caused by inflation, an overperforming fund, etc. to be addressed. If γ_m is supposed to be constant depending on the year a contract was issued and the age of an insured, we get for a contract issued in $u = \textit{calendar year} - 1971$:

$$\frac{I_u}{L_u} = \sum_{k=1}^{5} P(u,u+k) + \sum_{k=6}^{T^*-x} \mathbb{Q}\left(\tau_u^m(x) > k|\mathcal{G}_u\right) P(u,u+k).$$

The index u in $\tau_u^m(x)$ denotes the year the contract was issued. I_u and L_u stand for its *initial premium* and the agreed annual repayment of the *level annuity*. Using (30), the mortality tables of Figure 1 (upper limit in age is 101 years) and the fact that a person aged x in u was $x-u$ in 1971 it follows that:

$$\frac{I_u}{L_u} = \sum_{k=1}^{5} P(u,u+k) + \sum_{k=6}^{36} \left[\mathbb{P}\left(\tau_u^m(x) > k|\mathcal{G}_u\right) \exp\left(\mathrm{M}_{x-u}(u,u+k)\right) P(u,u+k)\right].$$

The annuities in Cannon and Tonks (2004) have been offered in the U.K. implying that the estimated financial market model based on EURIBOR rates and DAX cannot be used for pricing the bonds $P(u,u+k)$. We aim to show how the chosen mortality risk premium may be estimated. In doing so, we do not claim that this solution is the one and only way. Depending on the intention and needs of the user alternative approaches might be more appropriate. We replace $P(u,u+k)$ through the corresponding discount factors derived from the nominal rates of U.K. government bonds[6] published by the Bank of England and illustrated in Figure 5. Besides the nominal rates of U.K. government bonds, the discount factors of an insurance company possibly take into account corporate bond yields, and equity and other returns, which significantly affects the estimated mortality risk premium γ_m. Across the full range of insurance companies and annuity products, the internal discount factors may vary considerably. As Cannon and Tonks (2004) provide averaged annuity rates which are not restricted to a single provider, we cannot construct discount factors covering the entire annuity business. Furthermore, as soon as the discount factors are based on some defaultable products such as corporate bonds the inherent default risk has to be incorporated and separated from the mortality risk. If a risk-free rate is used for discounting, there are no default risks requiring particular attention. Concerning the annuity rates in Cannon and Tonks (2004), the nominal rates of U.K. government bonds might be a good approximation for the risk-free rate as their default risk is quite low and each insurance company is able to invest in them. Using linear interpolation whenever inner maturities are missing and constant extrapolation for maturities greater than 25 years results in the term structures displayed in Figure 5. The estimated parameters of the mortality model are summarized in Table 4.

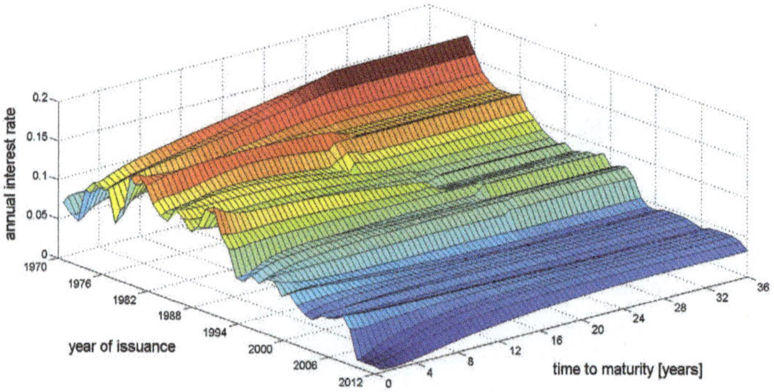

Figure 5. U.K. Nominal Rates (1970–2012).

[6] The data can be downloaded from http://www.bankofengland.co.uk/statistics/Pages/yieldcurve/archive.aspx.

Table 4. Mortality Parameters

Parameter	b	z	κ	γ	σ_ξ	γ_m
Estimated Value	12.1104	76.1390	0.4806	0.0195	0.0254	10.6482

On the one hand, Figure 4 confirms that the combination of the static Gompertz model and the mortality improvement ratio, i.e., the mortality model under $\mathbb{P}$, is able to properly map the real-world mortality tables. On the other hand, the plot on the left of Figure 6 indicates that the constant mortality risk premium γ_m and the nominal rates of the U.K. government bonds are suitable for the replication of the annuity rates of Cannon and Tonks (2004), as there are only minor deviations between the original annuity rates and their theoretical counterparts based on the estimated parameters of Table 4. All in all, the mortality model provides convincing results regarding the real-world measure $\mathbb{P}$ and the risk-neutral pricing measure $\mathbb{Q}$. However, the interpretation of $\gamma_m = 10.6482$ is still missing. Using the plot on the right in Figure 6 we can conclude: First, the blue and red curves are shaped similarly such that the constant mortality risk premium γ_m does not change the structure of the survival probabilites; Second, for any fixed age the risk-neutral survival probability exceeds its real-world analog. From the perspective of an annuity provider this makes sense. The $\mathbb{P}$-survival probabilities arise from the real mortality tables, whereas the $\mathbb{Q}$-survival probabilities are used for pricing annuities. If the difference between the $\mathbb{Q}$- and $\mathbb{P}$-survival probabilities is positive, an annuity provider implicitly assumes in his annuity prices that the insureds live on average longer than the mortality tables reflect. So, in addition to the mortality risk derived from real mortality tables, a premium in the form of the spread between the $\mathbb{Q}$- and $\mathbb{P}$-survival probabilities is charged by the insurance company for taking the insureds' longevity risk. Within our modeling framework γ_m covers the magnitude and direction of this longevity risk premium. The larger the absolute value of γ_m the larger the absolute value of the spread between both survival probabilities. Whenever γ_m is negative, the $\mathbb{Q}$-survival probabilities are smaller than their $\mathbb{P}$-analogues. For instance, in case of term life assurances, insurance companies are facing the opposite risk, i.e., that the insureds die earlier than expected.

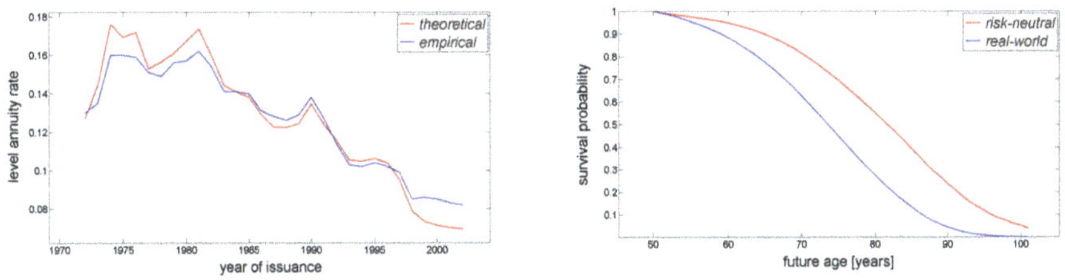

(a) (b)

Figure 6. Level Annuities of Cannon and Tonks (2004) (**a**) and Survival Probabilities (**b**).

4.3. Surrender Model

For $1 \leq i \leq K$, let q_i denote the probability that the early surrender option is exercised before t_i. To be precise, let $q_1, \ldots, q_K$ represent the (hypothetical) surrender probabilities we want to use for product pricing. Then, (27) provides for all $1 \leq i \leq K$:

$$1 - q_i \approx \exp\left(-C \cdot t_i\right) \cdot S_{11}^{\mathbb{Q}^{S(t_i)}}\left(D, \alpha, \beta, \tilde{\mathbf{t}}_\mathbf{i}\right).$$

Using (19) and (20), we obtain:

$$S_{11}^{\mathbb{Q}^{S(t_i)}}(D,\alpha,\beta,\tilde{\mathbf{t}}_i) = 1 + \Sigma_{j=1}^{i} \exp\left(\bar{h}_1(\beta,D,t_j)\right)\Phi\left(\bar{h}_2(0,\beta,D,t_j)\right) - \Sigma_{j=1}^{i} \exp\left(\bar{h}_1(\beta,D,t_j)\right)\Phi\left(\bar{h}_2(\alpha,\beta,D,t_j)\right)$$
$$+ \Sigma_{j=1}^{i} \exp\left(-\beta\alpha\Delta t_j\right)\Phi\left(\bar{h}_2(\alpha,0,D,t_j)\right) - \Sigma_{j=1}^{i} \Phi\left(\bar{h}_2(0,0,D,t_j)\right),$$

where it holds for all $1 \leq j \leq i$:

$$\bar{h}_1(\beta,D,t_j) := -\beta\Delta t_j \mathbb{E}_{\mathbb{Q}^{S(t_i)}}\left[D(t_j)\right] + \frac{1}{2}\beta^2\Delta t_j^2 \mathbb{V}\mathrm{ar}_{\mathbb{Q}^{S(t_i)}}\left[D(t_j)\right],$$
$$\bar{h}_2(\alpha,\beta,D,t_j) := \frac{\mathbb{E}_{\mathbb{Q}^{S(t_i)}}\left[D(t_j)\right] - \alpha}{\sqrt{\mathbb{V}\mathrm{ar}_{\mathbb{Q}^{S(t_i)}}\left[D(t_j)\right]}} - \beta\Delta t_j\sqrt{\mathbb{V}\mathrm{ar}_{\mathbb{Q}^{S(t_i)}}\left[D(t_j)\right]}.$$

The moments $\mathbb{E}_{\mathbb{Q}^{S(t_i)}}\left[D(t_j)\right]$ and $\mathbb{V}\mathrm{ar}_{\mathbb{Q}^{S(t_i)}}\left[D(t_j)\right]$ are given in Appendix A.1. After the calibration results of the financial market have been determined, an ordinary least-squares regression yields the estimation of the unknown surrender parameters α, β and C.

Due to a lack of data, the hypothetical parameters in Table 5 are considered. Case 1 neglects early surrender such that we are able to analyze the value of the surrender option and to test the quality of the approximation without any disturbances resulting from the surrender add-on. The parameters of Case 2 and Case 3 were chosen to get first-year surrender probabilities within a range of 1%–5% and 5%–10%, respectively[7]. The first-year surrender intensities based on Case 2 and Case 3 are illustrated in Figure 7. For the remaining drivers of the decision criterion D, i.e., δ, f and T, see Table 6.

Table 5. Parameters of Surrender Model.

	Case 1	Case 2	Case 3
α	0.00	1.00	0.25
β	0.00	0.04	0.20
C	0.00	0.01	0.05

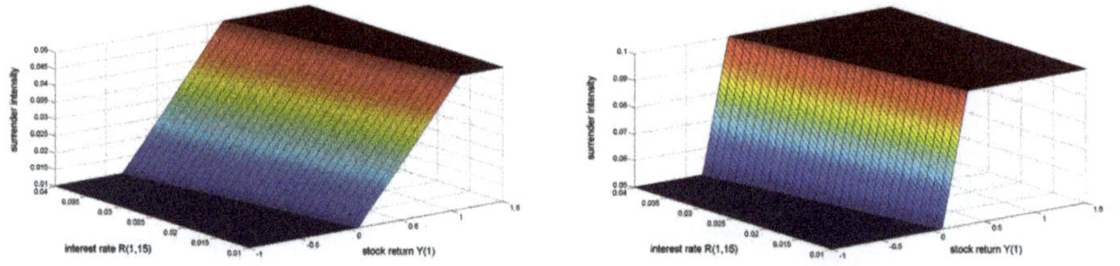

(**a**) (**b**)

Figure 7. First-Year Surrender Probability 1%–4.88% (**a**) and 4.88%–9.52% (**b**).

7 For the parameters in Table 5 the actual boundaries are 1%–4.88% and 4.88%–9.82%.

Table 6. Specification of Variable Annuity (VA) Contract.

Insured	man, aged 50 years
Premium	100
Maturity	15 years
δ	1.00 %
Termination dates	$1, \ldots, 14$ (once per year)
Repayment Dates	$1, \ldots, 15$ (once per year)
Surrender Fees	7%, ..., 1% (years 1–7, linear) 0% (years 8–14, no fee)

5. Numerical Example

To check the quality of the presented pricing framework, in particular, to detect its errors and limitations we price the VAs in (9) twice, that is, using our closed-form approximation and MC. The simulated prices will serve as a benchmark for the approximated ones; we generate 500,000 trajectories of the processes Y and r on a monthly basis. For the model parameters the calibration results in Tables 2–5 are taken. The contract specification of the considered VA is defined in Table 6.

The authors of Krayzler *et al.* (2016) derive an analytic solution for GMABs in the absence of early surrender. Since the work in (28) provides a closed-form solution for GMDBs and the value of the SB is zero, for Case 1 of Table 5 an analytic solution exists. The positive γ_m in Table 4 implies that the $\mathbb{Q}$-survival probabilities exceed their $\mathbb{P}$-counterparts (see Figure 6) reflecting the premium charged for longevity risk. In the case of GMDBs an insurer is facing the reverse risk, i.e., that an insured dies earlier than expected. Here, we keep the γ_m from Table 4 for the pricing of the GMDB, as we are not able to estimate the risk premium due to missing data. A summary of the priced VAs is displayed in Table 7.

Table 7. VA Prices, Standard Deviations and Differences.

	Case 1	Case 2	Case 3
GMAB			
	Case 1	**Case 2**	**Case 3**
Analytic Sol.	110.6804	x	x
Approximation	110.6804	79.2336	36.2581
Sim. (mean, 500K)	110.9925	81.2484	39.0351
Sim. (std, 500K)	0.1200	0.0662	0.0303
Delta (abs.)[8]	−0.3121	−2.0148	−2.7771
Delta (rel.)[9]	−0.0028	−0.0248	−0.0711
SB			
	Case 1	**Case 2**	**Case 3**
Analytic Sol.	0	x	x
Approximation	0	26.3468	62.9797
Sim. (mean, 500K)	0	27.7328	63.2259
Sim. (std, 500K)	0	0.0397	0.0519
Delta (abs.)	0	−1.3860	−0.2462
Delta (rel.)	x	−0.0500	−0.0039
GMDB			
	Case 1	**Case 2**	**Case 3**
Analytic Sol.	12.2560	x	x
Approximation	12.2560	10.3374	6.9443
Sim. (mean, 500K)	12.2589	10.4157	7.0785
Sim. (std, 500K)	0.0078	0.0049	0.0027
Delta (abs.)	−0.0029	−0.0783	−0.1343
Delta (rel.)	−0.0002	−0.0075	−0.0190
VA = GMAB + SB + GMDB			
	Case 1	**Case 2**	**Case 3**
Analytic Sol.	122.9363	x	x
Approximation	122.9363	115.9177	106.1820
Sim. (mean, 500K)	123.2514	119.3968	109.3395
Sim. (std, 500K)	0.1270	0.1007	0.0731
Delta (abs.)	−0.3150	−3.4791	−3.1575
Delta (rel.)	−0.0026	−0.0291	−0.0289

Table 7 shows that high first-year surrender probabilities (Case 1: 0%; Case 2: 1%–5%; Case 3: 5%–10%) reduce the GMAB prices. An increased surrender probability decreases the likelihood that a policyholder is entitled to the GMAB payoff, justifying the price decline. A high termination probability makes claims from the SB more likely (prices increase). A high likelihood of surrender enhances the chance that a policyholder surrenders his contract before he dies so that the decreased GMDB prices are reasonable. If early surrender occurs, a policyholder's right of refund is restricted to the fund reduced by the prevailing surrender fee. The absence of any guarantee diminishes the financial distress of the insurance company compared to the GMAB and GMDB. The theoretical assumption that the increase in the SB prices is smaller than the aggregated decrease in the GMAB and GMDB prices is supported by the decreasing VA prices.

In Case 1, the analytic solution and the closed-form approximation provide the same prices indicating that our approach works properly, if early surrender is neglected. MC prices of GMABs and GMDBs are slightly different, but these small deviations are acceptable. In the sequel, the MC

8 Delta (abs.) represents the difference between the approximated and the corresponding simulated prices.
9 Delta (rel.) is equal to the ratio of Delta (abs.) and the simulated price. Hence, it refers to the relative price deviations.

prices will serve as a benchmark for their approximated counterparts. Table 7 shows for GMABs, SBs and GMDBs an increase in the absolute error when their values decline. That is to say, the less the worth of a component is the higher its pricing error becomes. This is important, since the most valuable constituents are properly priced. Due to (28) a GMDB may be regarded as a portfolio of GMABs. Therefore, it is no coincidence that for all cases the pricing errors of GMABs and GMDBs have the same sign. Note that for the overall VA the absolute value of Delta (rel.) remains smaller than 3.00% for all considered cases.

For a better understanding of the assumed surrender behavior Figure 8 illustrates for all termination dates the empirical means of the simulated surrender intensities. Recalling Table 5 we can see that both time series meet the initial conditions. The surrender intensity of Case 2 is increasing while the one of Case 3 does the opposite. In both cases the same decision criterion is applied, but different parametrizations of the surrender intensity result in different admissible upper and lower bounds. In total, they cause distinct s-curves such that the simulated decision criterion reaches/exceeds their upper and lower limits in different scenarios.

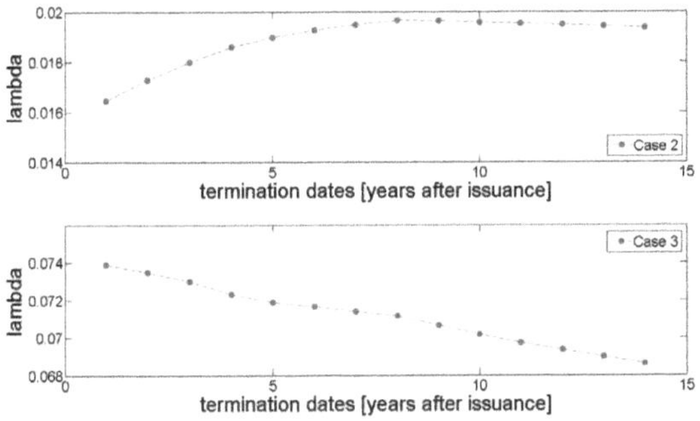

Figure 8. Means of Simulated Surrender Intensities

Finally, we briefly repeat the main advantage of the presented pricing scheme. Simulation techniques often require a sufficient number of scenarios together with an appropriate grid size (e.g., monthly steps). This may call for a lot of computational power and can be quite time consuming. By contrast, the derived closed-form approximation requires simple calculations. Each run takes a fraction of the simulation time, and thus, causes significant savings in computation time.

6. Emergency Fund Extension

The emergency fund hypothesis assumes that personal financial distress or other factors (e.g., unemployment or illness) force policyholders to prematurely surrender their contracts. In the sequel, let a major drop in stock market prices be one of these factors resulting in financial distress for some policyholders (in addition to the ones already covered by the lower limit C). To be precise, let the time-dependent function $l : [0, T] \rightarrow [-\infty, 0]$ denote the lower limit at time t triggering additional surrender arising from a badly performing fund. Then, for any point in time $t \in [0, T]$ with $Y(t) < l(t)$ we have an increased surrender intensity. In general, a steep decline in stock market prices should exert pressure on more policyholders than a small one does. Thus, we assume for any fixed $t \in [0, T]$ the more $Y(t)$ decreases on the interval $Y(t) \in [-\infty, l(t)]$, i.e., the bigger the loss on the fund account, the more the surrender intensity increases up to an upper limit. For an illustration of the new surrender intensity $\tilde{\lambda}^s(t)$ based on different parameters see Figure 9. If we assume a piecewise linear relation between $Y(t)$ and $\tilde{\lambda}^s(t)$ in the form of two s-curves (one covering the policyholders' surrender behavior described in Section 2.3 and one covering the emergency fund hypothesis), for any fixed point in time $t \in [0, T]$ we get:

$$\tilde{\lambda}^s(t) := \beta \max\left[\min\left[D(t), \alpha\right], 0\right] - \tilde{\beta} \max\left[\min\left[\tilde{D}(t), \tilde{\alpha}\right], 0\right] + \tilde{C}, \tag{31}$$

with $\alpha, \tilde{\alpha}, \beta, \tilde{\beta}, \tilde{C} \in \mathbb{R}_0^+$ and $\tilde{D}(t) := Y(t) - l(t)$.

Because of its relevance for applications in practice we show how the surrender model definded by Case 2 in Table 5 can be properly extended to the emergency fund hypothesis. On the interval $[0, \infty]$ the behavior of new intensity $\tilde{\lambda}^s$ shall coincide with the behavior of the old intensity λ^s. Therefore, we keep the parameters α and β of Table 5. The constant $\tilde{C}$ has to be adjusted to end up with the original lower limit C. For this purpose, $\tilde{C}$ has to satisfy:

$$\tilde{C} - \tilde{\alpha}\tilde{\beta} = C.$$

Since we are not able to calibrate this extended surrender model due to the lack of appropriate surrender data, we use the hypothetical values in Table 8. The corresponding surrender intensities are displayed in Figure 9. Using the contract specification in Table 6 we obtain the probabilities in Figure 10. These surfaces present the probability that the early surrender option is not exercised within the first year depending on the accumulated stock return $Y(1)$ and long-term interest rate $R(1, 15)$.

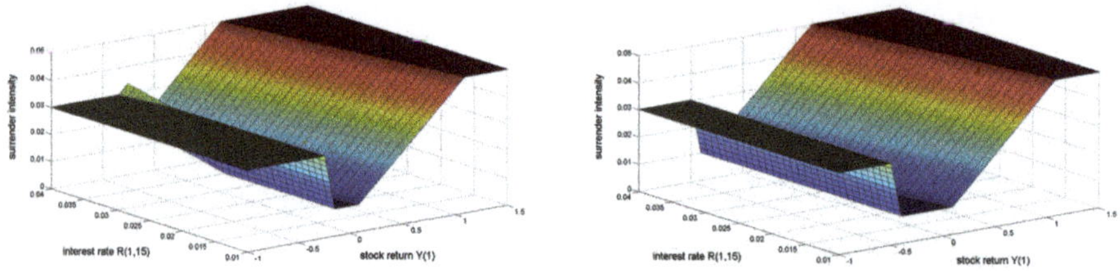

(a) **(b)**

Figure 9. Surrender Intensities of Cases 4 (**a**) and 5 (**b**).

The only difference between Cases 4 and 5 is given by the lower limit $l(t) \equiv l$ which has to be explained, in particular, regarding the assumed surrender behavior of the policyholders. In Case 4 we have that if the value of the fund drops to 86.07% = exp(−0.15) of the initial investment, the emergency add-on is activated. As soon as the fund further declines to 77.88% = exp(−0.25) the one-year surrender probability increases from 1% to 2.96% where it is capped. Similarly, we have in Case 5 that if the value of the fund drops from 67.03% = exp(−0.40) to 60.65% = exp(−0.50), the one-year surrender probability increases from 1% to 2.96% where it is again capped. Hence, in Case 4 additional surrender due to the emergency fund hypothesis is triggered earlier, indicating that the policyholders characterized by Case 4 suffer more from a downturn on the stock market than the ones described by Case 5. In both scenarios a negative fund performance causes an increase in the one-year surrender probability of almost 2%.

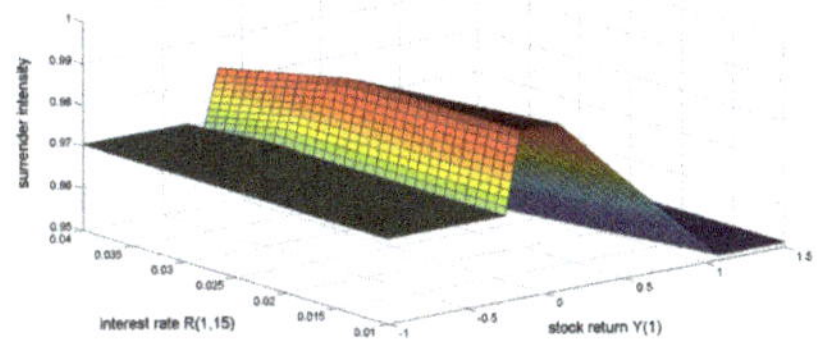

(a)

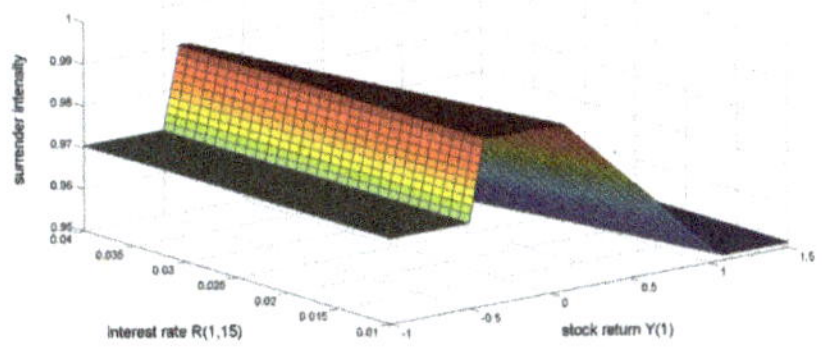

(b)

Figure 10. Survival Probabilities of Cases 4 (**a**) and 5 (**b**).

Table 8. Parameters of the Extended Surrender Model.

	Case 4	Case 5
α	1.00	1.00
β	0.04	0.04
$\tilde{\alpha}$	0.10	0.10
$\tilde{\beta}$	0.20	0.20
$\tilde{C}$	0.03	0.03
l	−0.25	−0.50

Using (10) we can price GMABs based on $\tilde{\lambda}^s$. As λ^s enters $E_1[\lambda^s]$ and $E_2[\lambda^s]$ only, we just have to derive equivalent solutions for $E_1[\tilde{\lambda}^s]$ and $E_2[\tilde{\lambda}^s]$. To do this, we apply the same methods as before and get:

$$E_1\left[\tilde{\lambda}^s\right] \approx \exp\left(-\tilde{C}\cdot t_K\right)\cdot\left(\tilde{S}_{11}^{\mathbb{Q}^T}\left(D,\tilde{D},\alpha,\tilde{\alpha},\beta,\tilde{\beta},\mathbf{t}\right)+\tilde{S}_{12}^{\mathbb{Q}^T}\left(D,\tilde{D},\alpha,\tilde{\alpha},\beta,\tilde{\beta},\mathbf{t}\right)\right),$$
$$E_2\left[\tilde{\lambda}^s\right] \approx \exp\left(-\tilde{C}\cdot t_K\right)\cdot\tilde{S}_{2}^{\mathbb{Q}^T}\left(D,\tilde{D},\tilde{Y},\alpha,\tilde{\alpha},\beta,\tilde{\beta},\mathbf{t}\right),$$

with

$$\tilde{S}_{11}^{\mathbb{Q}^T}\left(D,\tilde{D},\alpha,\tilde{\alpha},\beta,\tilde{\beta},\mathbf{t}\right)=S_{11}^{\mathbb{Q}^T}\left(D,\alpha,\beta,\mathbf{t}\right)-1+S_{11}^{\mathbb{Q}^T}\left(\tilde{D},\tilde{\alpha},-\tilde{\beta},\mathbf{t}\right),$$
$$\tilde{S}_{12}^{\mathbb{Q}^T}\left(D,\tilde{D},\alpha,\tilde{\alpha},\beta,\tilde{\beta},\mathbf{t}\right)=S_{12}^{\mathbb{Q}^T}\left(D,\alpha,\beta,\mathbf{t}\right)+S_{12}^{\mathbb{Q}^T}\left(\tilde{D},\tilde{\alpha},-\tilde{\beta},\mathbf{t}\right),$$
$$\tilde{S}_{2}^{\mathbb{Q}^T}\left(D,\tilde{D},\tilde{Y},\alpha,\tilde{\alpha},\beta,\tilde{\beta},\mathbf{t}\right)=S_{2}^{\mathbb{Q}^T}\left(D,\tilde{Y},\alpha,\beta,\mathbf{t}\right)-\mathbb{E}_{\mathbb{Q}^T}\left[\exp\left(\tilde{Y}\left(T\right)\right)\mathbb{1}_{\{\tilde{Y}(T)\geq 0\}}\right]$$
$$+S_{2}^{\mathbb{Q}^T}\left(\tilde{D},\tilde{Y},\tilde{\alpha},-\tilde{\beta},\mathbf{t}\right)+\mathbb{Q}^T\left(\tilde{Y}\left(T\right)\geq 0\right).$$

The new pricing formula for GMABs and (28) enable the pricing of GMDBs based on $\tilde{\lambda}^s$ without any further calculations. Eventually, the SB pricing in (25) requires the probability that no surrender takes place before a certain point in time. Similar to (27), it follows for $\tilde{\lambda}^s$:

$$\mathbb{Q}^{S(t_i)}\left(\tilde{\tau}^s>t_i\right)\approx\exp\left(-\tilde{C}\cdot t_i\right)\cdot\tilde{S}_{11}^{\mathbb{Q}^{S(t_i)}}\left(D,\tilde{D},\alpha,\tilde{\alpha},\beta,\tilde{\beta},\mathbf{t}\right),$$

where $\tilde{\tau}^s$ is the counterpart of τ^s for $\tilde{\lambda}^s$.

Table 9 states the simulated and approximated GMAB, SB, GMDB and VA prices for the original surrender intensity λ^s (Case 2) and its extended version $\tilde{\lambda}^s$ (Cases 4 and 5). On the one hand, a comparison between Cases 4 and 5 detects how the lower limit l affects the prices. On the other hand, Case 2 serves as a benchmark such that we are able to analyze the impact of the emergency fund component in $\tilde{\lambda}^s$ on the prices.

Table 9. VA Prices, Standard Deviations and Differences.

	GMAB		
	Case 2	**Case 4**	**Case 5**
Approximation	79.2336	75.4547	78.1821
Sim. (mean, 500 K)	81.2484	74.6267	77.2791
Sim. (std, 500 K)	0.0662	0.0680	0.0678
Delta (abs.)	−2.0148	0.8280	0.9031
Delta (rel.)	−0.0248	0.0111	0.0117
	SB		
	Case 2	**Case 4**	**Case 5**
Approximation	26.3468	28.5614	26.8172
Sim. (mean, 500 K)	27.7328	31.5358	29.6096
Sim. (std, 500 K)	0.0397	0.0367	0.0381
Delta (abs.)	−1.3860	−2.9744	−2.7924
Delta (rel.)	−0.0500	−0.0943	−0.0943
	GMDB		
	Case 2	**Case 4**	**Case 5**
Approximation	10.3374	9.9925	10.2123
Sim. (mean, 500 K)	10.4157	9.9483	10.1630
Sim. (std, 500 K)	0.0049	0.0051	0.0050
Delta (abs.)	−0.0783	0.0442	0.0493
Delta (rel.)	−0.0075	0.0044	0.0048
	VA = GMAB + SB + GMDB		
	Case 2	**Case 4**	**Case 5**
Approximation	115.9177	114.0086	115.2116
Sim. (mean, 500 K)	119.3968	116.1108	117.0517
Sim. (std, 500 K)	0.1007	0.1017	0.1021
Delta (abs.)	−3.4791	−2.1022	−1.8401
Delta (rel.)	−0.0291	−0.0181	−0.0157

The additional s-curve covering the emergency fund hypothesis increases the SB prices and decreases the GMAB and GMDB prices. If the probability of premature contract termination increases, the probability that a policyholder is entitled to the repayment of the GMAB decreases. Similarly, a higher surrender probability increases the chance that a contract will be surrendered before the death of the insured, reducing the payment obligations of the GMDB. By contrast, the policyholder is more likely to receive the payoffs of the SB.

The prices in Table 9 encourage the aforementioned assumption that termination based on the emergency hypothesis is triggered earlier in Case 4 than in Case 5, as the SB price in Case 4 exceeds its analog in Case 5. The opposite holds for the prices of the GMABs and GMDBs. Although the overall VA is worth more or less the same, the fair values of its single constituents have significantly changed. For instance, compare the GMAB and SB prices in Cases 2 and 4.

In spite of the emergency fund hypothesis, the magnitude of the relative pricing errors has not considerably changed. Hence, the presented approximation is able to properly price the VAs in (9) when additional sources for early surrender are taken into account. Note, this extended example shows once again the modularity and the inherent flexibility of the presented pricing framework which could be particularly useful for practitioners.

7. Conclusion and Future Research

In this paper we construct an affine linear framework with stochastic models for the financial market, the insureds' mortality and the policyholders' surrender behavior. The financial market includes a risk-free interest rate and a risky asset which is supposed to be a stock or a fund. Two distinct intensity based approaches map the insureds' mortality and the policyholders' surrender behavior. A static Gompertz model and an Ornstein-Uhlenbeck process covering the increasing life expectancy of humans form the mortality intensity. Some empirical studies detect an irrationality in the surrender behavior of policyholders. For instance, they surrender their contracts, although it is not rational from the perspective of maximizing portfolio value. Furthermore, some empirical studies confirm the *interest-rate hypothesis* that rising interest rates cause increased contract termination. To take into account both findings we deploy an s-shaped surrender intensity using a deterministic function with stochastic inputs from the financial market.

We focus on variable annuities requiring an upfront payment which is paid by the policyholder and is fully invested in the risky asset. The surrender benefit strongly affects the behavior of the policyholders. To avoid additional incentives for premature surrender a policyholder's right of refund is restricted to the current value of the risky investment reduced by the prevailing surrender fee. If the insured dies before the early surrender option is exercised, in particular, before the maturity of the contract, the payoff is given by the maximum of the current value of the risky investment and a preliminary agreed minimum benefit. The same choice is offered at maturity.

The main result of this paper is the derived closed-form approximation. Although the financial market, the insureds' mortality and the policyholders' surrender behavior are stochastic, we price certain variable annuities using a closed-form approximation. Despite some lengthy expressions, the presented pricing framework can be easily implemented. Compared to simulation techniques it requires less computational power and time, which could be particularly important for applications in practice. Additionally, we show how the stochastic models can be calibrated using actively traded financial products and historic mortality data. Due to missing data the calibration of the surrender model is based on hypothetical values. All in all, the displayed solution represents one possible way of calibrating the models. Depending on the needs of the user and the area of application (risk management, pricing, etc.) alternative calibration methods could be preferred. The usage of actively traded products supports subsequent hedging activities. The calibration of the mortality model incorporates primary market quotes of annuities (unfortunately, there were no quotes of variable annuties available). Hence, we are able to analyze the differences between the survival-probabilities derived from mortality tables and the ones entering product pricing. In terms of the considered quotes the annuity providers seem to work with higher survival probabilities than the current mortality tables suggest. In this context, the premium resulting from the increased survival probabilities could be charged for taking the insureds' longevity risk. Another advantage of the presented approach is its flexibility. Since some empricial studies confirm the *emergency fund hypothesis*, i.e., the assumption that policyholders cancel their contracts due to personal financial distress, we demonstrate how the original scheme can be properly adjusted.

Due to a lack of data we are not able to calibrate the surrender model. Therefore, future research may focus on possible calibration approaches and model extensions. In this article the mortality risk premium is supposed to be constant with respect to the year a contract was issued and the age of the insured. The development of more sophisticated models covering the mortality risk premium together with an accordingly adjusted calibration method might be interesting as well. Finally, products like guaranteed minimum withdrawal benefits (GMWBs) and guaranteed minimum living benefits (GMLBs) as well as other types of guarantees like ratchets should be investigated.

Acknowledgments: Franz Ramsauer gratefully acknowledges the support from Pioneer Investments during his doctoral phase. Mikhail Krayzler acknowledges support from risklab during his doctoral studies. David Saunders and Marcos Escobar acknowledge support of the Natural Sciences and Engineering Research Council of Canada, in the form of Discovery Grants.

Author Contributions: All authors contributed equally to this research work by providing new ideas, discussing existing results and sharing their profound knowledge in this field. In case of the derivation and implementation of the closed-form approximation as well as the model calibration F.R. did the most within the scope of Ramsauer (2013).

Conflicts of Interest: The authors declare no conflict of interest. The founding sponsors had no role in the design of the study; in the collection, analyses, or interpretation of data; in the writing of the manuscript, and in the decision to publish the results.

Abbreviations

The following abbreviations are used in this manuscript:

ATM	at-the-money
bn	billion
CDF	cumulative distribution function
DAX	Deutscher Aktienindex
EURIBOR	Euro Interbank Offered Rate
GMAB	guaranteed minimum accumulation benefit
GMDB	guaranteed minimum death benefit
GMLB	guaranteed minimum living benefit
GMWB	guaranteed minimum withdrawal benefit
GMXB	guaranteed minimum benefit
MC	Monte Carlo Simulation
SB	surrender benefit
U.K.	United Kingdom
U.S.	United States
VA	Variable annuity

Appendix A. Required Distributions

Appendix A.1. Financial Market Model

The closed-form approximation requires expectations and variances under the risk-neutral measure $\mathbb{Q}$, the forward measure $\mathbb{Q}^T$ in (12) and the equity measure $\mathbb{Q}^{S(t_i)}$ in (26). For all $0 \le t \le T$ we define:

$$V(t) = \frac{\sigma_r^2}{a_r^3}\left[2\exp(-a_r t) - \frac{1}{2}\exp(-2a_r t) + a_r t - \frac{3}{2}\right].$$

Then, it follows from (1) that the stock return is normally distributed under $\mathbb{Q}$ with:

$$\mathbb{E}_{\mathbb{Q}}[Y(t)] = \frac{1}{2}V(t) - \ln(P(0,t)) - \frac{1}{2}\int_0^t \sigma_S^2(s)\,\mathrm{d}s,$$
$$\mathbb{V}\mathrm{ar}_{\mathbb{Q}}[Y(t)] = \int_0^t \sigma_S^2(s)\,\mathrm{d}s - \frac{2\rho_{Sr}\sigma_r}{a_r}\int_0^t \sigma_S(s)\left[\exp(a_r(s-t)) - 1\right]\mathrm{d}s + V(t).$$

Using (12), the Girsanov theorem preserves the normal distribution and provides for all $0 \le t \le T$:

$$\mathbb{E}_{\mathbb{Q}^T}[Y(t)] = \rho_{Sr}\frac{\sigma_r}{a_r}\int_0^t \sigma_S(s)\left[\exp(a_r(s-T)) - 1\right]\mathrm{d}s - \frac{\sigma_r^2}{2a_r^3}\left[a_r t + \frac{1}{2}(\exp(-2a_r t) - 1)\right] - \ln(P(0,t))$$
$$+ \frac{\sigma_r^2}{2a_r^3}\left[\exp(a_r(t-T)) + \exp(-a_r(t+T)) - 2\exp(-a_r T)\right] - \frac{1}{2}\int_0^t \sigma_S^2(s)\,\mathrm{d}s.$$

As the performed measure change only adjusts the drift, the variances of $Y(t)$ under $\mathbb{Q}^T$ and $\mathbb{Q}$ coincide. For $0 \le t \le T$ the expectation $\mathbb{E}_{\mathbb{Q}^{S(t)}}[Y(t)]$ and the variance $\mathbb{V}\mathrm{ar}_{\mathbb{Q}^{S(t)}}[Y(t)]$ are stated in Theorem 3.1 in Krayzler *et al.* (2016). The rollup rate δ and the lower limit function $l(t), 0 \le t \le T$, are deterministic. Thus, for all $0 \le t \le T$ the preceding variances are the same for $\tilde{Y}(t) = Y(t) - \delta t$ and $\tilde{D}(t) = Y(t) - l(t)$. The expectations of $\tilde{Y}(t)$ and $\tilde{D}(t)$ are equal to the expectation of $Y(t)$ reduced by δt and $l(t)$, respectively.

For all $0 \le t \le T$ the decision criterion $D(t)$ is normally distributed with:

$$\mathbb{E}_{\mathbb{Q}}[D(t)] = \frac{\sigma_r^2}{2a_r^3}\left[a_r t + 2(\exp(-a_r T) - \exp(a_r(t-T)))\right] - \frac{1}{2}\int_0^t \sigma_S^2(s)\,\mathrm{d}s$$

$$
\begin{aligned}
&-\frac{\sigma_r^2}{4a_r^3}\left[\exp\left(-2a_rT\right)-\exp\left(2a_r\left(t-T\right)\right)\right]-f\left(t\right)-\delta T-\ln\left(P\left(0,T\right)\right),\\
\mathbb{V}\mathrm{ar}_{\mathbb{Q}}\left[D\left(t\right)\right] &= \frac{\sigma_r^2}{2a_r^3}\left[\exp\left(2a_r\left(t-T\right)\right)-\exp\left(-2a_rT\right)\right]+2\rho_{Sr}\frac{\sigma_r}{a_r}\int_0^t\sigma_S\left(s\right)\left(1-\exp\left(a_r\left(s-T\right)\right)\right)\mathrm{d}s\\
&+\frac{\sigma_r^2}{a_r^3}\left[a_rt-2\left(\exp\left(a_r\left(t-T\right)\right)-\exp\left(-a_rT\right)\right)\right]+\int_0^t\sigma_S^2\left(s\right)\mathrm{d}s.
\end{aligned}
$$

Again, a change of measure provides for the expectation under the forward measure $\mathbb{Q}^T$:

$$
\begin{aligned}
\mathbb{E}_{\mathbb{Q}^T}\left[D\left(t\right)\right] &= \frac{\sigma_r^2}{4a_r^3}\left[\exp\left(-2a_rT\right)-\exp\left(2a_r\left(t-T\right)\right)\right]-\frac{1}{2}\int_0^t\sigma_S^2\left(s\right)\mathrm{d}s-\delta T-\ln\left(P\left(0,T\right)\right)-f\left(t\right)\\
&-\frac{\sigma_r^2}{2a_r^3}\left[a_rt+2\left(\exp\left(-a_rT\right)-\exp\left(a_r\left(t-T\right)\right)\right)\right]-\rho_{Sr}\frac{\sigma_r}{a_r}\int_0^t\sigma_S\left(s\right)\left(1-\exp\left(a_r\left(s-T\right)\right)\right)\mathrm{d}s.
\end{aligned}
$$

In the case of the variance no change occurs, that is, the variances under $\mathbb{Q}^T$ and $\mathbb{Q}$ coincide. Next, we have:

$$
\begin{aligned}
\mathbb{C}\mathrm{ov}_{\mathbb{Q}^T}\left[D\left(t\right),Y\left(T\right)\right] &= \int_0^t\sigma_S^2\left(s\right)\mathrm{d}s+2\rho_{Sr}\frac{\sigma_r}{a_r}\int_0^t\sigma_S\left(s\right)\left(1-\exp\left(a_r\left(s-T\right)\right)\right)\mathrm{d}s\\
&+\frac{\sigma_r^2}{a_r^3}\left[a_rt-\frac{1}{2}\left(\exp\left(-2a_rT\right)-\exp\left(2a_r\left(t-T\right)\right)\right)+2\left(\exp\left(-a_rT\right)-\exp\left(a_r\left(t-T\right)\right)\right)\right].
\end{aligned}
$$

Finally, for $0\leq t\leq T$ we obtain the following expectation of $D\left(t\right)$ under the equity measure $\mathbb{Q}^{S(T)}$:

$$
\begin{aligned}
\mathbb{E}_{\mathbb{Q}^{S(T)}}\left[D\left(t\right)\right] &= \frac{\sigma_r^2}{2a_r^3}\left[a_rt+2\left(\exp\left(-a_rT\right)-\exp\left(a_r\left(t-T\right)\right)\right)\right]+\frac{1}{2}\int_0^t\sigma_S^2\left(s\right)\mathrm{d}s-\delta T-\ln\left(P\left(0,T\right)\right)\\
&-\frac{\sigma_r^2}{4a_r^3}\left[\exp\left(-2a_rT\right)-\exp\left(2a_r\left(t-T\right)\right)\right]+\rho_{Sr}\frac{\sigma_r}{a_r}\int_0^t\sigma_S\left(s\right)\left(1-\exp\left(a_r\left(s-T\right)\right)\right)\mathrm{d}s-f\left(t\right).
\end{aligned}
$$

As before, $\mathbb{V}\mathrm{ar}_{\mathbb{Q}^{S(T)}}\left[D\left(t\right)\right]$ remains unaffected by the measure change and thus it coincides with $\mathbb{V}\mathrm{ar}_{\mathbb{Q}}\left[D\left(t\right)\right]$.

Appendix A.2. Insurance Market Model

Using Itô's Lemma as well as Equations (2) and (3), it can be shown that the mortality intensity at time T is normally distributed with the moments $\mu_\lambda^{\mathbb{Q}},\sigma_\lambda^{\mathbb{Q}}$ for the risk-neutral case and $\mu_\lambda^{\mathbb{P}},\sigma_\lambda^{\mathbb{P}}$ for the real-world case:

$$
\begin{aligned}
\mu_{\lambda(T)}^{\mathbb{P}} &= \mathbb{E}_{\mathbb{P}}[\lambda_T(x+T)] = \lambda_0(x)\exp\left(-c_3T\right)+\frac{c_1}{c_2+c_3}\left(\exp\left(c_2T\right)-\exp\left(-c_3T\right)\right),\\
\left(\sigma_{\lambda(T)}^{\mathbb{P}}\right)^2 &= \mathbb{V}\mathrm{ar}_{\mathbb{P}}[\lambda_T(x+T)] = \frac{c_4^2}{2c_5+2c_3}\left(\exp\left(2c_5T\right)-\exp\left(-2c_3T\right)\right),\\
\mu_{\lambda(T)}^{\mathbb{Q}} &= \mathbb{E}_{\mathbb{Q}}[\lambda_T(x+T)] = \lambda_0(x)\exp\left(-c_3T\right)+\frac{c_1}{c_2+c_3}\left(\exp\left(c_2T\right)-\exp\left(-c_3T\right)\right)\\
&- \frac{c_4\gamma_m}{c_5+c_3}\left(\exp\left(c_5T\right)-\exp\left(-c_3T\right)\right),\\
\left(\sigma_{\lambda(T)}^{\mathbb{Q}}\right)^2 &= \mathbb{V}\mathrm{ar}_{\mathbb{Q}}[\lambda_T(x+T)] = \frac{c_4^2}{2c_5+2c_3}\left(\exp\left(2c_5T\right)-\exp\left(-2c_3T\right)\right).
\end{aligned}
$$

Then, the probability of negative mortality intensity can be calculated analytically as:

$$
\mathbb{P}(\lambda_T(x+T)<0)=\mathbb{P}\left(\frac{\lambda_T(x+T)-\mu_{\lambda(T)}}{\sigma_{\lambda(T)}}<-\frac{\mu_{\lambda(T)}}{\sigma_{\lambda(T)}}\right)=\Phi\left(-\frac{\mu_{\lambda(T)}}{\sigma_{\lambda(T)}}\right),
$$

where $\Phi(\cdot)$ is the cumulative distribution function of the standard normal distribution and $\mu_{\lambda(T)}$ and $\sigma_{\lambda(T)}$ are the corresponding moments of the mortality intensity at time T taken either under the risk-neutral or the real-world measure.

Appendix B. Required Theorems

Within this section we provide some general results which are important for the proofs in Appendix C.

Appendix B.1. Exponential of Truncated Univariate Gaussian

Assume $a \in \mathbb{R}$ and $b \in \mathbb{R}\setminus\{0\}$ and let X be a normally distributed random variable on the probability space $(\Omega, \mathcal{F}, \mathbb{P})$ with mean μ and variance σ^2, i.e., $X \sim \mathcal{N}(\mu, \sigma^2)$. Then, we have that:

1. if $b > 0$:

$$\mathbb{E}_{\mathbb{P}}\left[\exp(a+bX)\,\mathbb{1}_{\{a+bX\geq 0\}}\right] = \exp\left(a+b\mu+\frac{1}{2}b^2\sigma^2\right)\Phi\left(\frac{a/b+b\sigma^2+\mu}{\sigma}\right),$$
$$\mathbb{E}_{\mathbb{P}}\left[\exp(-a-bX)\,\mathbb{1}_{\{a+bX\geq 0\}}\right] = \exp\left(-a-b\mu+\frac{1}{2}b^2\sigma^2\right)\Phi\left(\frac{a/b-b\sigma^2+\mu}{\sigma}\right),$$

2. if $b < 0$:

$$\mathbb{E}_{\mathbb{P}}\left[\exp(a+bX)\,\mathbb{1}_{\{a+bX\geq 0\}}\right] = \exp\left(a+b\mu+\frac{1}{2}b^2\sigma^2\right)\Phi\left(-\frac{a/b+b\sigma^2+\mu}{\sigma}\right),$$
$$\mathbb{E}_{\mathbb{P}}\left[\exp(-a-bX)\,\mathbb{1}_{\{a+bX\geq 0\}}\right] = \exp\left(-a-b\mu+\frac{1}{2}b^2\sigma^2\right)\Phi\left(-\frac{a/b-b\sigma^2+\mu}{\sigma}\right).$$

Proof. For $b > 0$ we obtain:

$$\begin{aligned}
\mathbb{E}_{\mathbb{P}}\left[\exp(a+bX)\,\mathbb{1}_{\{a+bX\geq 0\}}\right] &= \frac{1}{\sqrt{2\pi}\sigma}\int_{-a/b}^{\infty}\exp(a+bx)\exp\left(-\frac{1}{2}\left(\frac{x-\mu}{\sigma}\right)^2\right)dx \\
&= \exp\left(a+b\mu+\frac{1}{2}b^2\sigma^2\right)\frac{1}{\sqrt{2\pi}\sigma}\int_{-a/b}^{\infty}\exp\left(-\frac{1}{2}\left(\frac{x-(b\sigma^2+\mu)}{\sigma}\right)^2\right)dx \\
&= \exp\left(a+b\mu+\frac{1}{2}b^2\sigma^2\right)\left(1-\Phi\left(-\frac{a/b+b\sigma^2+\mu}{\sigma}\right)\right) \\
&= \exp\left(a+b\mu+\frac{1}{2}b^2\sigma^2\right)\Phi\left(\frac{a/b+b\sigma^2+\mu}{\sigma}\right).
\end{aligned}$$

The remaining formulas can be similarly proved.

□

Appendix B.2. Exponential of Truncated Multivariate Gaussian

Let $(\Omega, \mathcal{F}, \mathbb{P})$ be a probability space and let $X := (X_1, \ldots, X_n)' \in \mathbb{R}^n$ be a Gaussian random variable with mean $\mu := (\mu_1, \ldots, \mu_n)'$ and covariance matrix Σ, i.e., $X \sim \mathcal{N}(\mu, \Sigma)$. For any lower limit $l := (l_1, \ldots, l_n)'$ and any transformation matrix $D \in \mathbb{R}^{n\times n}$ the moment generating function of the D-transformed random variable X at $u := (u_1, \ldots, u_n)'$ called $M(u, \mu, \Sigma, l, D)$ is given by:

$$M(u,\mu,\Sigma,l,D) := \mathbb{E}_{\mathbb{P}}\left[\exp(u'DX)\,\mathbb{1}_{\{X\geq l\}}\right] = \mathbb{P}\left(\hat{X}\geq l-\mu\right)\exp\left(u'D\mu+\frac{1}{2}u'D\Sigma D'u\right),$$

where $\hat{X} \geq l-\mu$ holds component-by-component, i.e $\hat{X}_i \geq l_i - \mu_i\ \forall\, 1 \leq i \leq n$, and $\hat{X} \sim \mathcal{N}(\Sigma D'u, \Sigma)$.

Proof. Similar to the steps in Horrace (2005) we define $Z := X - \mu$ and use that:

$$-\frac{1}{2}z'\Sigma^{-1}z + u'Dz = \frac{1}{2}u'D\Sigma D'u - \frac{1}{2}\left(z - \Sigma D'u\right)'\Sigma^{-1}\left(z - \Sigma D'u\right)$$

holds for all $z \in \mathbb{R}$. Then, we get:

$$\begin{aligned} M\left(u,\mu,\Sigma,l,D\right) :&= \mathbb{E}_{\mathbb{P}}\left[\exp\left(u'DX\right)\mathbb{1}_{\{X\geq l\}}\right] \\ &= \exp\left(u'D\mu\right)\int_{l-\mu}^{\infty}\left(\frac{1}{2\pi}\right)^{n/2}\left(\frac{1}{|\Sigma|}\right)^{1/2}\exp\left(u'Dz - \frac{1}{2}z'\Sigma^{-1}z\right)dz \\ &= \mathbb{P}\left(\hat{X} \geq l - \mu\right)\exp\left(u'D\mu + \frac{1}{2}u'D\Sigma D'u\right), \end{aligned}$$

with $\hat{X} \sim \mathcal{N}\left(\Sigma D'u, \Sigma\right)$.

□

Appendix B.3. First Order Moments of Truncated Bivariate Gaussian

Let $(\Omega, \mathcal{F}, \mathbb{P})$ be a probability space and let $(X,Y)' \in \mathbb{R}^2$ be a Gaussian random variable with mean zero and standardized covariance matrix, i.e.,:

$$\mu := \begin{pmatrix} 0 \\ 0 \end{pmatrix} \quad \text{and} \quad \Sigma := \begin{pmatrix} 1 & \rho \\ \rho & 1 \end{pmatrix}.$$

Then, for any $h, k \in \mathbb{R}$ it follows:

$$\begin{aligned} \mathbb{E}_{\mathbb{P}}\left[X\mathbb{1}_{\{X>h,Y>k\}}\right] &= \varphi(h)\,\Phi\left(-\frac{k-\rho h}{\sqrt{1-\rho^2}}\right) + \rho\varphi(k)\,\Phi\left(-\frac{h-\rho k}{\sqrt{1-\rho^2}}\right), \\ \mathbb{E}_{\mathbb{P}}\left[X\mathbb{1}_{\{X<h,Y<k\}}\right] &= -\varphi(h)\,\Phi\left(\frac{k-\rho h}{\sqrt{1-\rho^2}}\right) - \rho\varphi(k)\,\Phi\left(\frac{h-\rho k}{\sqrt{1-\rho^2}}\right), \end{aligned}$$

with $\varphi(\cdot)$ denoting the probability density function of the univariate standard normal distribution.

Proof. The original proof of this claim is given in Rosenbaum (1961). However, as there are some errors in that reference, we prove it here. For $h, k \in \mathbb{R}$ the linear transformation $x := \sqrt{1-\rho^2}z + \rho y$ provides:

$$\begin{aligned} \mathbb{E}_{\mathbb{P}}\left[X\mathbb{1}_{\{X>h,Y>k\}}\right] &= \frac{1}{2\pi\sqrt{1-\rho^2}}\int_k^{\infty}\int_h^{\infty} x\exp\left(-\frac{1}{2}\left(\frac{x^2-2\rho xy+y^2}{1-\rho^2}\right)\right)\mathrm{d}x\mathrm{d}y \\ &= \frac{1}{2\pi}\int_k^{\infty}\int_{\frac{h-\rho y}{\sqrt{1-\rho^2}}}^{\infty}\left(z\sqrt{1-\rho^2}+\rho y\right)\exp\left(-\frac{1}{2}\left(z^2+y^2\right)\right)\mathrm{d}z\mathrm{d}y \\ &= \frac{\sqrt{1-\rho^2}}{2\pi}\int_k^{\infty}\left[-\exp\left(-\frac{1}{2}z^2\right)\right]_{\frac{h-\rho y}{\sqrt{1-\rho^2}}}^{\infty}\exp\left(-\frac{1}{2}y^2\right)\mathrm{d}y \\ &+ \frac{\rho}{2\pi}\int_{\frac{h-\rho k}{\sqrt{1-\rho^2}}}^{\infty}\int_k^{\infty} y\exp\left(-\frac{1}{2}y^2\right)\mathrm{d}y\exp\left(-\frac{1}{2}z^2\right)\mathrm{d}z \\ &+ \frac{\rho}{2\pi}\int_{-\infty}^{\frac{h-\rho k}{\sqrt{1-\rho^2}}}\int_{\frac{h-\sqrt{1-\rho^2}z}{\rho}}^{\infty} y\exp\left(-\frac{1}{2}y^2\right)\mathrm{d}y\exp\left(-\frac{1}{2}z^2\right)\mathrm{d}z \\ &= \frac{\sqrt{1-\rho^2}}{2\pi}\int_k^{\infty}\exp\left(-\frac{1}{2}\frac{y^2+h^2-2h\rho y}{1-\rho^2}\right)dy + \rho\varphi(k)\,\Phi\left(-\frac{h-\rho k}{\sqrt{1-\rho^2}}\right) \end{aligned}$$

$$+\frac{\rho}{2\pi}\int_{-\infty}^{\frac{h-\rho k}{\sqrt{1-\rho^2}}}\exp\left(-\frac{1}{2}\frac{h^2+z^2-2hz\sqrt{1-\rho^2}}{\rho^2}\right)dz.$$

After the linear transformation $y := \frac{h-\sqrt{1-\rho^2}z}{\rho}$ has been applied to the last integral, the first and the last expression can be summarized, and we end up with:

$$\mathbb{E}_{\mathbb{P}}\left[X\mathbb{1}_{\{X>h,Y>k\}}\right] = \frac{1}{2\pi\sqrt{1-\rho^2}}\int_k^{\infty}\exp\left(-\frac{1}{2}\frac{y^2+h^2-2h\rho y}{1-\rho^2}\right)dy + \rho\varphi(k)\,\Phi\left(-\frac{h-\rho k}{\sqrt{1-\rho^2}}\right).$$

The linear transformation $z := \frac{y-h\rho}{\sqrt{1-\rho^2}}$ provides the assertion. The second result is similarly derived. □

Let $(\tilde{X},\tilde{Y})' \in \mathbb{R}^2$ be a Gaussian random variable with mean $\tilde{\mu}$ and covariance matrix $\tilde{\Sigma}$ defined by:

$$\tilde{\mu} := \begin{pmatrix}\mu_X\\ \mu_Y\end{pmatrix} \quad \text{and} \quad \tilde{\Sigma} := \begin{pmatrix}\sigma_X^2 & \rho\sigma_X\sigma_Y\\ \rho\sigma_X\sigma_Y & \sigma_Y^2\end{pmatrix}.$$

Then, the standardized Gaussian random variables are given by:

$$X := \frac{\tilde{X}-\mu_X}{\sigma_X} \quad \text{and} \quad Y := \frac{\tilde{Y}-\mu_Y}{\sigma_Y}. \tag{B1}$$

For any fixed $\tilde{h},\tilde{k} \in \mathbb{R}$ we set:

$$h := \frac{\tilde{h}-\mu_X}{\sigma_X} \quad \text{and} \quad k := \frac{\tilde{k}-\mu_Y}{\sigma_Y}, \tag{B2}$$

and obtain:

$$\begin{aligned}\mathbb{E}_{\mathbb{P}}\left[\tilde{X}\mathbb{1}_{\{\tilde{X}>\tilde{h},\tilde{Y}>\tilde{k}\}}\right] &= \sigma_X\mathbb{E}_{\mathbb{P}}\left[X\mathbb{1}_{\{X>h,Y>k\}}\right] + \mu_X\mathbb{P}(X>h,Y>k),\\ \mathbb{E}_{\mathbb{P}}\left[\tilde{X}\mathbb{1}_{\{\tilde{X}<\tilde{h},\tilde{Y}<\tilde{k}\}}\right] &= \sigma_X\mathbb{E}_{\mathbb{P}}\left[X\mathbb{1}_{\{X<h,Y<k\}}\right] + \mu_X\mathbb{P}(X<h,Y<k),\end{aligned}$$

using the above expectations of the truncated, standardized Gaussian $(X,Y)'$.

Proof. Follows directly from Appendix (B1) and the characteristics of the expectation. □

Appendix B.4. Second Order Moments of Truncated Bivariate Gaussian

Let $(X,Y)' \in \mathbb{R}^2$ be the standardized Gaussian of Appendix B.3 with $0 < \rho < 1$. For $h,k \in \mathbb{R}$ we define:

$$l_1 := \frac{k-\rho h}{\sqrt{1-\rho^2}}, \quad l_2 := \frac{h-\rho k}{\sqrt{1-\rho^2}} \quad \text{and} \quad \bar{\Sigma} := \begin{pmatrix}1 & -\sqrt{1-\rho^2}\\ -\sqrt{1-\rho^2} & 1\end{pmatrix}.$$

Then, we have that:

$$\begin{aligned}\mathbb{E}_{\mathbb{P}}\left[X^2\mathbb{1}_{\{X>h,Y>k\}}\right] &= \varphi(h)\left[h\Phi(-l_1) + \rho\sqrt{1-\rho^2}\varphi(l_1)\right] + \left(1-\rho^2\right)\mathbb{P}(X>h,Y>k)\\ &\quad + \rho^2\Phi(-l_2)\left[\Phi(-k)+k\varphi(k)\right] + \rho^2\mathbb{P}(\bar{X}<-h,\bar{Y}<l_2),\\ \mathbb{E}_{\mathbb{P}}\left[XY\mathbb{1}_{\{X>h,Y>k\}}\right] &= \varphi(h)\left[\sqrt{1-\rho^2}\varphi(l_1) + h\rho\Phi(-l_1)\right] + \rho\Phi(-l_2)\left[k\varphi(k)+\Phi(-k)\right]\end{aligned}$$

$$
\begin{aligned}
&+\rho\mathbb{P}\left(\bar{X}<-h,\bar{Y}<l_2\right),\\
\mathbb{E}_{\mathbb{P}}\left[X^2\mathbb{1}_{\{X<h,Y<k\}}\right]&=\varphi\left(h\right)\left[\rho\sqrt{1-\rho^2}\varphi\left(l_1\right)-h\Phi\left(l_1\right)\right]+\left(1-\rho^2\right)\mathbb{P}\left(X<h,Y<k\right)\\
&+\rho^2\Phi\left(l_2\right)\left[\Phi\left(k\right)-k\varphi\left(k\right)\right]+\rho^2\mathbb{P}\left(\bar{X}<h,\bar{Y}<-l_2\right),\\
\mathbb{E}_{\mathbb{P}}\left[XY\mathbb{1}_{\{X<h,Y<k\}}\right]&=\varphi\left(h\right)\left[\sqrt{1-\rho^2}\varphi\left(l_1\right)-h\rho\Phi\left(l_1\right)\right]+\rho\Phi\left(l_2\right)\left[\Phi\left(k\right)-k\varphi\left(k\right)\right]\\
&+\rho\mathbb{P}\left(\bar{X}<h,\bar{Y}<-l_2\right),
\end{aligned}
$$

where $(\bar{X},\bar{Y})'$ denotes a bivariate Gaussian random variable with mean zero and variance $\bar{\Sigma}$.

Proof. The work in Rosenbaum (1961) shows for $h,k\in\mathbb{R}$:

$$
\begin{aligned}
\mathbb{E}_{\mathbb{P}}\left[X^2\mathbb{1}_{\{X>h,Y>k\}}\right]&=\int_k^\infty \exp\left(-\frac{1}{2}\left(\frac{h^2-2\rho hy+y^2}{1-\rho^2}\right)\right)\frac{\sqrt{1-\rho^2}\left(h+\rho y\right)}{2\pi}dy\\
&+\int_k^\infty \exp\left(-\frac{1}{2}y^2\right)\left(\frac{1-\rho^2+\rho^2y^2}{2\pi}\right)\int_{\frac{h-\rho y}{\sqrt{1-\rho^2}}}^\infty \exp\left(-\frac{1}{2}\right)dzdy.
\end{aligned}
$$

Next, we apply $y:=\sqrt{1-\rho^2}z+h\rho$ to the first integral, $x:=\sqrt{1-\rho^2}z+\rho y$ to the first two summands of the second integral and change the order of integration for the third term of the second integral:

$$
\begin{aligned}
\mathbb{E}_{\mathbb{P}}\left[X^2\mathbb{1}_{\{X>h,Y>k\}}\right]&=\int_{\frac{k-h\rho}{\sqrt{1-\rho^2}}}^\infty \frac{\left(1-\rho^2\right)\left(h+\rho\sqrt{1-\rho^2}z+\rho^2h\right)}{2\pi}\exp\left(-\frac{1}{2}\left(z^2+h^2\right)\right)dz\\
&+\frac{\sqrt{1-\rho^2}}{2\pi}\int_k^\infty\int_h^\infty \exp\left(-\frac{1}{2}\frac{x^2-2\rho xy+y^2}{1-\rho^2}\right)dxdy\\
&+\frac{\rho^2}{2\pi}\int_{\frac{h-\rho k}{\sqrt{1-\rho^2}}}^\infty\int_k^\infty y^2e^{-\frac{1}{2}y^2}dy\exp\left(-\frac{1}{2}z^2\right)dz\\
&+\frac{\rho^2}{2\pi}\int_{-\infty}^{\frac{h-\rho k}{\sqrt{1-\rho^2}}}\int_{\frac{h-\sqrt{1-\rho^2}z}{\rho}}^\infty y^2\exp\left(-\frac{1}{2}y^2\right)dy\exp\left(-\frac{1}{2}z^2\right)dz.
\end{aligned}
$$

Using (partial) integration we get after the substitution of $x:=\sqrt{1-\rho^2}z+\rho y$:

$$
\begin{aligned}
\mathbb{E}_{\mathbb{P}}\left[X^2\mathbb{1}_{\{X>h,Y>k\}}\right]&=\varphi\left(h\right)\left[\left(1-\rho^2\right)h\left(1+\rho^2\right)\Phi\left(-l_1\right)+\rho\left(1-\rho^2\right)^{3/2}\varphi\left(l_1\right)\right]\\
&+\left(1-\rho^2\right)\mathbb{P}\left(X>h,Y>k\right)+\rho^2\Phi\left(-l_2\right)\left[k\varphi\left(k\right)+\Phi\left(-k\right)\right]\\
&+\frac{\rho}{2\pi}\int_{-\infty}^{l_2}\left(h-\sqrt{1-\rho^2}z\right)\exp\left(-\frac{1}{2}\frac{h^2-2hz\sqrt{1-\rho^2}+z^2}{\rho^2}\right)\mathrm{d}z\\
&+\frac{\rho}{2\pi}\int_{-\infty}^{l_2}\int_h^\infty \exp\left(-\frac{1}{2}\frac{x^2-2xz\sqrt{1-\rho^2}+z^2}{\rho^2}\right)dxdz.
\end{aligned}
$$

If $w:=\frac{1}{\rho}(z-\sqrt{1-\rho^2}h)$ is used for the first integral and the direction of integrating x (second integral) is turned by $\tilde{x}:=-x$, summarizing all terms yields the statement. Similarly, the remaining can be proved.

□

Let $(\tilde{X},\tilde{Y})' \in \mathbb{R}^2$ be the Gaussian of Appendix B.3 with $0 < \rho < 1$ and let $(X,Y)'$ be its standardized counterpart in Appendix (B1). For any $\tilde{h},\tilde{k} \in \mathbb{R}$ let h and k be given by Appendix (B2). Then, it holds that:

$$\begin{aligned}
\mathbb{E}_{\mathbb{P}}\left[\tilde{X}^2\mathbb{1}_{\{\tilde{X}>\tilde{h},\tilde{Y}>\tilde{k}\}}\right] &= \sigma_X^2\mathbb{E}_{\mathbb{P}}\left[X^2\mathbb{1}_{\{X>h,Y>k\}}\right] + 2\sigma_X\mu_X\mathbb{E}_{\mathbb{P}}\left[X\mathbb{1}_{\{X>h,Y>k\}}\right] + \mu_X^2\mathbb{P}\left(X>h,Y>k\right),\\
\mathbb{E}_{\mathbb{P}}\left[\tilde{X}\tilde{Y}\mathbb{1}_{\{\tilde{X}>\tilde{h},\tilde{Y}>\tilde{k}\}}\right] &= \sigma_X\sigma_Y\mathbb{E}_{\mathbb{P}}\left[XY\mathbb{1}_{\{X>h,Y>k\}}\right] + \sigma_X\mu_Y\mathbb{E}_{\mathbb{P}}\left[X\mathbb{1}_{\{X>h,Y>k\}}\right]\\
&\quad + \sigma_Y\mu_X\mathbb{E}_{\mathbb{P}}\left[Y\mathbb{1}_{\{X>h,Y>k\}}\right] + \mu_X\mu_Y\mathbb{P}\left(X>h,Y>k\right).
\end{aligned}$$

In case of upper truncation $\mathbb{1}_{\{X>h,Y>k\}}$ has to be replaced by $\mathbb{1}_{\{X<h,Y<k\}}$.

Proof. Follows directly from Appendix (B1) and the characteristics of the expectation. □

Appendix C. Approximation Proofs

Appendix C.1. Proof of $S_{11}^{\mathbb{Q}^T}(D,\alpha,\beta,\mathbf{t})$

The $S_{11}^{\mathbb{Q}^T}(D,\alpha,\beta,\mathbf{t})$ in (15) is equal to:

$$\begin{aligned}
S_{11}^{\mathbb{Q}^T}(D,\alpha,\beta,\mathbf{t}) = 1 &+ \sum_{i=1}^{K}\mathbb{E}_{\mathbb{Q}^T}\left[\exp\left(-\beta\Delta t_i D\left(t_i\right)\right)\mathbb{1}_{\{0<D(t_i)\}}\right] - \sum_{i=1}^{K}\mathbb{E}_{\mathbb{Q}^T}\left[\exp\left(-\beta\Delta t_i D\left(t_i\right)\right)\mathbb{1}_{\{D(t_i)\geq\alpha\}}\right]\\
&- \sum_{i=1}^{K}\mathbb{Q}^T\left(0<D\left(t_i\right)<\alpha\right) + \sum_{i=1}^{K}\left(\exp\left(-\beta\alpha\Delta t_i\right)-1\right)\mathbb{Q}^T\left(D\left(t_i\right)\geq\alpha\right).
\end{aligned}$$

Since α and β are non-negative, we have that:

$$\begin{aligned}
S_{11}^{\mathbb{Q}^T}(D,\alpha,\beta,\mathbf{t}) &= 1 + \sum_{i=1}^{K}\mathbb{E}_{\mathbb{Q}^T}\left[\exp\left(-\beta\Delta t_i D\left(t_i\right)\right)\mathbb{1}_{\{0<\beta\Delta t_i D(t_i)\}}\right]\\
&\quad - \sum_{i=1}^{K}\exp\left(-\alpha\beta\Delta t_i\right)\mathbb{E}_{\mathbb{Q}^T}\left[\exp\left(-\beta\Delta t_i\left(D\left(t_i\right)-\alpha\right)\right)\mathbb{1}_{\{D(t_i)-\alpha\geq 0\}}\right]\\
&\quad - \sum_{i=1}^{K}\left(\mathbb{Q}^T\left(D\left(t_i\right)<\alpha\right) - \mathbb{Q}^T\left(D\left(t_i\right)\leq 0\right)\right)\\
&\quad + \sum_{i=1}^{K}\left(\exp\left(-\beta\alpha\Delta t_i\right)-1\right)\left(1-\mathbb{Q}^T\left(D\left(t_i\right)<\alpha\right)\right).
\end{aligned}$$

with the help of Appendix B.1 we obtain that:

$$\begin{aligned}
S_{11}^{\mathbb{Q}^T}(D,\alpha,\beta,\mathbf{t}) &= 1 + \sum_{i=1}^{K}\Bigg[\exp\left(-\beta\Delta t_i\mathbb{E}_{\mathbb{Q}^T}\left[D\left(t_i\right)\right] + \frac{1}{2}\beta^2\Delta t_i^2\mathbb{V}\mathrm{ar}_{\mathbb{Q}^T}\left[D\left(t_i\right)\right]\right)\\
&\qquad \cdot\Phi\left(\frac{\mathbb{E}_{\mathbb{Q}^T}\left[D\left(t_i\right)\right] - \beta\Delta t_i\mathbb{V}\mathrm{ar}_{\mathbb{Q}^T}\left[D\left(t_i\right)\right]}{\sqrt{\mathbb{V}\mathrm{ar}_{\mathbb{Q}^T}\left[D\left(t_i\right)\right]}}\right)\Bigg]\\
&\quad - \sum_{i=1}^{K}\Bigg[\exp\left(-\alpha\beta\Delta t_i - \beta\Delta t_i\mathbb{E}_{\mathbb{Q}^T}\left[D\left(t_i\right)-\alpha\right] + \frac{1}{2}\beta^2\Delta t_i^2\mathbb{V}\mathrm{ar}_{\mathbb{Q}^T}\left[D\left(t_i\right)-\alpha\right]\right)\\
&\qquad \cdot\Phi\left(\frac{\mathbb{E}_{\mathbb{Q}^T}\left[D\left(t_i\right)-\alpha\right] - \beta\Delta t_i\mathbb{V}\mathrm{ar}_{\mathbb{Q}^T}\left[D\left(t_i\right)-\alpha\right]}{\sqrt{\mathbb{V}\mathrm{ar}_{\mathbb{Q}^T}\left[D\left(t_i\right)-\alpha\right]}}\right)\Bigg]\\
&\quad - \sum_{i=1}^{K}\left[\Phi\left(\frac{\alpha-\mathbb{E}_{\mathbb{Q}^T}\left[D\left(t_i\right)\right]}{\sqrt{\mathbb{V}\mathrm{ar}_{\mathbb{Q}^T}\left[D\left(t_i\right)\right]}}\right) - \Phi\left(\frac{-\mathbb{E}_{\mathbb{Q}^T}\left[D\left(t_i\right)\right]}{\sqrt{\mathbb{V}\mathrm{ar}_{\mathbb{Q}^T}\left[D\left(t_i\right)\right]}}\right)\right]
\end{aligned}$$

$$+\sum_{i=1}^{K}\left(\exp\left(-\alpha\beta\Delta t_i\right)-1\right)\left(1-\Phi\left(\frac{\alpha-\mathbb{E}_{\mathbb{Q}^T}\left[D\left(t_i\right)\right]}{\sqrt{\mathbb{V}\text{ar}_{\mathbb{Q}^T}\left[D\left(t_i\right)\right]}}\right)\right).$$

Summarizing terms results in:

$$\begin{aligned}
S_{11}^{\mathbb{Q}^T}\left(D,\alpha,\beta,\mathbf{t}\right)=1+\sum_{i=1}^{K}&\left[\exp\left(-\beta\Delta t_i\mathbb{E}_{\mathbb{Q}^T}\left[D\left(t_i\right)\right]+\frac{1}{2}\beta^2\Delta t_i^2\mathbb{V}\text{ar}_{\mathbb{Q}^T}\left[D\left(t_i\right)\right]\right)\right.\\
&\cdot\left(\Phi\left(\frac{\mathbb{E}_{\mathbb{Q}^T}\left[D\left(t_i\right)\right]-\beta\Delta t_i\mathbb{V}\text{ar}_{\mathbb{Q}^T}\left[D\left(t_i\right)\right]}{\sqrt{\mathbb{V}\text{ar}_{\mathbb{Q}^T}\left[D\left(t_i\right)\right]}}\right)\right.\\
&\left.\left.-\Phi\left(\frac{\mathbb{E}_{\mathbb{Q}^T}\left[D\left(t_i\right)\right]-\alpha-\beta\Delta t_i\mathbb{V}\text{ar}_{\mathbb{Q}^T}\left[D\left(t_i\right)\right]}{\sqrt{\mathbb{V}\text{ar}_{\mathbb{Q}^T}\left[D\left(t_i\right)\right]}}\right)\right)\right]\\
&-\sum_{i=1}^{K}\left[\Phi\left(\frac{\alpha-\mathbb{E}_{\mathbb{Q}^T}\left[D\left(t_i\right)\right]}{\sqrt{\mathbb{V}\text{ar}_{\mathbb{Q}^T}\left[D\left(t_i\right)\right]}}\right)-\Phi\left(\frac{-\mathbb{E}_{\mathbb{Q}^T}\left[D\left(t_i\right)\right]}{\sqrt{\mathbb{V}\text{ar}_{\mathbb{Q}^T}\left[D\left(t_i\right)\right]}}\right)\right]\\
&+\sum_{i=1}^{K}\left(\exp\left(-\alpha\beta\Delta t_i\right)-1\right)\left(1-\Phi\left(\frac{\alpha-\mathbb{E}_{\mathbb{Q}^T}\left[D\left(t_i\right)\right]}{\sqrt{\mathbb{V}\text{ar}_{\mathbb{Q}^T}\left[D\left(t_i\right)\right]}}\right)\right)
\end{aligned}$$

Finally, we use the definitions of $h_1\left(\beta_l,D,t_i\right)$ and $h_2\left(\alpha_l,\beta_l,D,t_i\right)$ in (19) to derive (20). □

Appendix C.2. Proof of $S_2^{\mathbb{Q}^T}\left(D,\alpha,\beta,\mathbf{t}\right)$

At first, we get rid of the products in $S_2^{\mathbb{Q}^T}\left(D,\tilde{Y},\alpha,\beta,\mathbf{t}\right)$ in (18) and properly split the indicator sets. For the first expression we use Appendix B.1. Then, we summarize the $\mathbb{Q}^T$-probabilities and so, we get:

$$\begin{aligned}
S_2^{\mathbb{Q}^T}\left(D,\tilde{Y},\alpha,\beta,\mathbf{t}\right)=&\exp\left(\mathbb{E}_{\mathbb{Q}^T}\left[\tilde{Y}\left(T\right)\right]+\frac{1}{2}\mathbb{V}\text{ar}_{\mathbb{Q}^T}\left[\tilde{Y}\left(T\right)\right]\right)\Phi\left(\frac{\mathbb{E}_{\mathbb{Q}^T}\left[\tilde{Y}\left(T\right)\right]+\mathbb{V}\text{ar}_{\mathbb{Q}^T}\left[\tilde{Y}\left(T\right)\right]}{\sqrt{\mathbb{V}\text{ar}_{\mathbb{Q}^T}\left[\tilde{Y}\left(T\right)\right]}}\right)\\
&+\sum_{i=1}^{K}\mathbb{E}_{\mathbb{Q}^T}\left[\exp\left(-\beta\Delta t_iD\left(t_i\right)+\tilde{Y}\left(T\right)\right)\mathbb{1}_{\{0<D(t_i)\}}\mathbb{1}_{\{\tilde{Y}(T)\geq 0\}}\right]\\
&-\sum_{i=1}^{K}\mathbb{E}_{\mathbb{Q}^T}\left[\exp\left(-\beta\Delta t_iD\left(t_i\right)+\tilde{Y}\left(T\right)\right)\mathbb{1}_{\{\alpha\leq D(t_i)\}}\mathbb{1}_{\{\tilde{Y}(T)\geq 0\}}\right]\\
&-\sum_{i=1}^{K}\mathbb{E}_{\mathbb{Q}^T}\left[\exp\left(-\beta\Delta t_iD\left(t_i\right)\right)\mathbb{1}_{\{0<D(t_i)\}}\mathbb{1}_{\{\tilde{Y}(T)\geq 0\}}\right]\\
&+\sum_{i=1}^{K}\mathbb{E}_{\mathbb{Q}^T}\left[\exp\left(-\beta\Delta t_iD\left(t_i\right)\right)\mathbb{1}_{\{\alpha\leq D(t_i)\}}\mathbb{1}_{\{\tilde{Y}(T)\geq 0\}}\right]\\
&-\sum_{i=1}^{K}\mathbb{E}_{\mathbb{Q}^T}\left[\exp\left(\tilde{Y}\left(T\right)\right)\mathbb{1}_{\{0<D(t_i)\}}\mathbb{1}_{\{\tilde{Y}(T)\geq 0\}}\right]\\
&+\sum_{i=1}^{K}\mathbb{E}_{\mathbb{Q}^T}\left[\exp\left(\tilde{Y}\left(T\right)\right)\mathbb{1}_{\{\alpha\leq D(t_i)\}}\mathbb{1}_{\{\tilde{Y}(T)\geq 0\}}\right]\\
&+\sum_{i=1}^{K}\mathbb{Q}^T\left(0<D\left(t_i\right),\tilde{Y}\left(T\right)\geq 0\right)\\
&+\sum_{i=1}^{K}\exp\left(-\beta\alpha\Delta t_i\right)\mathbb{E}_{\mathbb{Q}^T}\left[\exp\left(\tilde{Y}\left(T\right)\right)\mathbb{1}_{\{D(t_i)\geq\alpha\}}\mathbb{1}_{\{\tilde{Y}(T)\geq 0\}}\right]
\end{aligned}$$

$$- \sum_{i=1}^{K} \exp(-\beta\alpha\Delta t_i)\, \mathbb{Q}^T \left(D(t_i) \geq \alpha, \tilde{Y}(T) \geq 0\right)$$
$$- \sum_{i=1}^{K} \mathbb{E}_{\mathbb{Q}^T} \left[\exp\left(\tilde{Y}(T)\right) \mathbb{1}_{\{D(t_i)\geq\alpha\}} \mathbb{1}_{\{Y(T)\geq 0\}}\right] - \left(1 - \mathbb{Q}^T \left(\tilde{Y}(T) < 0\right)\right).$$

Using the notation in (23) and Appendix B.2 we obtain (24).

□

References

Bacinello, A.; Millossovich, P.; Olivieri, A.; Pitacco, E. Variable annuities: A unifying valuation approach. *Insur. Math. Econ.* **2011**, *49*, 285–297.

Ledlie, M.; Corry, D.; Finkelstein, G.; Ritchie, A.; Su, K.; Wilson, D. Variable Annuities. *Br. Actuar. J.* **2008**, *14*, 327–389.

Gatzert, N. The secondary market for life insurance in the United Kingdom, Germany, and the United States: Comparison and overview. *Risk Manag. Insur. Rev.* **2010**, *13*, 279–301.

Shevchenko, P.; Luo, X. A unified pricing of variable annuity guarantees under the optimal stochastic control framework. *Risks* **2016**, *4*, 22, doi:10.3390/risks4030022.

Knoller, C.; Kraut, G.; Schoenmaekers, P. On the propensity to surrender a variable annuity contract. *J. Risk Insur.* **2015**, doi:10.1111/jori.12076.

Krayzler, M.; Zagst, R.; Brunner, B. Closed-form solutions for guaranteed minimum accumulation and death benefits. *Eur. Actuar. J.* **2016**, *6*, 197–231.

Tsai, C.; Kuo, W.; Chen, W. Early surrender and the distribution of policy reserves. *Insur. Math. Econ.* **2002**, *31*, 429–445.

Kuo, W.; Tsai, C.; Chen, W. An empirical study on the lapse rate: The cointegration approach. *J. Risk Insur.* **2003**, *70*, 489–508.

Outreville, A. Whole-life insurance lapse rates and the emergency fund hypothesis. *Insur. Math. Econ.* **1990**, *9*, 249–255.

Kim, C. Modeling surrender and lapse rates with economic variables. *N. Am. Actuar. J.* **2005**, *9*, 56–70.

Jiang, S. Voluntary termination of life insurance policies: Evidence from the U.S. market. *N. Am. Actuar. J.* **2010**, *14*, 369–380.

Kiesenbauer, D. Main determinants of lapse in the German life insurance industry. *N. Am. Actuar. J.* **2012**, *16*, 52–73.

Kent, J.; Ed, M. *Dynamic Policyholder Behaviour*; Presentation; Staple Inn Actuarial Society: London, UK, 2008.

Eling, M.; Kiesenbauer, D. Does surplus participation reflect market discipline? An analysis of the German life insurance market. *J. Financ. Serv. Res.* **2012**, *42*, 1–27.

Bacinello, A. Fair valuation of a guaranteed life insurance participating contract embedding a surrender option. *J. Risk Insur.* **2003**, *70*, 461–487.

Bacinello, A. Endogenous model of surrender conditions in equity-linked life insurance. *Insur. Math. Econ.* **2005**, *37*, 270–296.

Milevsky, M.; Salisbury, T. Financial valuation of guaranteed minimum withdrawal benefits. *Insur. Math. Econ.* **2006**, *38*, 21–38.

Chen, Z.; Vetzal, K.; Forsyth, P. The effect of modeling parameters on the value of GMWB guarantees. *Insur. Math. Econ.* **2008**, *43*, 165–173.

Kling, A.; Ruez, F.; Ruß, J. The impact of stochastic volatility on pricing, hedging, and hedge efficiency of variable annuity guarantees. *ASTIN Bull.* **2011**, *41*, 511–545.

Moore, K. Optimal surrender strategies for equity-indexed annuity investors. *Insur. Math. Econ.* **2009**, *44*, 1–18.

Moenig, T.; Bauer, D. Revisiting the risk-neutral approach to optimal policyholder behavior: A study of withdrawal guarantees in variable annuities. *Rev. Financ.* **2015**, doi:10.1093/rof/rfv018.

Albizzati, M.; Geman, H. Interest rate risk management and valuation of the surrender option in life insurance policies. *J. Risk Insur.* **1994**, *61*, 616–637.

Mudavanhu, B.; Zhuo, J. Valuing Guaranteed Minimum Death Benefits in Variable Annuities and the Option to Lapse. Working Paper, 2002.
Kolkiewicz, A.; Tan, K. Unit-linked life insurance contracts with lapse rates dependent on economic factors. *Ann. Actuar. Sci.* **2006**, *1*, 49–78.
De Giovanni, D. Lapse rate modeling: A rational expectation approach. *Scand. Actuar. J.* **2010**, *2010*, 56–67.
Loisel, S.; Milhaud, X. From deterministic to stochastic surrender risk models: Impact of correlation crises on economic capital. *Eur. J. Oper. Res.* **2011**, *214*, 348–357.
Hull, J.; White, A. Numerical procedures for implementing term structure models I: Single-factor models. *J. Deriv.* **1994**, *2*, 7–16.
Dahl, M. Stochastic mortality in life insurance: Market reserves and mortality-linked insurance contracts. *Insur. Math. Econ.* **2004**, *35*, 113–136.
Dahl, M.; Møller, T. Valuation and hedging of life insurance liabilities with systematic mortality risk. *Insur. Math. Econ.* **2006**, *39*, 193–217.
Biffis, E. Affine processes for dynamic mortality and actuarial valuations. *Insur. Math. Econ.* **2005**, *37*, 443–468.
Harrison, D. Is failure imminent for the United Kingdom's annuity market? *Pensions* **2012**, *17*, 71–79.
Biffis, E.; Denuit, M.; Devolder, P. Stochastic mortality under measure changes. *Scand. Actuar. J.* **2010**, *2010*, 284–311.
Lando, D. On cox processes and credit risky securities. *Rev. Deriv. Res.* **1998**, *2*, 99–120.
Duffie, D.; Pan, J.; Singleton, K. Transform analysis and asset pricing for affine jump-diffusions. *Econometrica* **2000**, *68*, 1343–1376.
Flanders, H. Differentiation under the integral sign. *Am. Math. Mon.* **1973**, *80*, 615–627.
Zagst, R. *Interest Rate Management*; Springer Finance: Berlin, Germany, 2002.
Cannon, E.; Tonks, I. UK annuity price series, 1957–2002. *Financ. Hist. Rev.* **2004**, *11*, 165–196.
Ramsauer, F. Pricing of Variable Annuities—Incorporation of Policyholder Behavior. Master's Thesis, Technical University of Munich, München, Germany, 2013.
Horrace, W. Some results on the multivariate truncated normal distribution. *J. Multivar. Anal.* **2005**, *94*, 209–221.
Rosenbaum, S. Moments of a truncated bivariate normal distribution. *J. R. Stat. Soc. Ser. B* **1961**, *23*, 405–408.

risks

MDPI

Article

Evaluating Extensions to Coherent Mortality Forecasting Models

Syazreen Shair [1], Sachi Purcal [2,*,†] and Nick Parr [3,†]

1 Actuarial Science Department, Faculty of Computer & Mathematical Sciences, University of Technology MARA, Shah Alam 40450, Malaysia; syazreen@tmsk.uitm.edu.my
2 Department of Applied Finance & Actuarial Studies, Faculty of Business and Economics, Macquarie University, Sydney, NSW 2109, Australia
3 Department of Marketing & Management, Macquarie University, Sydney, NSW 2109, Australia; nick.parr@mq.edu.au
* Correspondence: sachi.purcal@mq.edu.au; Tel.: +61-2-9850-8571
† These authors contributed equally to this work.

Academic Editor: Pavel Shevchenko
Received: 25 October 2016; Accepted: 10 February 2017; Published: 10 March 2017

Abstract: Coherent models were developed recently to forecast the mortality of two or more sub-populations simultaneously and to ensure long-term non-divergent mortality forecasts of sub-populations. This paper evaluates the forecast accuracy of two recently-published coherent mortality models, the Poisson common factor and the product-ratio functional models. These models are compared to each other and the corresponding independent models, as well as the original Lee–Carter model. All models are applied to age-gender-specific mortality data for Australia and Malaysia and age-gender-ethnicity-specific data for Malaysia. The out-of-sample forecast error of log death rates, male-to-female death rate ratios and life expectancy at birth from each model are compared and examined across groups. The results show that, in terms of overall accuracy, the forecasts of both coherent models are consistently more accurate than those of the independent models for Australia and for Malaysia, but the relative performance differs by forecast horizon. Although the product-ratio functional model outperforms the Poisson common factor model for Australia, the Poisson common factor is more accurate for Malaysia. For the ethnic groups application, ethnic-coherence gives better results than gender-coherence. The results provide evidence that coherent models are preferable to independent models for forecasting sub-populations' mortality.

Keywords: coherent mortality forecasting models; Lee–Carter model; mortality forecasting accuracy; functional data model

1. Introduction

The widely-used Lee–Carter Lee and Carter (1992) model is an extrapolative mortality forecasting model that uses a single time-varying index of the mortality level. Despite its success forecasting U.S. mortality, the Lee–Carter model's assumptions have not been found to be universally appropriate (Booth et al. 2002), leading to a range of modifications being proposed in the literature (Booth et al. 2002; Lee and Miller 2001; Li 2010; Brouhns et al. 2002; Renshaw and Haberman 2003; Hyndman and Ullah 2007). It is noteworthy that the mortality forecasts of the modified Lee–Carter models have proven to be more accurate than those of the original model (Booth et al. 2005 2006; Shang et al. 2011). The Lee–Carter model and its earlier extensions are independent models (Li and Lee 2005) and, as such, forecast sub-populations (such as males and females) separately, failing to account for any relationship between groups (Li 2013). Such independent models may produce divergent forecasts between two or more sub-populations, which may poorly represent the smaller populations within the same larger region or country (Hyndman et al. 2013).

Coherent models were developed to forecast the mortality of two or more sub-populations simultaneously and to ensure long-term non-divergent forecasts of sub-populations (Li and Lee 2005; Li 2013; Hyndman et al. 2013). This type of joint forecasting is important, for example, to estimate deaths of both genders concurrently or to calculate premiums for life insurance and annuities that depend on the death or survival of more than one life (Li et al. 2016). The augmented common factor model Li and Lee (2005) extends the Lee–Carter model in two ways. It incorporates a mortality reference (the aggregated death rates of sub-populations) in the base model to maintain historic relationships between groups. It also restricts the time-component of sub-populations to $AR(1)$ forecasts, guaranteeing non-divergent forecasts in the long run. This technique improved the divergent forecasts of independent models over a variety of metrics and spawned the development of further new coherent models, including the Poisson common factor model Li (2013) and the product ratio functional model Hyndman et al. (2013). Both of these models are examined in detail in Section 2 below.

Which of the independent and coherent models provide better forecasts and why? While the literature includes comparisons between different independent models (Lee and Miller 2001; Booth et al. 2005 2006; Shang et al. 2011), as well as between independent and coherent functional time series models (Hyndman et al. 2013), no comparisons between types of coherent models have been made. Further, the application of coherent forecasting models has been limited to developed countries. The purpose of this research is to evaluate the forecast accuracy of two recent coherent models, the Poisson common factor model and the product ratio functional model. The two coherent models are compared to each other, as well as to their respective independent versions: the Poisson Lee–Carter model and the weighted functional model. In addition, as all four models are extensions of the Lee–Carter model, we include Lee–Carter forecasts as a performance benchmark. We also extend the application of coherent mortality forecasting to a less developed nation, Malaysia, as well as treating Australia, with gender-coherence being applied to Malaysian and Australian age-gender-specific mortality data. Furthermore, we apply two types of coherency: gender-coherence and ethnic-coherence to Malaysian age-gender-ethnic-specific mortality data. We forecast death rates, male-to-female death rate ratios and life expectancy at birth and compare the out-of-sample forecasts with the observations from official statistics.

Section 2 of this paper explains the coherent models and describes the error measures that we use to estimate the out-of-sample forecast errors. Section 3 discusses the observed mortality rates and their trends in Australia and Malaysia. In Sections 4 and 5, coherent and independent models are applied to gender-specific data for Australia and Malaysia, as well as ethnic-specific mortality data; the forecast accuracy of death rates, male-to-female sex ratios and life expectancy at birth are reported. Section 6 discusses the research outcomes in detail. Finally, Section 7 concludes.

2. Coherent Mortality Forecasting

2.1. Poisson Common Factor Model

The Poisson common factor model, based on the Poisson parametric distribution function, was extended by Li (2013) to estimate the number of deaths directly. The method extends the independent model Poisson–Lee–Carter model of Brouhns et al. (2002). The age-specific mortality rates, $m_{x,t,i}$, for lives aged x in year t and belonging to the i-th sub-population are given by:

$$\log(m_{x,t,i}) = a_{x,i} + \beta_x K_t + \sum_{j=1}^{J} b_{x,i,j} k_{t,i,j} + \epsilon_{x,t,i} \quad (1)$$

where $a_{x,i}$ is the average of the log age-specific death rates for the i-th group over the fitting period, $\beta_x K_t$ is the product of an age-component and time-component for the common factor, $b_{x,i,j} k_{t,i,j}$ is the product of an age-component and a time-component for the i-th subgroup and the j-th additional subgroup-specific factor and $\epsilon_{x,t,i}$ are the subgroup-specific residuals for age x and year t.

Equation (1) is identical to its independent version, the Poisson–Lee–Carter model (Brouhns et al. 2002), if the value of $\beta_x K_t$ is zero and just one gender-specific factor is considered. Clearly, without common factor variables, the model does not account for inter-relationships between sub-populations.

The parameters of the Poisson common factor model are estimated, as is the case with its independent version, using maximum log-likelihood. Deaths are assumed to follow the Poisson distribution function, with:

$$D_{x,t,i} = Poisson(E_{x,t,i}, m_{x,t,i}) \tag{2}$$

and:

$$m_{x,t,i} = \exp\left(a_{x,i} + \beta_x K_t + \sum_{j=1}^{J} b_{x,i,j} k_{t,i,j}\right), \tag{3}$$

where $D_{x,t,i}$ are the deaths of those aged x in year t belonging to the i-th sub-population and $E_{x,t,i}$ are the corresponding exposures. The age-specific mortality rates $m_{x,t,i}$ are considered unknown values and are estimated using (3) subject to the constraints $\sum_t K_t = 0$ and $\sum_x \beta_x = 1$ and $2IJ$ constraints of $\sum_t k_{t,i,j} = 0$ and $\sum_x b_{x,i,j} = 1$, where the number of factors I and J can be optimally determined using either the Bayesian Information Criterion (BIC) or the Akaike Information Criterion (AIC).

Following Brouhns et al. (2002), parameters $a_{x,i}$, β_x, K_t, $b_{x,i,j}$ and $k_{t,i,j}$ are estimated via an iterative updating scheme Li (2013). The time-component of the common factor is a non-stationary process; thus, a random walk with drift model is used to forecast the data. The subgroup-specific (like gender) time-components, on the other hand, are stationary; hence, a p-th order autoregressive model $AR(p)$ is used. Finally, age-specific death rate forecasts can be retrieved by placing the forecast time-component factors and estimated age factors into Equation (3).

2.2. Product-Ratio Functional Model

Hyndman et al. (2013) extended the independent Hyndman and Ullah (2007) functional time series model to model two quantities, the product function $p_{x,t}$ and the ratio function $r_{x,t,i}$, where:

$$p_{x,t} = \left(\prod_{i=1}^{I} f_{x,t,i}\right)^{1/I} \tag{4}$$

and:

$$r_{x,t,i} = \frac{f_{x,t,i}}{p_{x,t}}, \tag{5}$$

and where $i = 1, 2 \ldots, I$ refers to the i-th sub-population and the $f_{x,t,i}$ are the smoothed age and time-specific mortality rates for the i-th population. As a smoothing procedure, Hyndman et al. (2013) use weighted penalized regression splines. A monotonic increasing constraint over time is imposed on ages x and above. Intuitively, the product function $p_{x,t}$ is estimated as the geometric mean of the smoothed rates of sub-populations, which represents the general trend or mortality reference of sub-populations, while $r_{x,t,i}$ is the ratio of one sub-population's rates to the geometric mean, representing the mortality difference of a particular sub-population from the general trend.

The product and ratio functions have the advantage of being easy to use and are uncorrelated with each other on a log scale. Both are then used in the functional independent model (Hyndman and Ullah 2007) with:

$$\log p_{x,t} = ap_x + \sum_{l=1}^{L} \beta_{x,l} K_{t,l} + ep_{x,t} \tag{6}$$

and:

$$\log r_{x,t,i} = ar_{x,i} + \sum_{\xi=1}^{\Xi} b_{x,i,\xi} k_{t,i,\xi} + er_{x,t,i}, \tag{7}$$

where ap_x and $ar_{x,i}$ average the logs of the product and ratio functions respectively and l and ξ index the principal components. The time components $K_{t,l}$ and the $k_{t,i,\xi}$ and the age components $\beta_{x,l}$ and $b_{x,i,\xi}$ are estimated using weighted principal component analysis following Shang et al. (2011), which applies more weight to recent data. The weighting technique is used to cater for change over time in $\beta_{x,l}$ and $b_{x,i,\xi}$. In contrast to Li and Lee (2005), who used only the first principal component, the work of Hyndman et al. (2013) used up to six components. The time-component for the product function $K_{t,l}$ displays a linear decreasing trend and therefore is more appropriately forecast using a non-stationary series model, $ARIMA(p,d,q)$. A non-divergent mortality forecast is attained when $k_{t,i,\xi}$ is restricted to being forecast by a stationary time series model, either an autoregressive moving average $ARMA(p)$ or an auto-regressive fractional integrated moving average $ARFIMA(p,d,q)$.

The estimated average death rates and age factors, as well as the forecast of time components are put into Equations (6) and (7) to get the forecast values of the product and ratio functions. Subsequently, the age-specific mortality forecasts for each sub-population are obtained by simply multiplying the forecast rates of the product and ratio functions,

$$\log f_{x,t,i} = \log(p_{x,t} r_{x,t,i}) = a_{x,i} + \sum_{l=1}^{L} \beta_{x,l} K_{t,l} + \sum_{\xi=1}^{\Xi} b_{x,i,\xi} k_{t,i,\xi} + e_{x,t,i}, \tag{8}$$

where $a_{x,i} = ap_x + ar_{x,i}$ and $e_{x,t,i} = ep_{x,t} + er_{x,t,i}$ are the mortality average and error terms, respectively, for a particular group. Equation (8) is similar to that of Li (2013) given in (1) when there is no additional component for $\beta_x K_t$. The product-ratio functional model and its independent predecessor, the weighted functional model, were implemented using the demography package for R (Hyndman 2013).

2.3. Measurement of Forecast Accuracy

We divide T-year observations of a particular i-th sub-population into two parts. First, the in-sample data, which consist of the first n-year observations $\{y_{x,i,1}, y_{x,i,2}, \ldots, y_{x,i,n}\}$, are used in each model to estimate the parameters. Second, the out-of-sample data, comprising the remaining $T - n = t$ years of data $\{y_{x,i,n+1}, y_{x,i,n+2}, \ldots, y_{x,i,n+t}\}$, are compared to the forecast rates $\{F_{x,i,n+1|n}, F_{x,i,n+2|n}, \ldots, F_{x,i,n+t|n}\}$.

With the out-of-sample data, the forecast accuracy of each model is estimated using the following error measurements:

$$MAFE_i = \frac{\sum_{\tau=1}^{t} \sum_{x=1}^{p} \left| F_{x,i,n+\tau|n} - y_{x,i,n+\tau} \right|}{pt}, \tag{9}$$

$$MFE = \frac{\sum_{\tau=1}^{t} \sum_{x=1}^{p} \left(F_{x,i,n+\tau|n} - y_{x,i,n+\tau} \right)}{pt}, \tag{10}$$

and:

$$MAPFE_i = \frac{\sum_{\tau=1}^{t} \sum_{x=1}^{p} \left| \left(F_{x,i,n+\tau|n} - y_{x,i,n+\tau} \right) \Big/ y_{x,i,n+\tau} \right| \times 100}{pt} \tag{11}$$

for the p age groups. We use mean absolute forecast error ($MAFE_i$) and mean forecast error (MFE_i) to evaluate the forecast accuracy of the log death rates and life expectancy for the i-th sub-population.

For male-to-female death rate ratio forecasts, errors are estimated using the mean absolute percentage forecast error ($MAPFE_i$).

3. Mortality Data

In this study, we use central age-gender-specific death rates for Australia and Malaysia and age-gender-ethnic-specific death rates for Malaysia together with their respective mid-year exposures. The data for Australia are taken from University of California, Berkeley (USA), and Max Planck Institute for Demographic Research (Germany) (2013) for the period 1921 to 2009 for ages zero to 110. Data for Malaysia are from the Malaysian Department of Statistics from 1965 to 2011 for ages zero to 80.[1] According to Mikkelsen et al. (2015), Malaysia currently has 'good' quality mortality data, with substantial improvements having occurred since 2000.

The mortality rates at the oldest ages fluctuate widely. Following Li (2013), we exclude some of the oldest rates and include only data up to age 90 for Australia.[2] The original Lee and Carter (1992) model uses the data from the earliest available year regardless of whether or not the mortality index has been subject to change over time. Major shifts in the mortality index can be seen in the late 1960s for Australia and in the early 1970s and late 1990s for Malaysia (see Figure 1). Hence, to improve forecast accuracy, an appropriate starting year for the fitting period must be selected for the Lee–Carter extensions to ensure that the mortality index is reasonably linearly decreasing.

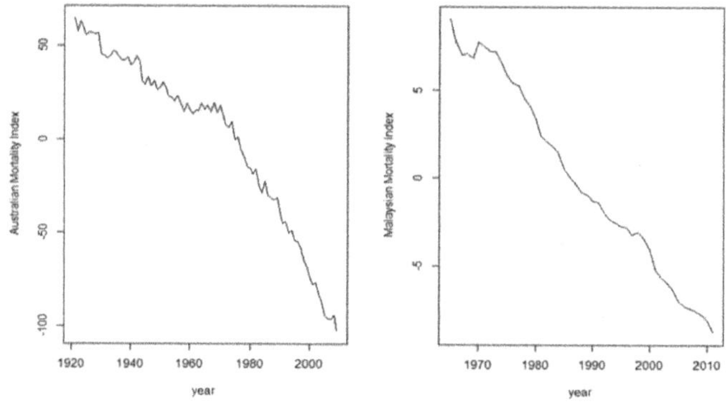

Figure 1. The mortality index, or time component, K_t, estimated from the Lee–Carter model for the Australian total population from 1921 to 2009 (**left**) and for the Malaysian total population from 1965 to 2011 (**right**).

Booth et al. (2002) suggest that 1968 and 1970 are the best starting years for the fitting period for Australian males and females, whereas Hyndman et al. (2013) used 1950 to fit the age-region-specific death rates to the product-ratio functional model. In this study, for comparative purposes, all models except for the original Lee–Carter model will use the same starting years, namely 1968 for Australia and 1975 for Malaysia.

The log age-specific death rate plots for males and females are shown in Figure 2. The top panel is Australian death rates, which clearly exhibit a similar pattern between males and females. The decreasing rates over the years from red to purple (1968 to 2009) occur in all ages. However, mortality has been decreasing at a slower rate in recent years: note the small decrease from blue to

1 The time period begins with the establishment of the modern Malaysian state. Data are not available for ages above 80.
2 Although Malaysian data runs to age 80, Australian data above age 80 were included in order to avoid loss of information.

purple curves (1990 to 2009). According to Parr et al. (2016), Australian mortality rates will continue decreasing, with the fastest decreases occurring at ages below 20 and between 40 and 80.

The male accident hump has decreased more rapidly than that for females in recent years. According to Pollard (1996), the disappearance of the accident hump among young males aged 14 to 24 and in the early adult ages 25 to 40 since the late 1980s is due to the declining rate of motor accident fatalities, a result of the introduction of random breath testing for alcohol and seat-belt regulations.

The bottom panel displays the inconsistent patterns between Malaysian female and male mortality, especially for the accident hump ages. Female mortality has declined consistently over the years (1975 to 2011) in all age groups, with a thin accident hump. The mortality of males over the accident hump ages (15 to 39) fluctuated in the early years (1975 to 1997). However, a decreasing trend can be seen in the later years, starting from 1998. The inconsistent pattern of change over time between the genders leads to the highest ratio of male-to-female death rates in this age group being from 1975 to 1997 (Mohamed et al. 2012).

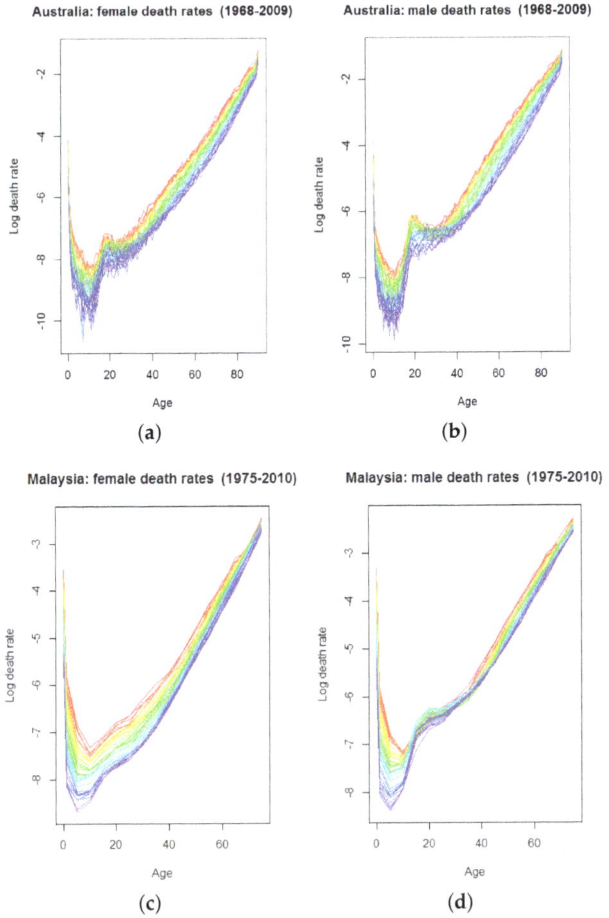

Figure 2. The rainbow age-specific log death rate plots for (**a**) Australian females, (**b**) Australian males, (**c**) Malaysian females and (**d**) Malaysian males.

4. Forecast Evaluation of Coherent Models Using Australian and Malaysian Male and Female Mortality

Our forecasts are based on five different mortality forecasting models, including two coherent models, the Poisson common factor and product-ratio functional models, and their independent versions, the Poisson Lee–Carter and weighted functional models. These four models are extensions of the Lee–Carter model; hence, the original model is included as a performance benchmark.

This section reports the forecast error of log age-gender-specific death rates, male-to-female death rate ratios and life expectancy at birth for the five different mortality forecasting methods (coherent and independent) for Australia and Malaysia.

4.1. Log Death Rate Forecasts

Table 1 presents the mean absolute forecast errors of log death rates for different methods averaged over age and year for male and female mortality rates in Australia and Malaysia.[3] In comparison to the independent models, both coherent models are more accurate for three out of four sub-populations—Australian males and females and Malaysian females—while the independent models perform better than the coherent models for Malaysian males. In terms of the overall accuracy (averaged over male and female errors), the coherent models perform better than the independent models for Australia, but underperform for Malaysia. The product-ratio functional model (coherent) performs the best for Australia, while the Poisson–Lee–Carter model (independent) performs the best for Malaysia.

Of the two coherent methods, the product-ratio functional model is more accurate than its counterpart, the Poisson common factor model, and proved to be the best model for three out of four sub-populations: Australian males and females and Malaysian females. When taking the average over genders, the product-ratio functional model performs better than the Poisson common factor model for Australia, but less well for Malaysia. Among the five models, all Lee–Carter extensions perform significantly better than the original model for both genders in Australia and for females in Malaysia. It is noteworthy that for Malaysian male mortality, the Lee–Carter model is more accurate than both coherent models, but underperforms the other independent models.

Table 1. Mean Absolute Forecast Error ($MAFE$) of log death rates for males and females by method, gender and country.

	$MAFE$					
	Australia			Malaysia		
	Male	Female	Overall	Male	Female	Overall
20-year forecasts						
Poisson–Lee–Carter	0.184	0.162	0.173	0.118	0.100	0.109
Poisson common factor	0.175	0.156	0.166	0.152	0.089	0.120
Weighted functional	0.171	0.135	0.153	0.123	0.111	0.117
Product-ratio functional	0.163	0.134	0.149	0.170	0.077	0.124
Lee–Carter	0.472	0.333	0.402	0.150	0.179	0.164

Table 2 summarises the corresponding mean forecast errors. The Lee–Carter model underestimates Australian male and female mortality rates substantially, in contrast to the other four models. For Malaysia, all models consistently underestimate both genders' mortality with the Lee–Carter model being the least accurate model for Malaysian females. Consistent with Table 1, in terms of overall accuracy, the product-ratio functional model is the most accurate for Australia, while the Poisson Lee–Carter is the most accurate for Malaysia.

---

3 Means are over age groups and years in the out-of-sample period; 'overall' refers to the average of the male and female errors.

Figure 3 shows the mean forecast errors by age. Clearly, the original Lee–Carter model produces significant errors for Australia and underestimates the mortality for people under 40 and overestimates the mortality of those who are aged above 40. However, for Malaysia, the Lee–Carter forecasts are fairly similar to the other four methods, especially for males. The errors for the coherent (dashed lines) and the independent (solid lines) models are generally similar in pattern for Australia. As can be seen from Figure 3, there is an extreme point of error for the Poisson-based methods around age 12 for both genders in Australia. However, no outlier is detected for the functional-based methods, which indicates the ability of the functional models to minimize the effect of extreme forecast values.

Table 2. Mean Forecast Error (*MFE*) of log death rates for males and females by method, gender and country.

	MFE					
	Australia			**Malaysia**		
	Male	**Female**	**Overall**	**Male**	**Female**	**Overall**
20-year forecasts						
Poisson–Lee–Carter	−0.094	−0.024	−0.059	0.072	0.060	0.066
Poisson common factor	−0.087	−0.031	−0.059	0.120	0.006	0.063
Weighted functional	−0.094	−0.036	−0.065	0.087	0.094	0.090
Product-ratio functional	−0.070	−0.030	−0.050	0.157	0.039	0.098
Lee–Carter	0.148	0.142	0.145	0.102	0.122	0.112

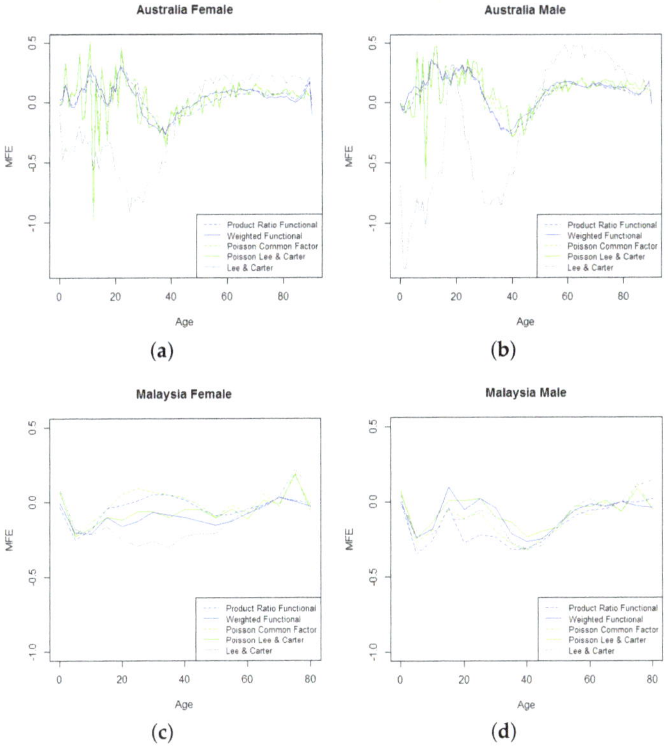

Figure 3. Mean Forecast Error (*MFE*) by age and methods for (**a**) Australian females, (**b**) Australian males, (**c**) Malaysian females and (**d**) Malaysian males.

4.2. *Male to Female Death Rate Ratio Forecasts*

The forecast error of male-to-female death rate ratios is presented in Table 3. The overall error shows that coherent models are more accurate than independent models for Australia, but less accurate for Malaysia. Results show substantial errors at younger ages (less than 40) for all methods in both countries. This indicates the difficulty in estimating the childhood mortality and the accident hump. Similar conclusions regarding log death rates appear in Shang et al. (2011), which examined such forecasts over fourteen countries.

Table 3. Mean Absolute Percentage Forecast Error ($MAPFE$) of the male-to-female death rate ratios by age, method and country.

			Australia $MAPFE$				
20-Year Forecasts	**0**	**1 to 14**	**15 to 39**	**40 to 54**	**55 to 69**	**70 to 90**	**Overall**
Poisson–Lee–Carter	4.60	62.07	30.21	11.64	9.41	8.90	21.14
Poisson common factor	3.74	55.31	23.15	11.65	11.46	6.21	18.59
Weighted functional	4.40	31.24	18.94	8.05	7.96	8.16	13.13
Product-ratio functional	3.67	30.36	15.93	8.46	10.00	5.13	12.26
Lee–Carter	45.78	41.39	45.23	14.45	26.22	10.89	30.66
			Malaysia $MAPFE$				
20-Year Forecasts	**0**	**1 to 14**	**15 to 39**	**40 to 54**	**55 to 69**	**70 to 80**	**Overall**
Poisson–Lee–Carter	3.24	8.35	14.67	7.67	5.20	6.20	7.55
Poisson common factor	2.28	4.71	22.32	10.61	4.32	5.32	8.26
Weighted functional	2.25	12.32	16.19	7.28	3.99	4.36	7.73
Product-ratio functional	3.71	6.35	24.98	10.58	3.25	4.14	8.84
Lee–Carter	6.79	10.18	18.70	7.66	4.20	7.54	9.18

For Australia, the coherent models have lower forecast errors than the independent models for the 0, 1 to 14, 15 to 39 and 70 to 90 age groups. Although the coherent models have higher errors than the independent models for Australian ages 40 to 69, the difference is insignificant, and the coherent models perform better than the independent models in overall terms. For Malaysia, the coherent models have lower forecast errors than the independent models for the 0, 1 to 14, 55 to 69 and 70 to 80 age groups and significantly higher errors for the 15 to 39 and 40 to 54 age groups; the errors of the young adult group aged 15 to 39 increase from 14.67 to 22.32 (by 52%) for the Poisson common factor model and from 16.19 to 24.98 (by 54%) for the product-ratio functional model. The high percentage error from this Malaysian young adult group causes the coherent models to perform less accurately than the independent models.

The comparisons between the two coherent models show that the product-ratio functional model is consistently more accurate than the Poisson common factor for all age groups in Australia and for the age group 40 and above in Malaysia. Similar to the results reported in Table 1, the overall errors show that the product-ratio functional model (a coherent model) is the best model for Australia, while Poisson–Lee–Carter (an independent model) is the best model for Malaysia.

Figures 4 and 5 present the forecasts of the male-to-female death rate ratio for Australia and Malaysia. As can be seen from both Figures 4 and 5, the coherent models (left panel) produce constant forecast ratios in most of the age groups in contrast to the diverging rates under the independent models (right panel), especially for the 15 to 39 age groups.

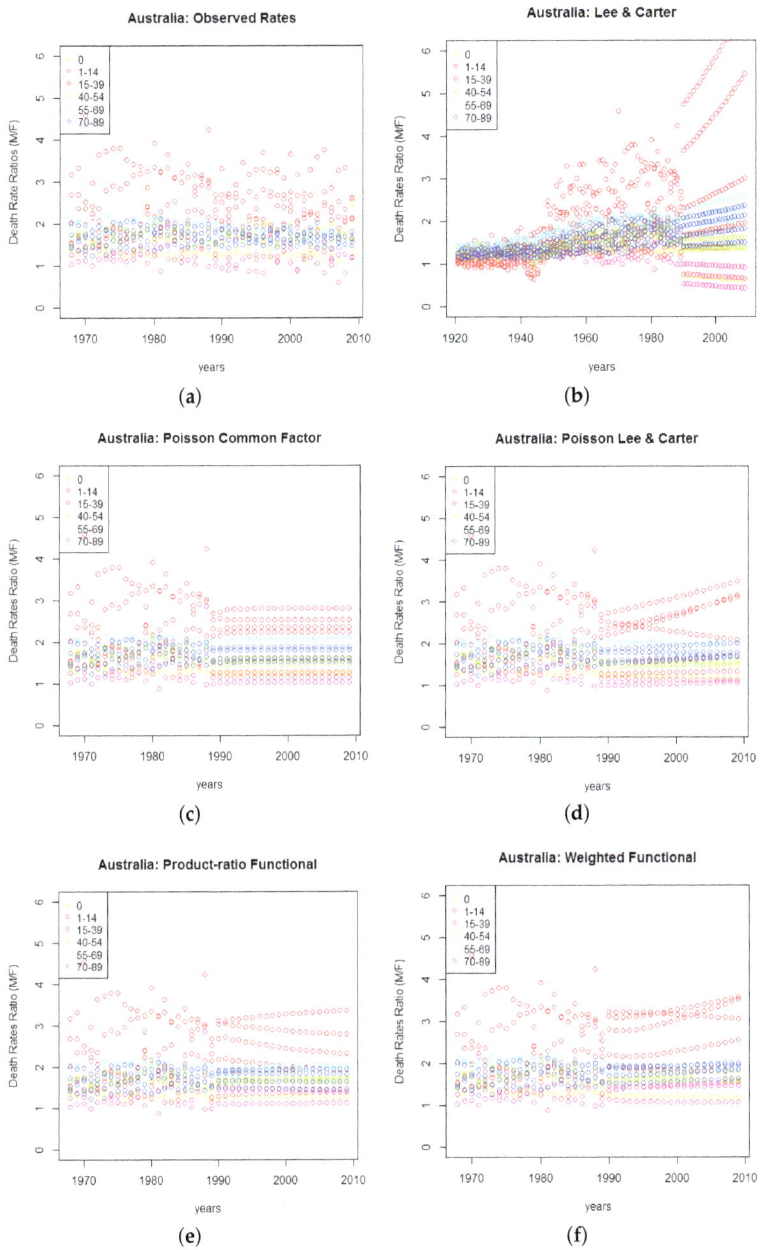

Figure 4. (**a**) Australian observed male-to-female death rate ratios 1968–2009, followed by forecasts of these ratios from 1989–2009 using (**b**) Lee-Carter, (**c**) Poisson common factor, (**d**) Poisson-Lee-Carter, (**e**) Product-ratio functional and (**f**) Weighted functional models.

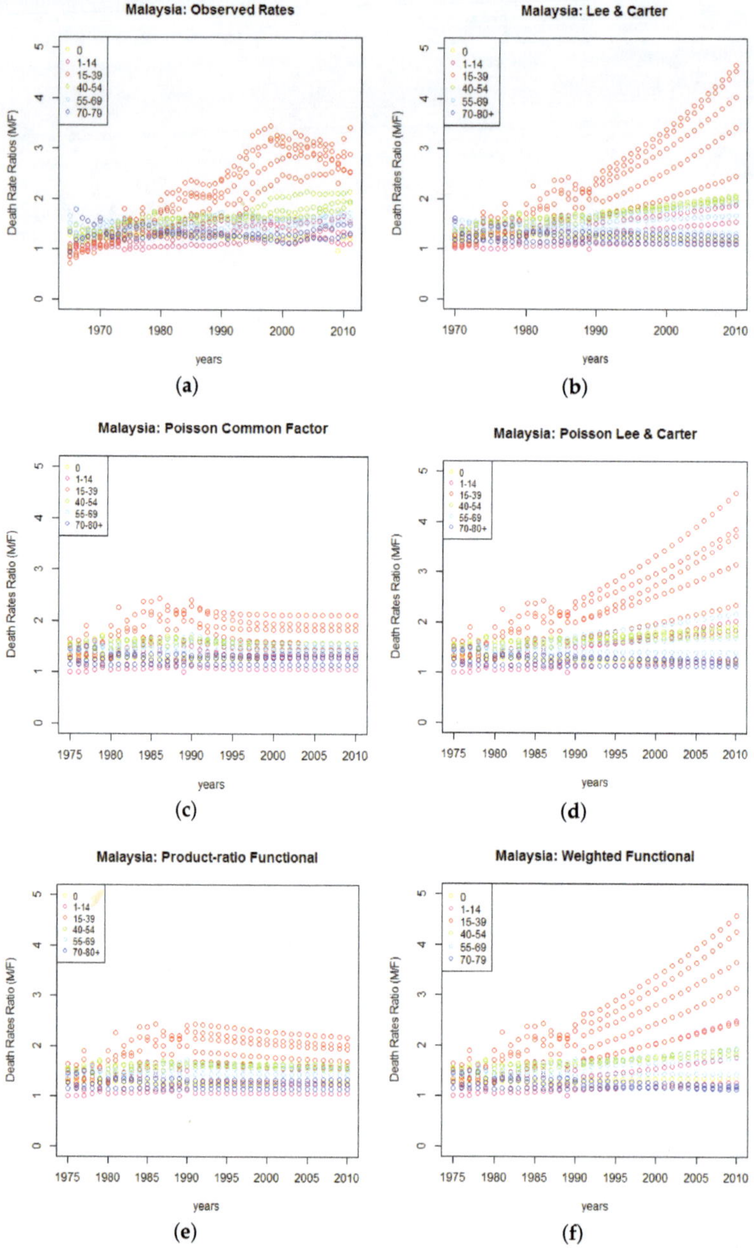

Figure 5. (**a**) Malaysian observed male-to-female death rate ratios 1965–2011, followed by forecasts of these ratios from 1990–2010 using (**b**) Lee-Carter, (**c**) Poisson common factor, (**d**) Poisson-Lee-Carter, (**e**) Product-ratio functional and (**f**) Weighted functional models.

4.3. Life Expectancy at Birth Forecasts

Next, we evaluate each model's accuracy using life expectancy at birth as the outcome measure. Table 4 shows the Mean absolute Forecast Error ($MAFE$) of life expectancy at birth by different methods. The overall errors in Table 4 appear to be consistent with the log death rates and male-to-female death rate ratio forecast errors in two ways. Firstly, the coherent models are more accurate than the independent models for Australia, but are less accurate for Malaysia. Secondly, the errors from the Lee–Carter extensions are reasonably similar. However, the error from the original Lee–Carter model is significantly higher for Australia.

Table 5 shows the Mean Forecast Error (MFE) of life expectancy at birth by different methods. From Table 5, it is clear that all models underestimate life expectancy at birth for both Australian males and females, with the forecast errors among males being more than double those of females. In other words, the methods used in this research tend to underestimate the rapid increase in life expectancy for Australian males that has occurred in recent years. In contrast, all of the models overestimate the life expectancy for Malaysian males, with the original Lee–Carter model providing the least error. The results for Malaysian females are less consistent.

Table 4. Mean Absolute Forecast Error ($MAFE$) of life expectancy at birth by method, gender and country.

	MAFE					
20-Year Forecasts	**Australia**			**Malaysia**		
	Male	**Female**	**Overall**	**Male**	**Female**	**Overall**
Poisson–Lee–Carter	1.289	0.567	0.928	0.466	0.213	0.339
Poisson common factor	1.202	0.521	0.861	0.724	0.295	0.509
Weighted functional	1.123	0.290	0.706	0.660	0.371	0.516
Product-ratio functional	0.945	0.355	0.650	0.945	0.223	0.584
Lee–Carter	2.044	1.201	1.622	0.289	0.302	0.296

Table 5. Mean Forecast Error (MFE) of life expectancy at birth by method, gender and country.

	MFE					
20-Year Forecasts	**Australia**			**Malaysia**		
	Male	**Female**	**Overall**	**Male**	**Female**	**Overall**
Poisson–Lee–Carter	−1.289	−0.567	−0.928	0.460	−0.035	0.213
Poisson common factor	−1.202	−0.521	−0.861	0.724	−0.203	0.261
Weighted functional	−1.123	−0.290	−0.706	0.660	0.372	0.516
Product-ratio functional	−0.945	−0.335	−0.650	0.938	0.131	0.534
Lee–Carter	−2.044	−1.201	−1.622	0.269	−0.187	0.041

As can be seen from Tables 4 and 5, the Lee–Carter model is the most accurate model for Malaysian males. This suggests that in some cases, such as in a developing country like Malaysia, where the available observed data are not extensive (available only since 1965), the original Lee–Carter model may still be relatively reliable. In addition, consistent with Booth et al. (2006), the results provide further empirical evidence that the most accurate model for mortality rates is not necessarily the best model for life expectancy.

Figure 6 shows that the Lee–Carter model significantly underestimates the life expectancy at birth for both genders in Australia. Conversely, this model outperforms the other models for Malaysian males. The significant underestimation of the Lee–Carter model for Australian life expectancy may be due to the fact that this model includes structural changes in the time-component that have happened since 1921. For Malaysia, there was no major structural change in the data after 1965; hence, the Lee–Carter model performs at least, as well as the other methods. Furthermore, the coherent forecasts (dashed lines) display proportional rates between males and females, whereas the independent forecasts (solid lines) tend to diverge and generally produce a bigger gap for the genders.

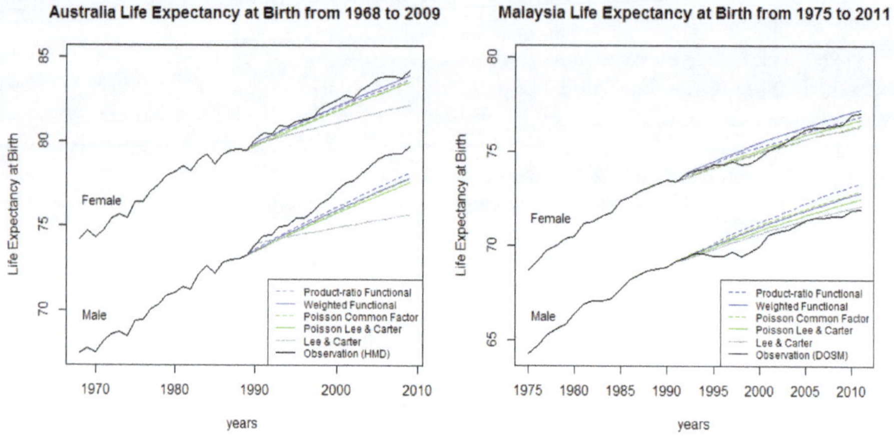

Figure 6. Observed and 20-year forecasts of Australian (**left**) and Malaysian (**right**) life expectancies at birth for males and females.

4.4. The Future Potential of Coherent Mortality Forecasting for Malaysia

Figure 2 shows that, from 1998 onwards (turquoise to purple), Malaysian male mortality for the accident hump group decreases consistently, in contrast to its earlier fluctuating pattern. This observation raises the question of whether this trend will continue in the future and thus improve the accuracy of the forecasts of the coherent models. For this section, we extend the fitting period for the Malaysia data to include the recent decreasing trend among males. About two thirds of the observations (i.e., from 1975 to 2001) are used for the fitting period, and rates are forecast for the remaining ten years (from 2002 to 2011). Tables 6 to 8 present the 10-year forecast errors of mortality rates, male-to-female death rates and life expectancy at birth.

Interestingly, the results show that for the 10-year forecasts, the coherent models are significantly more accurate than the independent models for both Malaysian genders. The error in the male-to-female death ratios at ages 15 to 39 is reduced substantially from 22.564 to 5.491 or by 76% for the Poisson common factor model and from 23.367 to 6.743 or by 71% for the product-ratio functional model, compared to the corresponding independent models (Table 7). These results confirm that the improvement in male mortality rates for people aged 15 to 39 plays an important role for the accuracy of coherent forecasts and consequently outperforms independent models. Nevertheless, the life expectancy forecasts show that the coherent models are still underperforming the independent models for Malaysia.

Table 6. Mean Absolute Forecast Error ($MAFE$) and Mean Forecast Error (MFE) of log death rates for males and females by method and gender for Malaysia.

	MAFE [1]					
10-Year Forecasts	*MAFE*			*MFE*		
	Male	**Female**	**Overall**	**Male**	**Female**	**Overall**
Poisson–Lee–Carter	0.072	0.082	0.077	−0.017	0.030	0.007
Poisson common factor	0.059	0.059	0.059	0.022	−0.002	0.010
Weighted functional	0.111	0.076	0.093	−0.049	0.012	−0.018
Product-ratio functional	0.071	0.060	0.065	0.024	−0.007	0.009
Lee–Carter	0.100	0.161	0.130	0.019	0.109	0.064

Table 7. Mean Absolute Percentage Forecast Error ($MAPFE$) of male-to-female death rate ratios by age and method for Malaysia.

	$MAPFE$						
10-Year Forecasts	**0**	**1 to 14**	**15 to 39**	**40 to 54**	**55 to 69**	**70 to 80**	**Overall**
Poisson–Lee–Carter	4.228	7.158	22.564	5.291	2.928	9.599	8.628
Poisson common factor	3.622	4.572	5.491	5.565	3.209	6.700	4.860
Weighted functional	17.614	15.948	23.367	4.108	2.754	8.973	12.127
Product-ratio functional	3.502	4.121	6.743	6.762	4.683	6.646	5.409
Lee–Carter	5.231	11.907	35.384	3.070	4.483	8.778	11.475

Table 8. Mean Absolute Forecast Error ($MAFE$) and Mean Forecast Error (MFE) of life expectancy at birth for males and females by method for Malaysia.

10-Year Forecasts	$MAFE$			MFE		
	Male	**Female**	**Overall**	**Male**	**Female**	**Overall**
Poisson–Lee–Carter	0.092	0.315	0.203	−0.073	−0.315	−0.194
Poisson common factor	0.191	0.272	0.232	0.183	−0.268	−0.043
Weighted functional	0.190	0.320	0.255	−0.188	−0.320	−0.254
Product-ratio functional	0.238	0.341	0.290	0.237	−0.342	−0.053
Lee–Carter	0.076	0.268	0.172	0.029	−0.246	−0.109

5. Forecast Evaluation of Coherent Models Using Malaysian Ethnic Group Mortality

Malaysia is a multicultural country, which consists of Malay and indigenous (henceforth Malay) groups (61.8%), Chinese (22.5%), Indian (6.7%), other ethnic groups (0.9%) and non-Malaysian citizens (8.1%) (DOSM 2010). In this study, we exclude other ethnic groups and non-Malaysian citizens due to data limitations. In view of the diversity of the Malaysian population, we investigate the suitability of the coherent models to forecast the mortality rates of these ethnic groups. Gender-coherence models are applied separately to Malay males and females, Chinese males and females and Indian males and females. Furthermore, ethnic-coherence models are applied to Malay, Chinese and Indian males and Malay, Chinese and Indian females. We report the results below.

5.1. Gender-Coherence

Table 9 presents the log death rates forecast error of different methods. We exclude the Lee–Carter model from this application as we wish to focus only on the modified versions of the Lee–Carter model. The patterns of errors of the Malay population forecasts are consistent with those of the national forecasts: both coherent models are more accurate than the independent models for females, but less accurate for males, resulting in the coherent forecasts having less accuracy than the independent forecasts overall. This may be due to the size of the Malay group, as it represents the majority of the Malaysian population. For Indians, the coherent models are less accurate than the independent models for both males and females. For the Chinese females, the forecasts generate results that are different from national forecasts, but similar in the patterns of error to those of a low mortality country, Australia, for which both the coherent models are more accurate than the independent models for the overall forecasts. The comparison between the two coherent models for the Chinese indicates that the Poisson common factor model outperforms the product-ratio functional model in the overall forecasts.

The results[4] for male-to-female death rate ratios tend to be consistent with the log death rates forecasts in terms of overall accuracy: the coherent models are less accurate than the independent models for Malays and Indians, but are more accurate than the independent models for Chinese.

---

4 While the results discussed in this paragraph are not displayed below, they are available from the authors on request.

However, the life expectancy at birth forecasts show that the coherent models are less accurate than the independent models for all ethnic groups.

Table 9. Mean Absolute Forecast Errors ($MAFE$) according to ethnic groups and gender in Malaysia. Gender-coherence is imposed on coherent models for Malay, Chinese and Indians.

20-Year Forecasts	**Malay**		
	Male	**Female**	**Overall**
Poisson–Lee–Carter	0.157	0.182	0.133
Poisson common factor	0.229	0.129	0.179
Weighted functional	0.150	0.161	0.156
Product-ratio functional	0.238	0.094	0.166
20-Year Forecasts	**Chinese**		
	Male	**Female**	**Overall**
Poisson–Lee–Carter	0.144	0.136	0.140
Poisson common factor	0.150	0.111	0.131
Weighted functional	0.138	0.185	0.162
Product-ratio functional	0.165	0.120	0.142
20-Year Forecasts	**Indian**		
	Male	**Female**	**Overall**
Poisson–Lee–Carter	0.155	0.187	0.171
Poisson common factor	0.173	0.260	0.216
Weighted functional	0.166	0.183	0.174
Product-ratio functional	0.198	0.199	0.198

5.2. Ethnic-Coherence

The application of coherent mortality forecasting models is extended to apply ethnic-coherence to male and female sub-ethnic populations and compare these results with those of the gender-coherence models. Past data suggest that Chinese mortality is consistently lower than Malay and Indian (refer to Figure 7). Therefore, we incorporate Chinese data in the forecasts of Malay and Indian mortality and report the impact of different types of coherency on the accuracy of coherent forecasts.

Table 10 shows that the coherent models that account for Chinese female mortality as part of the mortality reference for Malay females and Indian females (ethnic-coherence) can generally improve the forecasts of Malay females and Indian females. As can be seen in Table 10, the use of coherent (rather than independent) models reduces the error of Malay females from 0.182 to 0.142 and from 0.161 to 0.156. Similarly, the forecast errors of independent models are reduced from 0.187 to 0.152 and from 0.183 to 0.129 for Indian females. It is noteworthy that these improvements are attained at the expense of accuracy for Chinese female mortality, as indicated by the increase of errors from 0.136 to 0.179. For Chinese males, the coherent models consistently achieve higher forecast errors compared to the independent models; results for Malay males and Indian males are, however, mixed, resulting in the ethnic-coherence models underperforming the independent models in terms of overall errors.

In addition, the results show that the association of lower mortality groups of the same gender in the sub-population's model can improve the forecast of high mortality groups better than the association of the lower mortality group of the opposite gender. For example, ethnic-coherence models (that account for Indian female, Malay female and Chinese female mortality as part of the mortality reference) for Indian females outperform independent models, whereas when using gender-coherence, the coherent models underperform independent models. Based on these findings, we suggest that the ethnic-coherence models are more accurate than the gender-coherence models for forecasting the mortality of Indian females.

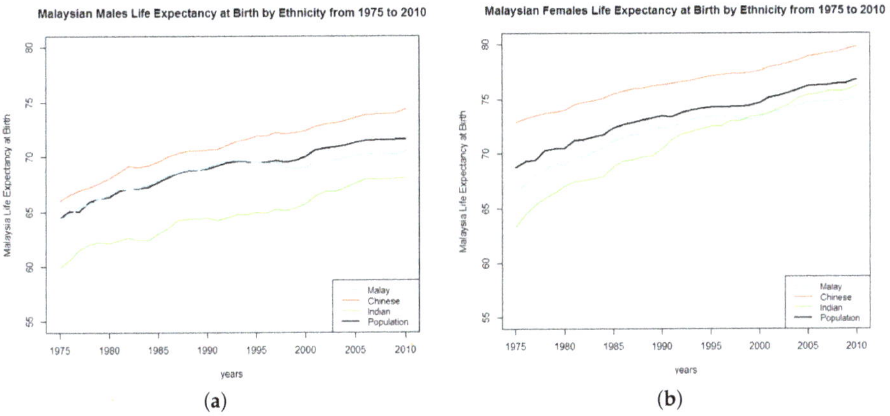

Figure 7. Malaysian observed life expectancy at birth by ethnic groups from 1975 to 2010 for males (**a**) and females (**b**).

Table 10. Mean Absolute Forecast Errors (*MAFE*) by ethnic groups and gender in Malaysia. Ethnic-coherence is imposed on coherent models for males and females.

Malaysian Males	**Malay**	**Chinese**	**Indian**	**Overall**
20-year forecasts				
Poisson–Lee–Carter	0.157	0.144	0.155	0.152
Poisson common factor	0.148	0.187	0.169	0.168
Weighted functional	0.150	0.138	0.166	0.151
Product-ratio functional	0.162	0.167	0.150	0.160
Malaysian Females	**Malay**	**Chinese**	**Indian**	**Overall**
20-year forecasts				
Poisson–Lee–Carter	0.182	0.136	0.187	0.168
Poisson common factor	0.142	0.179	0.152	0.157
weighted functional	0.161	0.185	0.183	0.176
Product-ratio functional	0.156	0.185	0.129	0.157

6. Discussion

6.1. Coherent Mortality Forecasts for Gender Sub-Populations in Malaysia and Australia

6.1.1. Comparison between Coherent and Independent Models

The comparison of the mortality forecasts of the coherent models shows that the coherent models are more accurate than the independent models for both genders in Australia. In contrast, the coherent models are less accurate than the independent models for Malaysian males, but produce better results for females. In terms of overall accuracy, the coherent models perform less well than the independent models for Malaysia. The better performance of the coherent models for Australia is in line with the findings of Hyndman et al. (2013), which show that coherent models tend to be more accurate overall than independent models for Swedish data. It may be that coherent models perform better than independent models for developed countries and are less accurate for developing countries like Malaysia.

It is noteworthy that the accuracy of the coherent models for Malaysian females is achieved at the expense of accuracy of Malaysian male mortality. Similarly, Hyndman et al. (2013) found that coherency improved the accuracy of the mortality forecast of Swedish males at the expense of the accuracy of Swedish female mortality. According to Yasmeen (2010), this trend is related to the first age component of the mortality reference ($\beta_{x,l}$).

This study shows that improved forecasts of male-to-female death ratios are another way in which the coherent models produce a better overall performance than the independent models for Australia. However, the data suggest that the accuracy of the coherent models varies between different age groups. This might be due to the fact that coherent models were designed to produce non-divergent sub-populations forecasts, and therefore, they tend to perform better than the independent models if the differentials between male and female mortality in particular groups are within a defined constant. For example, the coherent models outperform the independent models for Malaysia at ages 0, 1 to 14, 55 to 69 and 70 to 80 and at the same time significantly underperform the independent models for the 15 to 39 and 40 to 54 age groups. The poorer performance for the young adult and middle-age groups might be due to a diverging gap between male and female mortality, which contributes to the larger errors for the overall accuracy in Malaysia. Furthermore, the life expectancy forecasts show that the coherent models tend to produce a smaller forecast gender gap, which is in contrast with recent trends in Malaysia and is aligned with recent trends in Australia. Indeed, Malaysian life expectancies for males and females in recent years have been diverging due to a slow increase in male life expectancy that may be explained by the fluctuations in death rates among young adult males. Therefore, the short-term accuracy of coherent models appears to be strongly influenced by the constant differential of mortality rates between sub-populations. In other words, if some signs of dissimilar patterns are discernible between male and female mortality, then coherent models may not be the best models to forecast those sub-populations.

There is some evidence from our research that indicates the constant differential between male and female mortality is achievable through a careful choice of fitting period. Although the coherent models are less accurate than the independent models for Malaysia in the 20-year forecasts, our results show that these models perform better than the independent models in 10-year forecasts. A shorter forecast period extends the fitting period to include more recent linear decreasing rates in male mortality; hence, the rates tend to be proportional to female rates. In this case, the non-divergent forecast from the coherent models is more consistent with the observations. This finding suggests that coherent models may in the future be better suited to the sub-populations of Malaysia, provided that the recently observed decreasing pattern of death rates for males, which is consistent with that for females, continues in the future.

6.1.2. Comparison between the Two Coherent Models

To the best of our knowledge, the comparison of the forecast accuracy between the coherent models has not been documented in the literature before. This research fills the gap by comparing two recently-developed forms of coherent models: the product-ratio functional and Poisson common factor models. These two models adopt different statistical procedures, which may impact on the accuracy of forecasts in different ways.

This study finds that the product-ratio functional model produces slightly better forecasts than the Poisson common factor for Australia in all forecast components: log mortality rates, male-to-female mortality ratios and life expectancy at birth. One of the possible reasons why the product-ratio functional model might be better is that the model was developed based on the weighted functional method framework that combines the non-parametric smoothing and geometrically-decaying weight procedures. The smoothing procedure allows the observed error to be treated separately from the time series forecast, while the weighting technique gives a greater weight to more recent than earlier data. Prior research confirms that this weighted functional model successfully reduced the forecast error from other independent models for many developed countries, including Australia (Shang et al. 2011). Our findings support and complement this result by showing that the use of the weighted functional method in the product-ratio functional models can provide the most accurate forecast of the coherent models in Australia.

Nonetheless, this weighted functional technique does not seem to be suitable for Malaysian mortality and results in a less accurate performance of the product-ratio functional model compared to the Poisson common factor model. This might be because the observed Malaysian male mortality in the forecasting period is inconsistent with the most recent trend in the fitting period. Thus, applying greater weight on the most current trend may wrongly estimate the forecast trend. On the other hand, Australian male and female mortality and Malaysian female mortality in the forecasting period are in line with the most recent trends in the fitting period; hence, the weighting procedure tends to work more effectively for these groups.

6.2. Comparison between the Lee–Carter Model and Its Extensions

Our findings support previous studies by Booth et al. (2002 2006); Shang et al. (2011) in several ways. First, the original Lee–Carter model is substantially less accurate than all of the Lee–Carter extensions we consider in forecasting mortality. This may be due to the limitation of the Lee–Carter model, which requires a long data series for fitting. Hence, it violates the invariant age-component and linearly decreasing time-component assumptions. Longer fitting periods produce age-component estimates that are different from the age rate of change in the forecasting period and provide structural changes for the mortality index. Therefore the Lee–Carter model may be invalid for many developed countries.

Second, when forecasting life expectancy, the Lee–Carter model does not necessarily produce larger errors than its extensions. For example, we find that Lee–Carter forecasts produce the highest error for Malaysian overall log death rates and that, conversely, it produces the least error for overall life expectancy. According to Booth et al. (2006), the life expectancy estimate involves two types of transformation of log death rates, namely exponentiation and the life table. There will be some cancellation of errors and implicit weights during the process, which eventually could provide a different degree of accuracy for this measure. Therefore, it is insufficient to evaluate the accuracy of a mortality forecasting model merely based on life expectancy error: the error in log death rates is essential to gain a comprehensive understanding of the forecast error. Third, this study found that the weighted functional Lee–Carter extension is consistently more accurate than the Poisson–Lee–Carter model for independent forecasts in Australia. This finding supports results from Booth et al. (2006) that found that functional-based models produced the most accurate forecasts of log death rates. The work in Shang et al. (2011) showed that functional methods are better than the Lee–Carter method; the weighted functional version is the best among the 10 models they considered for male and female log mortality forecasts.

6.3. Coherent Mortality Forecasts for Gender and Ethnicity Sub-Populations in Malaysia

The application of coherent models to the smaller sub-populations (Malay, Chinese and Indian) may be advantageous to forecasters as it provides additional information and results that are specific to these particular sub-populations. For the gender-coherence applications, Malaysia's mortality forecasts indicate that the coherent models are less accurate than the independent models for overall accuracy. This result is applicable to the Malay population, which is the majority of the population. However, for the Chinese, we found that coherent models are more accurate than independent models, following the results for Australia. Therefore, preference between forecasting methods may differ between specific sub-populations.

Over recent decades, the life expectancy of the Chinese sub-population has been increasing and consistently higher than that of Malays and Indians for both genders. Our results suggest that the ethnic-coherence models are more accurate than the independent models and the gender-coherence model for the majority of sub-populations. This suggests that the incorporation of a lower mortality of the same gender sub-population in the coherent model increases accuracy by more than the incorporation of a lower mortality of the opposite gender sub-population.

For the Chinese, the ethnic-coherence models produce less accurate forecasts than gender-coherence forecasts. This indicates that the association of higher mortality population with lower mortality sub-populations in the model might jeopardize the accuracy for lower mortality groups. While Chinese female mortality is better forecast using gender-coherence, Chinese male mortality is better forecast individually or independently. Thus, it seems that Chinese males are the only group for which the best mortality reference is unavailable within the country.

Our findings suggest that coherent models have the potential to be more accurate than the independent models even when applied to high mortality populations provided an appropriate type of coherency is chosen. Further investigations are needed to establish the best mortality reference for the sub-populations. Other types of coherency, such as urban and rural coherence or developed and developing countries coherence, would make good topics for future research.

7. Conclusions

This research evaluated five mortality forecasting models: two coherent models (the product-ratio functional and the Poisson common factor models), their independent versions (the weighted functional model and the Poisson–Lee–Carter model) and the Lee–Carter model. All five models were applied to age- and gender-specific mortality rates from Australia and Malaysia in which gender-coherence was employed for coherent models.

The out-of-sample log death rate forecast errors of different models showed that both coherent models outperformed independent models for three out of the four sub-populations: Australian males and females and Malaysian females. In terms of overall accuracy (averaging over males and females), coherent models were more accurate than independent models for Australia, but less accurate for Malaysia. However, coherent models have the potential to outperform independent models for Malaysian sub-populations if an extended fitting period was employed, thus accounting for a recent decreasing mortality trend among Malaysian males in the estimation. Between coherent models, the Poisson common factor method was more accurate than the product-ratio functional method in Malaysia, while the reverse was true in Australia. It is noteworthy that the Lee–Carter model was significantly less accurate than the other models in both countries.

In addition to log death rates, we included the male-to-female death rate ratio and life expectancy at birth forecasts as outcomes to measure the performance of different mortality forecasting models. The out-of-sample male-to-female death ratio forecasts of independent models diverged, particularly for the 15 to 39 age group, whereas the forecasts from coherent models were approximately constant for almost all age groups, consistent with the observed pattern over the same time. The life expectancy at birth forecast errors showed similar results to the log death rates in which the overall errors indicated that coherent models were more accurate than independent models for Australia, but were less accurate for Malaysia.

Finally, the application of the coherent mortality models to age-, gender- and ethnic-specific mortality rates of Malaysian sub-populations showed that the association of a lower mortality group of the same gender (ethnic-coherence) in the sub-population's model can improve the accuracy of forecast values more than the association of a lower mortality group of opposite gender (gender-coherence).

Acknowledgments: The authors thank the reviewers for their valuable suggestions. Syazreen Shair is grateful for research funds from the Faculty of Business and Economics at Macquarie University, Australia, and the Ministry of Higher Education, Malaysia, in conjunction with the University of Technology MARA.

Author Contributions: Nick Parr, Syazreen Shair and Sachi Purcal conceived of and designed the experiments. Syazreen Shair performed the experiments. Syazreen Shair and Sachi Purcal analysed the data. Nick Parr contributed analysis and a review of the literature. Syazreen Shair wrote the paper.

Conflicts of Interest: The authors declare no conflict of interest.

References

Lee, R.D.; Carter, L.R. Modelling and Forecasting U.S Mortality. *J. Am. Stat. Assoc.* **1992**, *87*, 659–671.

Booth, H.; Maindonald, J.; Smith, L. Applying Lee-Carter under condition of variable mortality decline. *Popul. Stud.* **2002**, *56*, 325–336.

Lee, R.; Miller, T. Evaluating the Performance of Lee-Carter Method for Forecasting Mortality. *Demography* **2001**, *38*, 537–549.

Li, J. Projections of New Zealand Mortality Using the Lee-Carter Model and its Augmented Common Factor Extensions. *N. Z. Popul. Rev.* **2010**, *36*, 27–53.

Brouhns, N.; Denuit, M.; Vermunt, J.K. A Poisson log-bilinear regression approach to the construction of projected life tables. *Insur. Math. Econ.* **2002**, *31*, 372–393.

Renshaw, A.; Haberman, S. Lee-Carter Mortality Forecasting: A Parallel Generalized Linear Modelling Approach for England and Wales Mortality Projections. *J. R. Stat. Soc.* **2003**, *52*, 119–137.

Hyndman, R.J.; Ullah, M.S. Robust Forecasting of Mortality and Fertility Rates: A Functional Data Approach. *Comput. Stat. & Data Anal.* **2007**, *51*, 111–126.

Booth, H.; Tickle, L.; Smith, L. Evaluation of the variants of Lee-Carter method of forecasting mortality: A multi-country comparison. *N. Z. Popul. Rev.* **2005**, *31*, 13–34.

Booth, H.; Hyndman, R.J.; Tickle, L.; Jong, P.D. Lee-Carter Mortality Forecasting: A Multi-country Comparison of Variants and Extensions. *Demogr. Res.* **2006**, *15/9*, 289–310.

Shang, H.L.; Booth, H.; Hyndman, R.J. Point and interval forecasts of mortality rates and life expectancy: A comparison of ten principal component methods. *Demogr. Res.* **2011**, *25*, 173–214.

Li, N.; Lee, R. Coherent Mortality Forecasts for a Group of Population: An Extension of the Lee-Carter Method. *Demography* **2005**, *42*, 575–594.

Li, J. A Poisson Common Factor Model for Projecting Mortality and Life Expectancy Jointly for Females and Males. *Popul. Stud.* **2013**, *67*, 111–126.

Hyndman, R.J.; Booth, H.; Yasmeen, F. Coherent mortality forecasting: The product-ratio method with functional time series models. *Demography* **2013**, *50*, 261–283.

Li, J.; Tickle, L.; Parr, N. A multi-population evaluation of the Poisson common factor model for projecting mortality jointly for both sexes. *J. Popul. Res.* **2016**, *33*, 333–360.

Hyndman, R.J. Demography: Forecasting Mortality, Fertility, Migration and Population Data, 2013. R Package version 1.14. With Contributions from Heather Booth and Leonie Tickle and John Maindonald. Available online: http://robjhyndman.com/software/demography (accessed on 15 April 2013).

University of California, Berkeley (USA); Max Planck Institute for Demographic Research (Germany). Human Mortality Database, 2013. Available online: http://www.mortality.org (accessed on 19 June 2013).

Mikkelsen, L.; Phillips, D.; AbouZahr, C.; Setel, P.; de Savigny, D.; Lozano, R.; Lopez, A. A global assessment of civil registration and vital statistics systems: Monitoring data quality and progress. *Lancet* **2015**, *386*, 1395–1406.

Parr, N.; Li, J.; Tickle, L. A cost of living longer: Projections of the effects of prospective mortality improvements on economic support ratios for 14 advanced economics. *Popul. Stud.* **2016**, *70*, 181–200.

Pollard, J. On the Changing Shape of the Australian Mortality Curve. *Health Transit. Rev.* **1996**, *6*, 283–300.

Mohamed, B.; Hamid, A.; Zolkepli. Mortality rates by specific age group and gender in Malaysia: Trend of 16 years, 1995–2010. *J. Health Inf. Dev. Ctries.* **2012**, *6*, 521–529.

DOSM. *Kadar Demografi Utama, 1911–2010, Malaysia,* Technical Report; Department of Statistics Malaysia: Putrajaya, Malaysia, 2010.

Yasmeen, F. Functional Linear Models for Mortality Forecasting. Ph.D. Thesis, Department of Econometrics and Business Statistics, Monash University, Australia, 2010.

risks

MDPI

Article

Multivariate Functional Time Series Forecasting: Application to Age-Specific Mortality Rates

Yuan Gao † and Han Lin Shang *

Research School of Finance, Actuarial Studies and Statistics, Australian National University, Canberra, ACT 2601, Australia; u5758483@anu.edu.au

* Correspondence: hanlin.shang@anu.edu.au; Tel.: +61-2-6125-0535

† Current address: Research School of Finance, Actuarial Studies and Statistics, Level 4, Building 26C, Australian National University, Kingsley Street, Canberra, ACT 2601, Australia.

Academic Editor: Pavel Shevchenko

Received: 26 October 2016; Accepted: 21 March 2017; Published: 25 March 2017

Abstract: This study considers the forecasting of mortality rates in multiple populations. We propose a model that combines mortality forecasting and functional data analysis (FDA). Under the FDA framework, the mortality curve of each year is assumed to be a smooth function of age. As with most of the functional time series forecasting models, we rely on functional principal component analysis (FPCA) for dimension reduction and further choose a vector error correction model (VECM) to jointly forecast mortality rates in multiple populations. This model incorporates the merits of existing models in that it excludes some of the inherent randomness with the nonparametric smoothing from FDA, and also utilizes the correlation structures between the populations with the use of VECM in mortality models. A nonparametric bootstrap method is also introduced to construct interval forecasts. The usefulness of this model is demonstrated through a series of simulation studies and applications to the age-and sex-specific mortality rates in Switzerland and the Czech Republic. The point forecast errors of several forecasting methods are compared and interval scores are used to evaluate and compare the interval forecasts. Our model provides improved forecast accuracy in most cases.

Keywords: age-and sex-specific mortality rate; bootstrapping prediction interval; vector autoregressive model; vector error correction model; interval score

1. Introduction

Most countries around the world have seen steady decreases in mortality rates in recent years, which also come with aging populations. Policy makers from both insurance companies and government departments seek more accurate modeling and forecasting of the mortality rates. The renowned Lee–Carter model Lee and Carter (1992) is a benchmark in mortality modeling. Their model was the first to decompose mortality rates into one component, age, and the other component, time, using singular value decomposition. Since then, many extensions have been made based on the Lee–Carter model. For instance, Booth et al. Booth *et al.* (2002) address the non-linearity problem in the time component. Koissi et al. Koissi *et al.* (2006) propose a bootstrapped confidence interval for forecasts. Renshaw and Haberman Renshaw and Haberman (2006) introduce the age-period-cohort model that incorporates the cohort effect in mortality modeling. Other than the Lee–Carter model, Cairns et al. Cairns *et al.* (2006) propose the Cairns–Blake–Dowd (CBD) model that satisfies the new-data-invariant property. Chan et al. Chan *et al.* (2014) use a vector autoregressive integrated moving average (VARIMA) model for the joint forecast of CBD model parameters.

Mortality trends in two or more populations may be correlated, especially between sub-populations in a given population, such as females and males. This calls for a model that makes predictions in several populations simultaneously. We would also expect that the forecasts of similar populations do not diverge over the long run, so coherence between forecasts is a desired property. Carter and Lee Carter and Lee (1992) examine how mortality rates of female and male populations can be forecast together using only one time-varying component. Li and Lee Li and Lee (2005) propose a model with a common factor and a population-specific factor to achieve coherence. Yang and Wang Yang and Wang (2013) use a vector error correction model (VECM) to model the time-varying factors in multi-populations. Zhou et al. Zhou *et al.* (2014) argue that the VECM performs better than the original Lee–Carter and vector autoregressive (VAR) models, and that the assumption of a dominant population is not needed. Danesi et al. Danesi *et al.* (2015) compare several multi-population forecasting models and show that the preferred models are those providing a balance between model parsimony and flexibility. These mentioned approaches model mortality rates using raw data without smoothing techniques. In this paper, we propose a model under the functional data analysis (FDA) framework.

In functional data analysis settings (see Ramsay and Silverman Ramsay and Silverman (2005) for a comprehensive Introduction to FDA), it is assumed that there is an underlying smooth function of age as the mortality rate in each year. Since mortality rates are collected sequentially over time, we use the term functional time series for the data. Let $y_t(x)$ denote the log of the observed mortality rate of age x at year t. Suppose $f_t(x)$ is a underlying smooth function, where $x \in \mathcal{I}$ represents the age continuum defined on a finite interval. In practice, we can only observe functional data on a set of grid points and the data are often contaminated by random noise:

$$y_t(x_j) = f_t(x_j) + u_{t,j}, \quad t = 1, \ldots, n, \quad j = 1, \ldots, p,$$

where n denotes the number of years and p denotes the number of discrete data points of age observed for each function. The errors $\{u_{t,j}\}$ are independent and identically distributed (iid) random variables with mean zero and variances $\sigma_t^2(x_j)$. Smoothing techniques are thus needed to obtain each function $f_t(x)$ from a set of realizations. Among many others, localized least squares and spline-based smoothing are two of the approaches frequently used (see, for example, Wahba (1975); Rice and Silverman (1991)). We are not the first to use the functional data approach to model mortality rates. Hyndman and Ullah Hyndman and Ullah (2007) propose a model under the FDA framework, which is robust to outlying years. Chiou and Müller Chiou and Müller (2014) introduce a time-varying eigenfunction to address the cohort effect. Hyndman et al. Hyndman *et al.* (2013) propose a product–ratio model to achieve coherency in the forecasts of multiple populations.

Our proposed method is illustrated in Section 2 and the Appendices. It can be summarized in four steps:

1) smooth the observed data in each population;
2) reduce the dimension of the functions in each population using functional principal component analysis (FPCA) separately;
3) fit the first set of principal component scores from all populations with VECM. Then, fit the second set of principal component scores with another VECM and so on. Produce forecasts using the fitted VECMs; and
4) produce forecasts of mortality curves.

Yang and Wang Yang and Wang (2013) and Zhou et al. Zhou *et al.* (2014) also use VECM to model the time-varying factor, namely, the first set of principal component scores. Our model is different in the following three ways. First, the studied object is in an FDA setting. Nonparametric smoothing techniques are used to eliminate extraneous variations or noise in the observed data. Second, as with other Lee–Carter based models, only the first set of principal component scores are used for prediction in Yang and Wang (2013); Zhou *et al.* (2014). For most countries, the fraction of variance explained is not high enough for one time-varying factor to adequately explain the mortality change. Our approach uses more than one set of principal component scores, and we review some of the ways to choose the optimal number of principal component scores. Third, in their previous papers, only point forecasts are calculated, while we use a bootstrap algorithm for constructing interval forecasts. Point and interval forecast accuracies are both considered.

The article is organized as follows: in Section 2, we revisit the existing functional time series models and put forward a new functional time series method using a VECM. In Section 3, we illustrate how the forecast results are evaluated. Simulation experiments are shown in Section 4. In Section 5, real data analyses are conducted using age-and sex-specific mortality rates in Switzerland and the Czech Republic. Concluding remarks are given in Section 6, along with reflections on how the methods presented here can be further extended.

2. Forecasting Models

Let us consider the simultaneous prediction of multivariate functional time series. Consider two populations as an example: $f_t^{(\omega)}(x), \quad \omega = 1,2$ are the smoothed log mortality rates of each population. According to (A1) in the Appendices, for a sequence of functional time series $\{f_t^{(\omega)}(x)\}$, each element can be decomposed as:

$$\begin{aligned} f_t^{(\omega)}(x) &= \mu^{(\omega)}(x) + \sum_{k=1}^{\infty} \xi_{t,k}^{(\omega)} \phi_k^{(\omega)}(x) \\ &= \mu^{(\omega)}(x) + \sum_{k=1}^{K} \xi_{t,k}^{(\omega)} \phi_k^{(\omega)}(x) + e_t^{(\omega)}(x), \end{aligned}$$

where $e_t^{(\omega)}(x)$ denotes the model truncation error function that captures the remaining terms. Thus, with functional principal component (FPC) regression, each series of functions are projected onto a $K^{(\omega)}$-dimension space.

The functional time series curves are characterized by the corresponding principal component scores that form a time series of vectors with the dimension $K^{(\omega)}$: $\boldsymbol{\xi}_t^{(\omega)} = \left(\xi_{t,1}^{(\omega)}, \ldots, \xi_{t,K^{(\omega)}}^{(\omega)}\right)^\top$. To construct h-step-ahead predictions $\widehat{f}_{n+h|n}^{(\omega)}$ of the curve, we need to construct predictions for the $K^{(\omega)}$-dimension vectors of the principal component scores; namely, $\widehat{\boldsymbol{\xi}}_{n+h|n}^{(\omega)} = \left(\widehat{\xi}_{(n+h|n),1}^{(\omega)}, \cdots, \widehat{\xi}_{(n+h|n),K^{(\omega)}}^{(\omega)}\right)^\top$, with techniques from multivariate time series using covariance structures between multiple populations (see also Aue *et al.* (2015)). The h-step-ahead prediction for $f_{n+h|n}^{(\omega)}$ can then be constructed by forward projection

$$\begin{aligned} \widehat{f}_{n+h|n}^{(\omega)} &= \mathrm{E}\left[f_{n+h}^{(\omega)} | f_1^{(\omega)}(x), \ldots, f_n^{(\omega)}(x)\right] \\ &= \widehat{\mu}^{(\omega)}(x) + \widehat{\xi}_{(n+h|n),1}^{(\omega)} \widehat{\phi}_1^{(\omega)}(x) + \cdots + \widehat{\xi}_{(n+h|n),K^{(\omega)}}^{(\omega)} \widehat{\phi}_{K^{(\omega)}}^{(\omega)}(x), \quad \omega = 1,2. \end{aligned}$$

In the following material, we consider four methods for modeling and predicting the principal component scores $\boldsymbol{\xi}_{n+h}$, where h denotes a forecast horizon.

2.1. *Univariate Autoregressive Integrated Moving Average Model*

The FPC scores can be modeled separately as univariate time series using the autoregressive integrated moving average (ARIMA(p,d,q)) model:

$$\Phi(B)(1-B)^d \xi_{t,k}^{(\omega)} = \Theta(B) w_{t,k}^{(\omega)}, \quad k = 1, \cdots, K^{(\omega)}, \quad \omega = 1,2,$$

where B denotes the lag operator, and $\omega_{t,k}$ is the white noise. $\Phi(B)$ denotes the autoregressive part and $\Theta(B)$ denotes the moving average part. The orders p, d, q can be determined automatically according to either the Akaike information criterion or the Bayesian information criterion value Hyndman and Khandakar (2008). Then, the maximum likelihood method can be used to estimate the parameters.

This prediction model is efficient in some cases. However, Aue et al. Aue *et al.* (2015) argue that, although the FPC scores have no instantaneous correlation, there may be autocovariance at lags greater than zero. The following model addresses this problem by using a vector time series model for the prediction of each series of FPC scores.

2.2. Vector Autoregressive Model

2.2.1. Model Structure

Now that each function $f_t^{(\omega)}(x)$ is characterized by a $K^{(\omega)}$-dimension vector $\boldsymbol{\xi}_t^{(\omega)}$, we can model the $\boldsymbol{\xi}_t^{(\omega)}$s using a VAR($p$) model:

$$\boldsymbol{\xi}_t^{(\omega)} = \boldsymbol{v}^{(\omega)} + \boldsymbol{A}_1^{(\omega)}\boldsymbol{\xi}_{t-1}^{(\omega)} + \cdots + \boldsymbol{A}_p^{(\omega)}\boldsymbol{\xi}_{t-p}^{(\omega)} + \boldsymbol{\epsilon}_t,$$

where $\boldsymbol{A}^{(\omega)} = \{\boldsymbol{A}_1^{(\omega)}, \ldots, \boldsymbol{A}_p^{(\omega)}\}$ are fixed $K^{(\omega)} \times K^{(\omega)}$ coefficient matrices and $\{\boldsymbol{\epsilon}_t\}$ form a sequence of iid random $K^{(\omega)}$-vectors with a zero mean vector. There are many approaches to estimating the VAR model parameters in Lütkepohl (2005) including multivariate least squares estimation, Yule–Walker estimation and maximum likelihood estimation.

The VAR model seeks to make use of the valuable information hidden in the data that may have been lost by depending only on univariate models. However, the model does not fully take into account the common covariance structures between the populations.

2.2.2. Relationship between the Functional Autoregressive and Vector Autoregressive Models

As mentioned in the Introduction, Bosq Bosq (2012) proposes functional autoregressive (FAR) models for functional time series data. Although the computations for FAR(p) models are challenging, if not unfeasible, one exception is FAR(1), which takes the form of:

$$f_t = \Psi(f_{t-1}) + \epsilon_t, \tag{1}$$

where $\Psi : \mathcal{H} \to \mathcal{H}$ is a bounded linear operator. However, it can be proven that if a FAR(p) structure is indeed imposed on $(f_t : t \in Z)$, then the empirical principal component scores $\boldsymbol{\xi}_t$ should approximately follow a VAR(p) model. Let us consider FAR(1) as an example. Apply $\langle \cdot, \widehat{\phi}_k \rangle$ to both sides of Equation (1) to obtain:

$$\begin{aligned}
\langle f_t, \widehat{\phi}_k \rangle &= \langle \Psi(f_{t-1}), \widehat{\phi}_k \rangle + \langle \epsilon_t, \widehat{\phi}_k \rangle \\
&= \sum_{k'=1}^{\infty} \langle f_{t-1}, \widehat{\phi}_{k'} \rangle \langle \Psi(\widehat{\phi}_{k'}), \widehat{\phi}_k \rangle + \langle \epsilon_t, \widehat{\phi}_k \rangle \\
&= \sum_{k'=1}^{d} \langle f_{t-1}, \widehat{\phi}_{k'} \rangle \langle \Psi(\widehat{\phi}_{k'}), \widehat{\phi}_k \rangle + \delta_{t,k},
\end{aligned}$$

with remainder terms $\delta_{t,k} = d_{t,k} + \langle \epsilon_t, \widehat{\phi}_k \rangle$, where $d_{t,k} = \sum_{k'=d+1}^{\infty} \langle f_{t-1}, \widehat{\phi}_{k'} \rangle \langle \Psi(\widehat{\phi}_{k'}), \widehat{\phi}_k \rangle$.

With matrix notation, we get $\boldsymbol{\xi}_t = \boldsymbol{B}\boldsymbol{\xi}_{t-1} + \delta_t$, for $t = 2, \ldots, n$ where $\boldsymbol{B} \in \mathbb{R}^{d \times d}$. This is a VAR(1) model for the estimated principal component scores. In fact, it can be proved that the two models make asymptotically equivalent predictions Aue *et al.* (2015).

2.3. Vector Error Correction Model

The VAR model relies on the assumption of stationarity; however, in many cases, that assumption does not stand. For instance, age-and sex-specific mortality rates over a number of years show persistently varying mean functions. The extension we suggest here uses the VECMs to fit pairs of principal component scores of the two populations. In a VECM, each variable in the vector is non-stationary, but there is some linear combination between the variables that is stationary in the long run. Integrated variables with this property are called co-integrated variables, and the process involving co-integrated variables is called a co-integration process. For more details on VECMs, consult Lütkepohl (2005).

2.3.1. Fitting a Vector Error Correction Model to Principal Component Scores

For the kth principal component score in the two populations, suppose the two are both first integrated and have a relationship of long-term equilibrium:

$$\xi_{t,k}^{(1)} - \beta\xi_{t,k}^{(2)} = \delta_{t,k},$$

where β is a constant and $\delta_{t,k}$ is a stable process. According to Granger's Representation Theorem, the following VECM specifications exist for $\xi_{t,k}^{(1)}$ and $\xi_{t,k}^{(2)}$:

$$\begin{aligned}\Delta\xi_{t,k}^{(1)} &= \alpha_1(\xi_{t-1,k}^{(1)} - \beta\xi_{t-1,k}^{(2)}) + \gamma_{1,1}\Delta\xi_{t-1,k}^{(1)} + \gamma_{1,2}\Delta\xi_{t-1,k}^{(2)} + \epsilon_{t,k}^{(1)},\\ \Delta\xi_{t,k}^{(2)} &= \alpha_2(\xi_{t-1,k}^{(1)} - \beta\xi_{t-1,k}^{(2)}) + \gamma_{2,1}\Delta\xi_{t-1,k}^{(1)} + \gamma_{2,2}\Delta\xi_{t-1,k}^{(2)} + \epsilon_{t,k}^{(2)},\end{aligned} \tag{2}$$

where $k = 1, \ldots, K$, and $\alpha_1, \alpha_2, \gamma_{1,1}, \gamma_{1,2}, \gamma_{2,1}, \gamma_{2,2}$ are the coefficients, $\epsilon_{t,k}^{(1)}$ and $\epsilon_{t,k}^{(2)}$ are innovations. Note that further lags of $\Delta\xi_{t,k}$'s may also be included.

2.3.2. Estimation

Let us consider the VECM(p) without the deterministic term written in a more compact matrix form:

$$\Delta\boldsymbol{\xi}_k = \boldsymbol{\Pi}_k\boldsymbol{\xi}_{-1,k} + \boldsymbol{\Gamma}_k\Delta\boldsymbol{\Upsilon}_k + \boldsymbol{\epsilon}_k,$$

where

$$\begin{aligned}\Delta\boldsymbol{\xi}_k &= [\Delta\boldsymbol{\xi}_{1,k}, \ldots, \Delta\boldsymbol{\xi}_{t,k}],\\ \boldsymbol{\xi}_{-1,k} &= [\boldsymbol{\xi}_{0,k}, \ldots, \boldsymbol{\xi}_{n-1,k}],\\ \boldsymbol{\Gamma}_k &= [\boldsymbol{\Gamma}_{1,k}, \ldots, \boldsymbol{\Gamma}_{p-1,k}],\end{aligned}$$

$$\Delta\boldsymbol{\Upsilon}_k = [\Delta\boldsymbol{\Upsilon}_{0,k}, \ldots, \Delta\boldsymbol{\Upsilon}_{n-1,k}] \quad \text{with} \quad \Delta\boldsymbol{\Upsilon}_{t-1,k} = \begin{bmatrix}\Delta\boldsymbol{\xi}_{t-1,k}\\ \vdots\\ \Delta\boldsymbol{\xi}_{t-p+1,k}\end{bmatrix},$$

$$\boldsymbol{\epsilon}_k = [\boldsymbol{\epsilon}_{1,k}, \ldots, \boldsymbol{\epsilon}_{t,k}].$$

With this simple form, least squares, generalized least squares and maximum likelihood estimation approaches can be applied. The computation of the model with deterministic terms is equally easy, requiring only minor modifications. Moreover, the asymptotic properties of the parameter estimators are essentially unchanged. For further details, refer to Lütkepohl (2005). There is a sequence of tests to determine the lag order, such as the likelihood ratio test. Since our purpose is to make predictions, a selection scheme based on minimizing the forecast mean squared error can be considered.

2.3.3. Expressing a Vector Error Correction Model in a Vector Autoregressive Form

In a matrix notation, the model in Equation (2) can be written as:

$$\Delta\boldsymbol{\xi}_{t,k} = \boldsymbol{\alpha}\boldsymbol{\beta}^\top\boldsymbol{\xi}_{t-1,k} + \boldsymbol{\Gamma}_1\Delta\boldsymbol{\xi}_{t-1,k} + \boldsymbol{\epsilon}_{t,k},$$

or

$$\xi_{t,k} - \xi_{t-1,k} = \boldsymbol{\alpha}\boldsymbol{\beta}^{\top}\xi_{t-1,k} + \boldsymbol{\Gamma}_1(\xi_{t-1,k} - \xi_{t-2,k}) + \epsilon_{t,k}, \tag{3}$$

where

$$\boldsymbol{\alpha} = \begin{bmatrix} \alpha_1 \\ \alpha_2 \end{bmatrix}, \quad \boldsymbol{\beta}^{\top} = \begin{pmatrix} 1 & \beta \end{pmatrix}, \quad \boldsymbol{\Gamma}_1 = \begin{bmatrix} \gamma_{1,1} & \gamma_{1,2} \\ \gamma_{2,1} & \gamma_{2,2} \end{bmatrix}.$$

Rearranging the terms in Equation (3) gives the VAR(2) representation:

$$\xi_{t,k} = (\boldsymbol{I}_K + \boldsymbol{\Gamma}_1 + \boldsymbol{\alpha}\boldsymbol{\beta}^{\top})\xi_{t-1,k} - \boldsymbol{\Gamma}_1\xi_{t-2,k} + \epsilon_{t,k}.$$

Thus, a VECM(1) can be written in a VAR(2) form. When forecasting the scores, it is quite convenient to write the VECM process in the VAR form. The optimal h-step-ahead forecast with a minimal mean squared error is given by the conditional expectation.

2.4. Product–Ratio Model

Coherent forecasting refers to non-divergent forecasting for related populations Li and Lee (2005). It aims to maintain certain structural relationships between the forecasts of related populations. When we model two or more populations, joint modeling plays a very important role in terms of achieving coherency. When modeled separately, forecast functions tend to diverge in the long run. The product–ratio model forecasts the population functions by modeling and forecasting the ratio and product of the populations. Coherence is imposed by constraining the forecast ratio function to stationary time series models. Suppose $f^{(1)}(x)$ and $f^{(2)}(x)$ are the smoothed functions from the two populations to be modeled together, we compute the products and ratios by:

$$p_t(x) = \sqrt{f_t^{(1)}(x)f_t^{(2)}(x)},$$
$$r_t(x) = \sqrt{f_t^{(1)}(x)/f_t^{(2)}(x)}.$$

The product $\{p_t(x)\}$ and ratio $\{r_t(x)\}$ functions are then decomposed using FPCA and the scores can be modeled separately with a stationary autoregressive moving average (ARMA)(p,q) Box *et al.* (2015) in the product functions or an autoregressive fractionally integrated moving average (ARFIMA)(p,d,q) process Granger and Joyeux (1980); Hosking (1981) in the ratio functions, respectively. With the h-step-ahead forecast values for $\widehat{p}_{n+h|n}(x)$ and $\widehat{r}_{n+h|n}(x)$, the h-step-ahead forecast values for $\widehat{f}^{(1)}_{n+h|n}(x)$ and $\widehat{f}^{(2)}_{n+h|n}(x)$ can be derived by

$$\widehat{f}^{(1)}_{n+h|n}(x) = \widehat{p}_{n+h|n}(x)\widehat{r}_{n+h|n}(x),$$
$$\widehat{f}^{(2)}_{n+h|n}(x) = \widehat{p}_{n+h|n}(x)/\widehat{r}_{n+h|n}(x).$$

2.5. Bootstrap Prediction Interval

The point forecast itself does not provide information about the uncertainty of prediction. Constructing a prediction interval is an important part of evaluating forecast uncertainty when the full predictive distribution is hard to specify.

The univariate model proposed by Hyndman and Ullah (2007), discussed in Section 2.1, computes the variance of the predicted function by adding up the variance of each component as well as the estimated error variance. The $(1-\alpha) \times 100\%$ prediction interval is then constructed under the assumption of normality, where α denotes the level of significance. The same approach is used in the product–ratio model; however, when the normality assumption is violated, alternative approaches may be used.

Bootstrapping is used to construct prediction interval in the functional VECM that we propose. There are three sources of uncertainties in the prediction. The first is from the smoothing process. The second is from the remaining terms after the cut-off at K in the principal component regression: $\sum_{k=K+1}^{n} \xi_{t,k}\phi_k(x)$. If the correct number of dimensions of K is picked, the residuals can be regarded as independent. The last source of uncertainty is from the prediction of scores. The smoothing errors are generated under the assumption of normality and the other two kinds of errors are bootstrapped. All three uncertainties are added up to construct bootstrapped prediction functions. The steps are summarized in the following algorithm:

1) Smooth the functions with $y_t^{(\omega)}(x_j) = f_t^{(\omega)}(x_j) + u_t^{(\omega)}(x_j), \quad \omega = 1, 2$, where $u_t^{(\omega)}$ is the smoothing error with mean zero and estimated variance $\widehat{\sigma}_t^2(x_j)^{(\omega)}, \quad j = 1, \ldots, p$.

2) Perform FPCA on the smoothed functions $f_t^{(1)}$ and $f_t^{(2)}$ separately, and obtain K pairs of principal component scores $\boldsymbol{\xi}_{t,k} = \left(\xi_{t,k}^{(1)}, \xi_{t,k}^{(2)}\right)^\top$.

3) Fit K VECM models to the principal component scores. From the fitted scores $\widehat{\boldsymbol{\xi}}_{t,k}$, for $t = 1, \ldots, n$ and $k = 1, \ldots, K$, obtain the fitted functions $\widehat{\boldsymbol{f}}_t, = \left(\widehat{f}_t^{(1)}, \widehat{f}_t^{(2)}\right)^\top$.

4) Obtain residuals $\boldsymbol{e}_t$ from $\boldsymbol{e}_t = \boldsymbol{f}_t - \widehat{\boldsymbol{f}}_t$.

5) Express the estimated VECM from step 3 in its VAR form: $\boldsymbol{\xi}_{t,k} = \widehat{A}_1\boldsymbol{\xi}_{t-1,k} + \widehat{A}_2\boldsymbol{\xi}_{t-2,k} + \boldsymbol{\epsilon}_{t,k}$, $t = 1, \ldots, n$ and $k = 1, \ldots, K$. Construct K sets of bootstrap principal component scores time series $\boldsymbol{\xi}_{t,k}^* = \widehat{A}_1\boldsymbol{\xi}_{t-1,k}^* + \widehat{A}_2\boldsymbol{\xi}_{t-2,k}^* + \boldsymbol{\epsilon}_{t,k}^*$, where the error term $\boldsymbol{\epsilon}_{t,k}^*$ is re-sampled with replacement from $\boldsymbol{\epsilon}_{t,k}$.

6) Refit a VECM with $\boldsymbol{\xi}_{t,k}^*$ and make h-step-ahead predictions $\widehat{\boldsymbol{\xi}}_{n+h|n}^*$ and hence a predicted function $\widehat{\boldsymbol{f}}_{n+h|n}^*$.

7) Construct a bootstrapped h-step-ahead prediction for the function by

$$\widehat{\boldsymbol{f}}_{n+h|n}^{**}(x_j) = \widehat{\boldsymbol{f}}_{n+h|n}^*(x_j) + \boldsymbol{e}_t^* + \boldsymbol{u}_t^*(x_j),$$

where $\boldsymbol{e}_t^*$ is a re-sampled version of $\boldsymbol{e}_t$ from step 4 and $\boldsymbol{u}_t^*(x_j)$ are generated from a normal distribution with mean $\mathbf{0}$ and variance $\sigma_{t,j}^2$, where $\sigma_{t,j}^2$ is re-sampled from $\{\widehat{\sigma}_{1,j}^2, \ldots, \widehat{\sigma}_{n,j}^2\}$ from step 1).

8) Repeat steps 5 to 7 many times.

9) The $(1 - \alpha) \times 100\%$ point-wise prediction intervals can be constructed by taking the $\frac{\alpha}{2} \times 100\%$ and $(1 - \frac{\alpha}{2}) \times 100\%$ quantiles of the bootstrapped samples.

Koissi et al. Koissi *et al.* (2006) extend the Lee–Carter model with a bootstrap prediction interval. The prediction interval we suggest in this paper is different from their method. First, we work under a functional framework. This means that there is extra uncertainty from the smoothing step. Second, in both approaches, errors caused by dimension reduction are bootstrapped. Third, after dimension reduction, their paper uses an ARIMA(0, 1, 0) model to fit the time-varying component. There is no need to consider forecast uncertainty since the parameters of the time series are fixed. In our approach, parameters are estimated using the data. We adopt similar ideas from the early work of Masarotto Masarotto (1990) for the bootstrap of the autoregression process. This step can also be further extended to a bootstrap-after-bootstrap prediction interval Kim (2001). To summarize, we incorporate three sources of uncertainties in our prediction interval, whereas Koissi et al. Koissi *et al.* (2006) only considers one due to the simplicity of the Lee–Carter model.

3. Forecast Evaluation

We split the data set into a training set and a testing set. The four models are fitted to the data in the training set and predictions are made. The data in the testing set is then used for forecast evaluation. Following the early work by Faraway (2016), we allocate the first two-thirds of the observations into the training set and the last one-third into the testing set.

We use an expanding window approach. Suppose the size of the full data set is 60. The first 40 functions are modeled and one to 20-step-ahead forecasts are produced. Then, the first 41 functions are used to make one to 19-step-ahead forecasts. The process is iterated by increasing the sample size by one until reaching the end of the data. This produces 20 one-step-ahead forecasts, 19 two-step-ahead forecasts, ... and, finally, one 20-step-ahead forecast. The forecast values are compared with the true values of the last 20 functions. Mean absolute prediction errors (MAPE) and mean squared prediction errors (MSPE) are used as measures of point forecast accuracy Danesi *et al.* (2015). For each population, MAPE and MSPE can be calculated as:

$$\begin{aligned}
\text{MAPE}(h) &= \frac{1}{(21-h)\times p}\sum_{\eta=h}^{20}\sum_{j=1}^{p}\left|y_{n+\eta}(x_j)-\widehat{f}_{n+\eta|n+\eta-h}(x_j)\right|, \\
\text{MSPE}(h) &= \frac{1}{(21-h)\times p}\sum_{\eta=h}^{20}\sum_{j=1}^{p}\left[y_{n+\eta}(x_j)-\widehat{f}_{n+\eta|n+\eta-h}(x_j)\right]^2,
\end{aligned} \tag{4}$$

where $\widehat{f}_{n+\eta|n+\eta-h}$ represents the h-step-ahead prediction using the first $n+\eta-h$ years fitted in the model, and $y_{n+\eta}(x_j)$ denotes the true value.

For the interval forecast, coverage rate is a commonly used evaluation standard. However, coverage rate alone does not take into account the width of the prediction interval. Instead, the interval score is an appealing method that combines both a measure of the coverage rate and the width of the prediction interval Gneiting and Raftery (2007). If $\widehat{f}^{u}_{n+h|n}$ and $\widehat{f}^{l}_{n+h|n}$ are the upper and lower $(1-\alpha)\times 100\%$ prediction bounds, and y_{n+h} is the realized value, the interval score at point x_j is:

$$\begin{aligned}
S_\alpha(x_j) &= \left[\widehat{f}^{u}_{n+h|n}(x_j)-\widehat{f}^{l}_{n+h|n}(x_j)\right] \\
&+\frac{2}{\alpha}\left[\widehat{f}^{l}_{n+h|n}(x_j)-y_{n+h}(x_j)\right]\mathbb{1}\left\{y_{n+h}(x_j)<\widehat{f}^{l}_{n+h|n}(x_j)\right\} \\
&+\frac{2}{\alpha}\left[y_{n+h}(x_j)-\widehat{f}^{u}_{n+h|n}(x_j)\right]\mathbb{1}\left\{y_{n+h}(x_j)>\widehat{f}^{u}_{n+h|n}(x_j)\right\},
\end{aligned} \tag{5}$$

where α is the level of significance, and $\mathbb{1}\{\cdot\}$ is an indicator function. According to this standard, the best predicted interval is the one that gives the smallest interval score. In the functional case here, the point-wise interval scores are computed and the mean over the discretized ages is taken as a score for the whole curve. Then, the score values are averaged across the forecast horizon to get a mean interval score at horizon h:

$$\overline{S}_\alpha(h)=\frac{1}{(21-h)\times p}\sum_{\eta=h}^{20}\sum_{j=1}^{p}S_\alpha[\widehat{f}^{u}_{n+\eta|n+\eta-h}(x_j),\widehat{f}^{l}_{n+\eta|n+\eta-h}(x_j);y_{n+\eta}(x_j)], \tag{6}$$

where p denotes the number of age groups and h denotes the forecast horizons.

4. Simulation Studies

In this section, we report the results from the prediction of simulated non-stationary functional time series using the models discussed in Section 2. We generated two series of correlated populations, each with two orthogonal basis functions. The simulated functions are constructed by

$$f_t^{(\omega)}(x) = \xi_{t,1}^{(\omega)}\phi_1^{(\omega)}(x) + \xi_{t,2}^{(\omega)}\phi_2^{(\omega)}(x), \quad \omega = 1,2. \tag{7}$$

The construction of the basis functions is arbitrary, with the only restriction being that of orthogonality. The two basis functions for the first population we used are $\phi_1^{(1)}(x) = -\cos(\pi x)$ and $\phi_2^{(1)} = \sin(\pi x)$, and, for the second population, these are $\phi_1^{(2)}(x) = -\cos(\pi x + \pi/8)$ and $\phi_2^{(2)}(x) = \sin(\pi x + \pi/8)$, where $x \in [0,1]$. Here, we are using $n = 100$ discrete data points for each function. As shown in Figure 1, the basis functions are scaled so that they have an L_2 norm of 1.

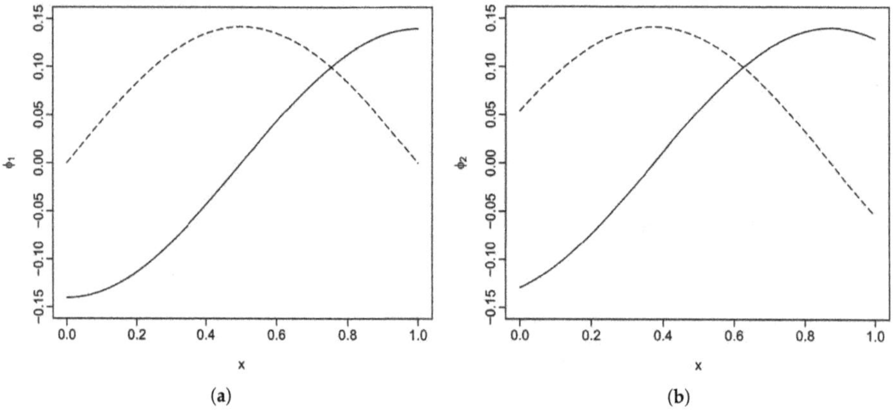

Figure 1. Simulated basis functions for the first and second populations. (**a**) basis functions for population 1; (**b**) basis functions for population 2.

The principal component scores, or coefficients $\xi_{t,k}$, are generated with non-stationary time series models and centered to have a mean of zero. In Section 4.1, we consider the case with co-integration, and, in Section 4.2, we consider the case without co-integration.

4.1. With Co-Integration

We first considered the case where there is a co-integration relationship between the scores of the two populations. Assuming that the principal component scores are first integrated, the two pairs of scores are generated with the following two models:

$$\begin{bmatrix}\Delta\xi_{t,1}^{(1)} \\ \Delta\xi_{t,1}^{(2)}\end{bmatrix} = \begin{bmatrix}-0.2 & 0.4 \\ 0.2 & -0.4\end{bmatrix}\begin{bmatrix}\xi_{t,1}^{(1)} \\ \xi_{t,1}^{(2)}\end{bmatrix} + \begin{bmatrix}0.4 & 0.3 \\ -0.3 & -0.4\end{bmatrix}\begin{bmatrix}\Delta\xi_{t-1,1}^{(1)} \\ \Delta\xi_{t-1,1}^{(2)}\end{bmatrix} + \begin{bmatrix}\epsilon_{t,1}^{(1)} \\ \epsilon_{t,1}^{(2)}\end{bmatrix},$$

$$\begin{bmatrix}\Delta\xi_{t,2}^{(1)} \\ \Delta\xi_{t,2}^{(2)}\end{bmatrix} = \begin{bmatrix}-0.4 & 0.4 \\ 0.4 & -0.4\end{bmatrix}\begin{bmatrix}\xi_{t,2}^{(1)} \\ \xi_{t,2}^{(2)}\end{bmatrix} + \begin{bmatrix}0.3 & -0.2 \\ -0.2 & 0.3\end{bmatrix}\begin{bmatrix}\Delta\xi_{t-1,2}^{(1)} \\ \Delta\xi_{t-1,2}^{(2)}\end{bmatrix} + \begin{bmatrix}\epsilon_{t,2}^{(1)} \\ \epsilon_{t,2}^{(2)}\end{bmatrix},$$

where $\epsilon_{t,k}$ are innovations that follow a Gaussian distribution with mean zero and variance σ_k^2. To satisfy the condition of decreasing eigenvalues: $\lambda_1 > \lambda_2$, we used $\sigma_1^2 = 0.1$ and $\sigma_2^2 = 0.01$.

It can easily be seen that the long-term equilibrium for the first pair of scores is $-\xi_{t,1}^{(1)} + 2\xi_{t,1}^{(2)}$ and, for the second pair of scores, it is $-\xi_{t,2}^{(1)} + \xi_{t,2}^{(2)}$.

4.2. Without Co-Integration

When co-integration does not exist, there is no long-term equilibrium between the two sets of scores, but they are still correlated through the coefficient matrix. We assumed that the first integrated scores follow a stable VAR(1) model:

$$\begin{bmatrix} \Delta\xi_{t,1}^{(1)} \\ \Delta\xi_{t,1}^{(2)} \end{bmatrix} = \begin{bmatrix} 0.4 & -0.3 \\ -0.2 & 0.4 \end{bmatrix} \begin{bmatrix} \Delta\xi_{t-1,1}^{(1)} \\ \Delta\xi_{t-1,1}^{(2)} \end{bmatrix} + \begin{bmatrix} \epsilon_{t,1}^{(1)} \\ \epsilon_{t,1}^{(2)} \end{bmatrix},$$

$$\begin{bmatrix} \Delta\xi_{t,2}^{(1)} \\ \Delta\xi_{t,2}^{(2)} \end{bmatrix} = \begin{bmatrix} 0.3 & 0.1 \\ 0.2 & 0.5 \end{bmatrix} \begin{bmatrix} \Delta\xi_{t-1,2}^{(1)} \\ \Delta\xi_{t-1,2}^{(2)} \end{bmatrix} + \begin{bmatrix} \epsilon_{t,2}^{(1)} \\ \epsilon_{t,2}^{(2)} \end{bmatrix}.$$

For a VAR(1) model to be stable, it is required that $\det(\boldsymbol{I}_p - \boldsymbol{A}_1 z) = 0$ should have all roots outside the unit circle.

4.3. Results

The principal component scores are generated using the aforementioned two models for observations $t = 1, \ldots, 60$. Two sets of simulated functions are generated using Equation (7). We performed an FPCA on the two populations separately. The estimated principal component scores are then modeled using the univariate model, the VAR model and the VECM.

We repeated the simulation procedures 150 times. In each simulation, 500 bootstrap samples are generated to calculate the prediction intervals. We show the MSPE and the mean interval scores at each forecast horizon in Figure 2. The three models performed almost equally well in the short-term forecasts. In the long run, however, the functional VECM produced better predictions than the other two models. This advantage grew bigger as the forecast horizons increased.

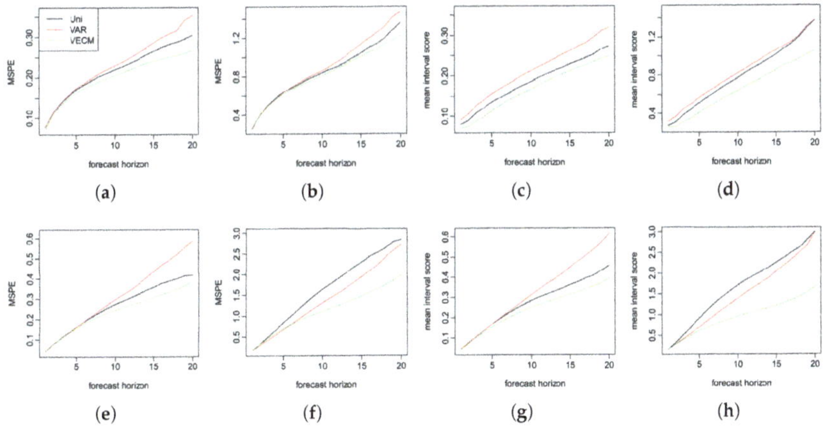

Figure 2. The first row presents the mean squared prediction error (MSPE) and the mean interval scores for the two populations in a co-integration setting. The second row presents the MSPE and the mean interval scores for the two populations without the co-integration. (**a**) 1st population; (**b**) 2nd population; (**c**) 1st population; (**d**) 2nd population; (**e**) 1st population; (**f**) 2nd population; (**g**) 1st population; and (**h**) 2nd population.

5. Empirical Studies

To show that the proposed model outperformed the existing ones using real data, we applied the four models illustrated in Section 2 to the sex-and age-specific mortality rates in Switzerland and the Czech Republic. The observations are yearly mortality curves from ages 0 to 110 years, where the age is treated as the continuum in the rate function. Female and male curves are available from 1908 to 2014 in Human Mortality Database (2016). We only used data from 1950 to 2014 for our analysis to avoid the possibly abnormal rates before 1950 due to war deaths. With the aim of forecasting, we considered the data before 1950 to be too distant to provide useful information. The data at ages 95 and older are grouped together, in order to avoid problems associated with erratic rates at these ages.

5.1. Swiss Age-Specific Mortality Rates

Figure 3 shows the smoothed log mortality rates for females and males from 1950 to 2014. We use a rainbow plot Hyndman and Shang (2010), where the red color represents the curves for more distant years and the purple color represents the curves for more recent years. The curves are smoothed using penalized regression splines with a monotonically increasing constraint after the age of 65 (see Hyndman and Ullah (2007); Wood (1994)). Over a span of 65 years, the mortality rates in general have decreased over all ages, with exceptions in the male population at around age 20. Female rates have been slightly lower than male rates over the years.

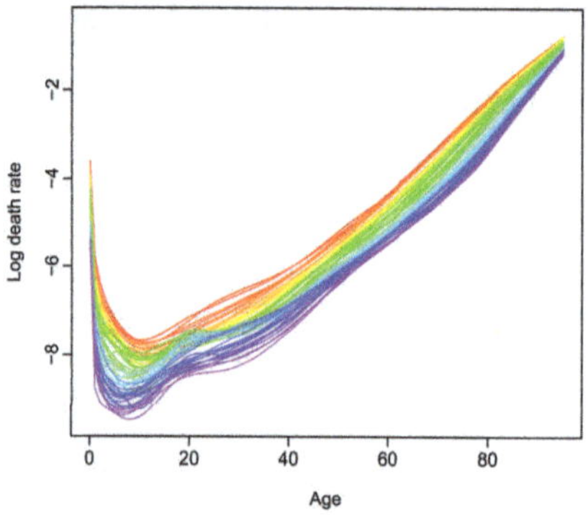

(a)

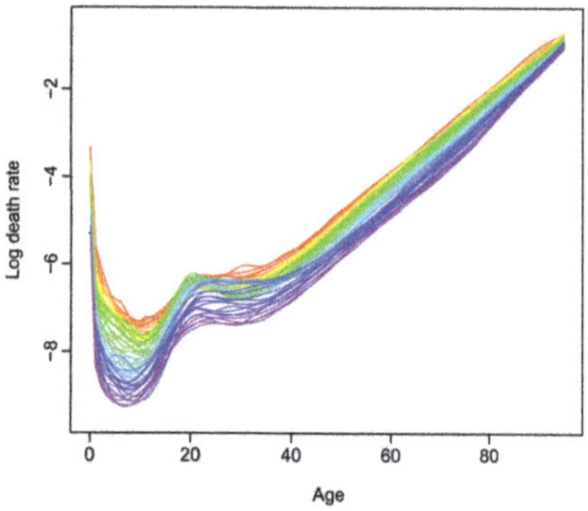

(b)

Figure 3. Smoothed log mortality rates in Switzerland from 1950 to 2014. (**a**) female population; (**b**) male population.

First, we tested the stationarity of our data set. The Monte Carlo test, in which the null hypothesis is stationarity, was applied to both the male and female populations. We used data from all 65 of the years in our range and performed 5000 Monte Carlo replications Horvath *et al.* (2014). The p-values for the male and female populations were 0.0256 and 0.0276, respectively. These small p-values indicated a strong deviation from stationary functional time series.

The first 45 years of data (from 1950 to 1994) were allocated to the training set, and the last 20 years of data from (1995 to 2014) were allocated to the testing set. To choose the order K, we further divided the training set into two groups of 30 and 15 years. The model was fitted to the first 30 years from (1950 to 1979) and forecasts were made for the next 15 years (from 1980 to 1994). In both the VAR model and the functional VECM, K is chosen using:

$$K = \underset{m}{\operatorname{argmin}} \left\{ \frac{1}{15} \sum_{h=1}^{15} \sum_{j=0}^{95} \left[\widehat{f}_{n'+h|n'}(x_j; m) - y_{n'+h}(x_j) \right]^2 \right\},$$

where $\widehat{f}_{n'+h|n'}(x_j;m)$ denotes the h-step-ahead forecast based on the first $n' = 30$ years of data, with m dimensions retained. $y_{n'+h}$ denotes the true rate at year $n' + h$. This selection scheme led to both the VAR and VECM models with $K = 3$ basis functions in this case, which explained 91.20%, 4.37% and 1.56% of the variation in the training set, respectively. These add up to 97.13% of the total variances in the training data being explained. In the univariate and the product–ratio models, order $K = 6$ is used as in Hyndman *et al.* (2013); Hyndman and Booth (2008), where they found that six components would suffice and that having more than six made no difference to the forecasts. With chosen K values, the four models were fitted using an expanding window approach (as explained in Section 3). This produced 20 one-step-ahead forecasts, 19 two-step-ahead forecasts... and, finally, one 20-step-ahead forecast. These forecasts are compared with the holdout data from the years 1995 to 2014. We calculated MAPE and MSPE as point forecast errors using Equation (4).

Table 1 presents the MSPE of the log mortality rates. The smallest errors at each forecast horizon are highlighted in bold face. For the prediction of the female rates, the proposed functional VECM has proved to make more accurate point forecasts for all forecast horizons except for the 20-step-ahead prediction. It should be noted that there is only one error estimate for the 20-step-ahead forecast, so the error estimate may be quite volatile. The other three approaches are somewhat competitive for the 11-step-ahead forecasts or less. For the longer forecast horizons, the errors of the product–ratio method increase quickly. For the forecasting of male mortality rates, although the VAR model produces slightly smaller values of the forecast errors, there is hardly any difference between the four models in the short term. For long-term predictions, the product–ratio approach performs much better than the univariate and the VAR models, but the VECM still dominates. In fact, the product–ratio model usually outperforms the existing models for the male mortality forecasts, while, for the female mortality forecasts, it is not as accurate. MAPEs of the models followed a similar pattern to the MSPE values and are not shown here.

Table 1. Mean squared prediction error (MSPE) for Swiss female and male rates (the smallest values are highlighted in bold).

h	Female				Male			
	UNI	VAR	PR	VECM	UNI	VAR	PR	VECM
1	0.081	0.082	0.076	**0.074**	0.050	**0.048**	0.049	0.049
2	0.085	0.088	0.079	**0.075**	0.056	**0.052**	0.053	0.053
3	0.090	0.094	0.084	**0.078**	0.065	**0.059**	0.060	0.060
4	0.096	0.104	0.091	**0.082**	0.077	**0.067**	0.070	0.069
5	0.103	0.112	0.098	**0.086**	0.090	**0.078**	0.080	**0.078**
6	0.109	0.119	0.107	**0.090**	0.107	0.093	0.093	**0.089**
7	0.117	0.130	0.119	**0.096**	0.129	0.115	0.109	**0.104**
8	0.125	0.140	0.130	**0.102**	0.149	0.136	0.124	**0.119**
9	0.136	0.151	0.145	**0.111**	0.171	0.160	0.139	**0.129**
10	0.145	0.163	0.157	**0.116**	0.198	0.191	0.160	**0.149**
11	0.156	0.171	0.173	**0.125**	0.224	0.223	0.178	**0.162**
12	0.167	0.186	0.195	**0.133**	0.261	0.269	0.206	**0.184**
13	0.174	0.192	0.210	**0.137**	0.299	0.317	0.232	**0.201**
14	0.188	0.203	0.238	**0.145**	0.344	0.361	0.260	**0.213**
15	0.183	0.209	0.254	**0.141**	0.396	0.414	0.293	**0.228**
16	0.197	0.219	0.281	**0.152**	0.460	0.444	0.332	**0.239**
17	0.209	0.223	0.327	**0.164**	0.538	0.556	0.373	**0.251**
18	0.209	0.233	0.354	**0.165**	0.649	0.652	0.416	**0.263**
19	0.197	0.232	0.457	**0.162**	0.792	0.733	0.502	**0.253**
20	**0.144**	0.249	0.493	0.175	0.904	0.753	0.525	**0.270**
Mean	0.145	0.165	0.203	**0.120**	0.298	0.286	0.213	**0.158**
Median	0.145	0.265	0.173	**0.120**	0.224	0.223	0.178	**0.158**

To examine how the models perform in interval forecasts, Equations (5) and (6) are used to calculate the mean interval scores. We generate 1,000 bootstrap samples in the functional VECM and VAR. Table 2 shows the mean interval scores. The 80% prediction intervals are produced using the four different approaches. As explained earlier, smaller mean interval score values indicate better interval predictions. For the female forecasts, functional VECM makes superior interval predictions at all forecast steps, while, for the male forecasts, the product–ratio model and VECM are very competitive, with the latter having a minor advantage for the mean value.

Table 2. Mean interval score (80%) for Swiss female and male rates (the smallest values are highlighted in bold).

h	Female				Male			
	UNI	VAR	PR	VECM	UNI	VAR	PR	VECM
1	1.089	1.042	0.865	**0.852**	0.871	0.767	**0.657**	0.715
2	1.114	1.042	0.878	**0.864**	0.964	0.786	**0.699**	0.748
3	1.153	1.059	0.909	**0.880**	1.088	0.852	**0.759**	0.791
4	1.204	1.102	0.954	**0.902**	1.243	0.911	**0.838**	0.839
5	1.254	1.136	0.997	**0.926**	1.407	1.011	0.909	**0.887**
6	1.306	1.169	1.046	**0.964**	1.594	1.134	1.005	**0.954**
7	1.358	1.234	1.113	**0.996**	1.789	1.289	1.113	**1.059**
8	1.413	1.276	1.166	**1.026**	1.969	1.430	**1.190**	1.133
9	1.483	1.349	1.241	**1.088**	2.134	1.587	1.282	**1.204**
10	1.532	1.426	1.287	**1.113**	2.326	1.798	1.388	**1.338**
11	1.608	1.479	1.358	**1.170**	2.476	2.012	1.475	**1.458**
12	1.661	1.591	1.437	**1.209**	2.655	2.303	**1.609**	1.628
13	1.716	1.647	1.463	**1.237**	2.819	2.618	**1.706**	1.767
14	1.766	1.723	1.540	**1.281**	3.001	2.892	**1.793**	1.891
15	1.705	1.775	1.571	**1.262**	3.145	3.082	1.892	1.963
16	1.774	1.790	1.638	**1.304**	3.309	3.180	**1.957**	1.986
17	1.852	1.860	1.760	**1.352**	3.521	3.692	2.041	**2.011**
18	1.819	1.884	1.767	**1.368**	3.632	4.148	**2.036**	2.051
19	1.795	1.986	1.941	**1.360**	3.683	4.254	2.175	**1.974**
20	1.679	2.347	2.176	**1.398**	3.873	3.595	2.375	**1.978**
Mean	1.514	1.496	1.355	**1.128**	2.375	2.167	1.445	**1.419**
Median	1.532	1.479	1.355	**1.128**	2.375	2.012	1.445	**1.419**

5.2. Czech Republic Age-Specific Mortality Rates

We have also applied the four models to other countries, such as the Czech Republic, to show that the proposed functional VECM does not only work in the case of the Swiss mortality rates. The raw data are grouped and smoothed as was done for the Swiss data. $K = 5$ is chosen in the VAR and the VECM, and the proportions of the explained variance are 93.04%, 1.99%, 1.55%, 1.18%, and 0.79% respectively, which add up to 98.55% of the total variance explained. Figure 4 shows the MSPE and mean interval scores for the point and interval forecast evaluations. In order to compare with the VECM model in the literature, we also try fitting only the first set of principal component scores, shown in the figure by VECM*. Among all five models, functional VECM produces better predictions in both the point and interval forecasts. Compared to our model that uses five principal component scores, VECM* produces larger errors, especially in the male forecasts. We consider that an important fraction of information is lost if only the first set of principal component scores is used.

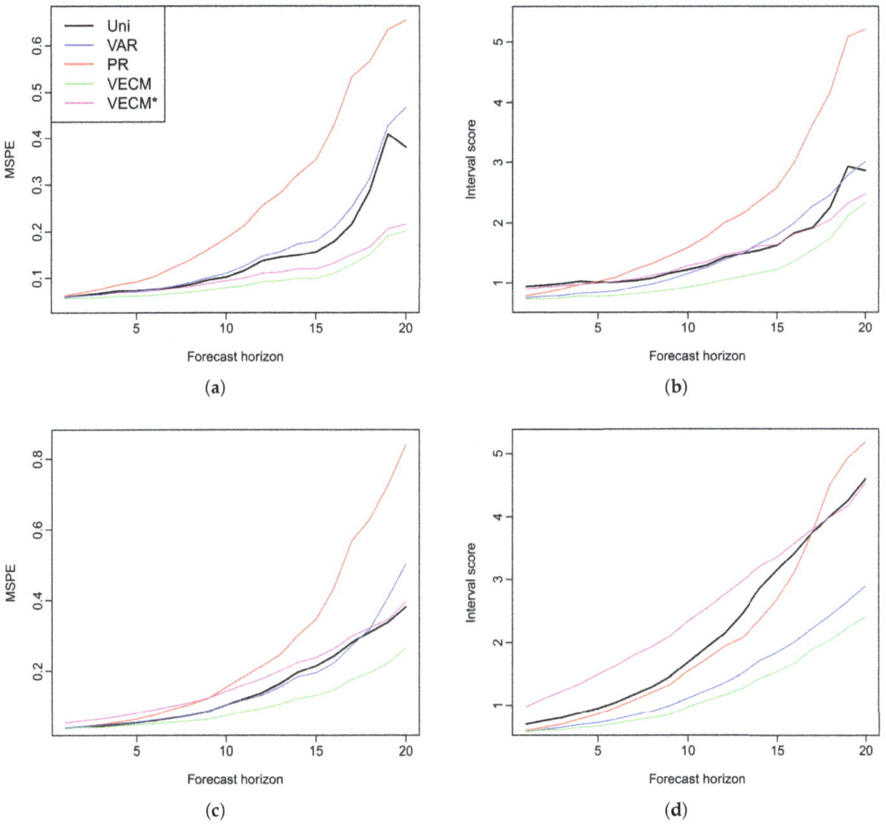

Figure 4. Czech Republic: forecast errors for female and male mortality rates (MSPE and interval scores are presented). (**a**) MSPE for female data; (**b**) mean interval score for female data; (**c**) MSPE for male data; (**d**) mean interval score for male data.

To examine whether or not the differences in the forecast errors are significant, we conduct the Diebold–Mariano test Diebold and Mariano (1995). We use a null hypothesis where the two prediction methods have the same forecast accuracy at each forecast horizon, while the three alternative hypotheses used are that the functional VECM method produces more accurate forecasts than the three other methods. Thus, a small p-value is expected in favor of the alternatives. A squared error loss function is used and the p-values for one-sided tests are calculated at each forecast horizon, as shown in Figure 5. The p-values are hardly greater than zero at most forecast horizons. Almost all are below $\alpha = 0.05$, denoted by the horizontal line, with the exception of the 19- and 20-step-ahead forecasts. We conclude that there is strong evidence that the functional VECM method produces more accurate forecasts than the other three methods for most of the forecast horizons.

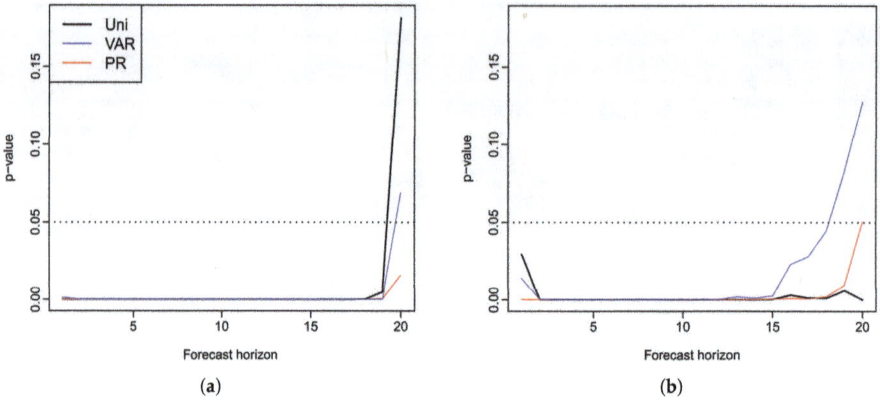

Figure 5. Czech Republic: p-values for the three tests comparing a functional VECM to the univariate, VAR, and product–ratio models, respectively (the horizontal line is the default level of significance $\alpha = 0.05$). (**a**) female population; (**b**) male population.

In summary, we have applied the proposed functional VECM to modeling female and male mortality rates in Switzerland and the Czech Republic, and proven its advantage in forecasting.

6. Conclusions

We have extended the existing models and introduced a functional VECM for the prediction of multivariate functional time series. Compared to the current forecasting approaches, the proposed method performs well in both simulations and in empirical analyses. An algorithm to generate bootstrap prediction intervals is proposed and the results give superior interval forecasts. The advantage of our method is the result of several factors: (1) the functional VECM model considers the covariance between different groups, rather than modeling the populations separately; (2) it can cope with data where the assumption of stationarity does not hold; (3) the forecast intervals using the proposed algorithm combine three sources of uncertainties. Bootstrapping is used to avoid the assumption of the distribution of the data.

We apply the proposed method as well as the existing methods to the male and female mortality rates in Switzerland and the Czech Republic. The empirical studies provide evidence of the superiority of the functional VECM approach in both the point and interval forecasts, which are evaluated by MAPE, MSPE and interval scores, respectively. Diebold–Mariano test results also show significantly improved forecast accuracy of our model. In most cases, when there is a long-run coherent structure in the male and female mortality rates, functional VECM is preferable. The long-term equilibrium constraint in the functional VECM ensures that divergence does not emerge.

While we use two populations for the illustration of the model and in the empirical analysis, functional VECM can easily be applied to populations with more than two groups. A higher rank of co-integration order may need to be considered and the Johansen test can then be used to determine the rank Johansen (1991).

In this paper, we have focused on comparing our model with others within functional time series frameworks. There are numerous other mortality models in the literature, and many of them try to deal with multiple populations. Further research is needed to evaluate our model against the performance of these models.

Acknowledgments: The authors would like to thank three reviewers for insightful comments and suggestions, which led to a much improved manuscript. The authors thank Professor Michael Martin for his helpful comments and suggestions. Thanks also go to the participants of a school seminar at the Australian National University and Australian Statistical Conference held in 2016 for their comments and suggestions. The first author would also like to acknowledge the financial support of a PhD scholarship from the Australian National University.

Author Contributions: The authors contributed equally to the paper. Yuan Gao analyzed the data and wrote the paper. Han Lin Shang initiated the project and contributed analysis and a review of the literature.

Conflicts of Interest: The authors declare no conflict of interest.

Appendix A. Functional Principal Component Analysis

Let $\{f_t(x), t \in Z\}$ be a set of functional time series in $L_2(\mathcal{I})$ from a separable Hilbert space $\mathcal{H}$. $\mathcal{H}$ is characterized by the inner product $\langle \cdot, \cdot \rangle$, where $\langle f_1, f_2 \rangle = \int_{\mathcal{I}} f_1(x) f_2(x) dx$. We assume that $f(x)$ has a continuous mean function $\mu(x)$ and covariance function $G(w, x)$:

$$\mu(x) = \mathrm{E}[f(x)],$$
$$G(w,x) = \mathrm{Cov}[f(w), f(x)] = \mathrm{E}\{[f(w) - \mu(w)][f(x) - \mu(x)]\},$$

and thus the covariance operator for any $f(x) \in \mathcal{H}$ is given by

$$C(w)(f) = \int_{\mathcal{I}} G(w,x) f(x) dx.$$

The eigenequation $C(w)(f) = \rho f$ has solutions with orthonormal eigenfunctions $\phi_k(x)$, and associated eigenvalues λ_k for $k = 1, 2, ...$ such that $\lambda_1 \geq \lambda_2 \geq ...$ and $\sum_k \lambda_k < \infty$.

According to the Karhunen–Loève theorem, the function $f(x)$ can be expanded by:

$$f(x) = \mu(x) + \sum_{k=1}^{\infty} \xi_k \phi_k(x), \tag{A1}$$

where $\{\phi_k(x)\}$ are orthogonal basis functions also on $L^2(\mathcal{I})$, and the principal component scores $\{\xi_k\}$ are uncorrelated random variables given by the projection of the centered function in the direction of the kth eigenfunction:

$$\xi_k = \int_{\mathcal{I}} [f(x) - \mu(x)] \phi_k(x) dx.$$

The principal component scores also satisfy:

$$\mathrm{E}(\xi_k) = 0, \quad \mathrm{Var}(\xi_k) = \lambda_k.$$

Appendix B. Functional Principal Component Regression

According to Equation (A1), for a sequence of functional time series $\{f_t(x)\}$, each element can be decomposed as:

$$\begin{aligned} f_t(x) &= \mu(x) + \sum_{k=1}^{\infty} \xi_{t,k} \phi_k(x) \\ &= \mu(x) + \sum_{k=1}^{K} \xi_{t,k} \phi_k(x) + e_t(x), \end{aligned}$$

where $e_t(x)$ denotes the model truncation error function that captures the remaining terms. It is assumed that the scores follow $\xi_k \sim N(0, \lambda_k)$. Thus, the functions can be characterized by the K-dimension vector $(\xi_1, \ldots, \xi_K)^\top$.

Assorted approaches for selecting the number of principal components, K, include: (a) ensuring that a certain fraction of the data variation is explained Chiou (2012); (b) cross-validation Rice and Silverman (1991); (c) bootstrapping Hall and Vial (2006); and (d) information criteria Yao *et al.* (2005).

With the smoothed functions $\{f_1(x), \ldots, f_n(x)\}$, the mean function $\mu(x)$ is estimated by

$$\widehat{\mu}(x) = \frac{1}{n}\sum_{t=1}^{n} f_t(x).$$

The covariance operator for a function g is estimated by

$$\widehat{C}(g) = \frac{1}{n}\sum_{t=1}^{n}\langle f_t - \widehat{\mu}, g\rangle(f_t - \widehat{\mu}),$$

where n is the number of observed curves. Sample eigenvalue and eigenfunction pairs $\widehat{\lambda}_k$ and $\widehat{\phi}_k(x)$ can be calculated from the estimated covariance operator using singular value decomposition. Empirical principal component scores $\xi_{t,k}$ are obtained by $\xi_{t,k} = \langle f_t, \widehat{\phi}_k\rangle$ with numerical integration $\int_{\mathcal{I}}[f_t(x) - \widehat{\mu}(x)]\widehat{\phi}_k(x)dx$. These simple estimators are proved to be consistent under weak dependence when the functions collected are dense and regularly spaced Yao and Lee (2006); Hörmann and Kokoszka (2010). In sparse data settings, other methods should be applied. For instance, Ref. Yao *et al.* (2005) proposes principal component conditional expectation using pooled information between the functions to undertake estimations.

References

Lee, R.D.; Carter, L.R. Modeling and Forecasting U. S. Mortality. *J. Am. Stat. Assoc.* **1992**, *87*, 659–671.

Booth, H.; Maindonald, J.; Smith, L. Applying Lee-Carter under conditions of variable mortality decline. *Popul. Stud.* **2002**, *56*, 325–336.

Koissi, M.C.; Shapiro, A.F.; Högnäs, G. Evaluating and extending the Lee–Carter model for mortality forecasting: Bootstrap confidence interval. *Insur. Math. Econ.* **2006**, *38*, 1–20.

Renshaw, A.E.; Haberman, S. A cohort-based extension to the Lee–Carter model for mortality reduction factors. *Insur. Math. Econ.* **2006**, *38*, 556–570.

Cairns, A.J.G.; Blake, D.; Dowd, K. A two-factor model for stochastic mortality with parameter uncertainty: theory and calibration. *J. Risk Insur.* **2006**, *73*, 687–718.

Chan, W.; Li, J.S.; Li, J. The CBD Mortality Indexes: Modeling and Applications. *N. Am. Actualrial J.* **2014**, *18*, 38–58.

Carter, L.R.; Lee, R.D. Modelling and Forecasting US sex differentials in Modeling. *Int. J. Forecast.* **1992**, *8*, 393–411.

Li, N.; Lee, R. Coherent mortality forecasts for a group of populations: An extension of the Lee–Carter method. *Demography* **2005**, *42*, 575–594.

Yang, S.S.; Wang, C. Pricing and securitization of multi-country longevity risk with mortality dependence. *Insur. Math. Econ.* **2013**, *52*, 157–169.

Zhou, R.; Wang, Y.; Kaufhold, K.; Li, J.S.H.; Tan, K.S. Modeling Mortality of Multiple Populations with Vector Error Correction Models: Application to Solvency II. *N. Am. Actuarial J.* **2014**, *18*, 150–167.

Danesi, I.L.; Haberman, S.; Millossovich, P. Forecasting mortality in subpopulations using Lee–Carter type models: A comparison. *Insur. Math. Econ.* **2015**, *62*, 151–161.

Ramsay, J.O.; Silverman, J.W. *Functional Data Analysis*; Springer: New York, NY, USA, 2005.

Wahba, G. Smoothing noisy data with spline function. *Numer. Math.* **1975**, *24*, 383–393.

Rice, J.; Silverman, B. Estimating the Mean and Covariance Structure Nonparametrically When the Data Are Curves. *J. R. Stat. Soc. Ser. B (Methodol.)* **1991**, *53*, 233–243.

Hyndman, R.J.; Ullah, M.S. Robust forecasting of mortality and fertility rates: A fucntional data approach. *Comput. Stat. Data Anal.* **2007**, *51*, 4942–4956.

Chiou, J.M.; Müller, H.G. Linear manifold modelling of multivariate functional data. *J. R. Soc. Stat. Ser. B (Stat. Methodol.)* **2014**, *76*, 605–626.

Hyndman, R.J.; Booth, H.; Yasmeen, F. Coherent Mortality Forecasting: The Product-Ratio Method with Functional Time Series Models. *Demography* **2013**, *50*, 261–283.

Aue, A.; Norinho, D.D.; Hörmann, S. On the prediction of stationary functional time series. *J. Am. Stat. Assoc.* **2015**, *110*, 378–392.

Hyndman, R.J.; Khandakar, Y. Automatic Time Series Forecasting: The forecast Package for R. *J. Stat. Softw.* **2008**, *27*, doi:10.18637/jss.v027.i03.

Lütkepohl, H. *New Introduction to Multiple Time Series Analysis*; Springer: New York, NY, USA, 2005.

Bosq, D. *Linear Processes in Function Spaces: Theory and Applications*; Springer Science & Business Media: New York, NY, USA, 2012; Volume 149.

Box, G.E.; Jenkins, G.M.; Reinsel, G.C.; Ljung, G.M. *Time Series Analysis: Forecasting and Control*, 5th ed.; John Wiley & Sons: Hoboken, NJ, USA, 2015.

Granger, C.W.; Joyeux, R. An introduction to long-memory time series models and fractional differencing. *J. Time Ser. Anal.* **1980**, *1*, 15–29.

Hosking, J.R. Fractional differencing. *Biometrika* **1981**, *68*, 165–176.

Masarotto, G. Bootstrap prediction intervals for autoregressions. *Int. J. Forecast.* **1990**, *6*, 229–239.

Kim, J. Bootstrap-after-bootstrap prediction invervals for autoregressive models. *J. Bus. Econ. Stat.* **2001**, *19*, 117–128.

Faraway, J.J. Does data splitting improve prediction? *Stat. Comput.* **2016**, *26*, 49–60.

Gneiting, T.; Raftery, A.E. Strictly Proper Scoring Rules, Prediction, and Estimation. *J. Am. Stat. Assoc.* **2007**, *102*, 359–378.

Human Mortality Database. *University of California, Berkeley (USA), and Max Planck Institute for Demographic Research (Germany)*. 2016. Availabele online: http://www.mortality.org (accessed on 8 March 2016).

Hyndman, R.J.; Shang, H.L. Rainbow plots, bagplots, and boxplots for functional data. *J. Comput. Graph. Stat.* **2010**, *19*, 29–45.

Wood, S.N. Monotonic smoothing splines fitted by cross validation. *SIAM J. Sci. Comput.* **1994**, *15*, 1126–1133.

Horvath, L.; Kokoszka, P.; Rice, G. Testing stationarity of functional time series. *J. Econ.* **2014**, *179*, 66–82.

Hyndman, R.J.; Booth, H. Stochastic population forecasts using functional data models for mortality, fertility and migration. *Int. J. Forecast.* **2008**, *24*, 323–342.

Diebold, F.X.; Mariano, R.S. Comparing predictive accuracy. *J. Bus. Econ. Stat.* **1995**, *13*, 253–263.

Johansen, S. Estimation and Hypothesis Testing of Cointegration Vectors in Gaussian Vector Autoregressive Models. *Econometrica* **1991**, *59*, 1551–1580.

Chiou, J.M. Dynamical functional prediction and classification with application to traffic flow prediction. *Ann. Appl. Stat.* **2012**, *6*, 1588–1614.

Hall, P.; Vial, C. Assessing the finite dimensionality of functional data. *J. R. Stat. Soc. Ser. B (Stat. Methodol.)* **2006**, *68*, 689–705.

Yao, F.; Müller, H.; Wang, J. Functional data analysis for sparse longitudinal data. *J. Am. Stat. Assoc.* **2005**, *100*, 577–590.

Yao, F.; Lee, T.C.M. Penalized spline models for functional principal component analysis. *J. R. Stat. Soc. Ser. B (Stat. Methodol.)* **2006**, *68*, 3–25.

Hörmann, S.; Kokoszka, P. Weakly dependent functional data. *Ann. Stat.* **2010**, *38*, 1845–1884.

Sample Availability: Computational code in R are available upon request from the authors.

risks

MDPI

Article

Actuarial Applications and Estimation of Extended CreditRisk$^+$

Jonas Hirz [1], Uwe Schmock [2] and Pavel V. Shevchenko [3,*]

1. BELTIOS GmbH, Lehargasse 1, Vienna 1060, Austria; jonas.hirz@beltios.com
2. Department of Financial and Actuarial Mathematics, TU Wien, Wiedner Hauptstr. 8–10, Vienna 1040, Austria; schmock@fam.tuwien.ac.at
3. Department of Applied Finance and Actuarial Studies, Macquarie University, NSW 2109, Australia

* Correspondence: pavel.shevchenko@mq.edu.au; Tel.: +61-2-9850-8492

Academic Editor: Mogens Steffensen

Received: 20 January 2017; Accepted: 26 March 2017; Published: 31 March 2017

Abstract: We introduce an additive stochastic mortality model which allows joint modelling and forecasting of underlying death causes. Parameter families for mortality trends can be chosen freely. As model settings become high dimensional, Markov chain Monte Carlo is used for parameter estimation. We then link our proposed model to an extended version of the credit risk model CreditRisk$^+$. This allows exact risk aggregation via an efficient numerically stable Panjer recursion algorithm and provides numerous applications in credit, life insurance and annuity portfolios to derive P&L distributions. Furthermore, the model allows exact (without Monte Carlo simulation error) calculation of risk measures and their sensitivities with respect to model parameters for P&L distributions such as value-at-risk and expected shortfall. Numerous examples, including an application to partial internal models under Solvency II, using Austrian and Australian data are shown.

Keywords: stochastic mortality model; extended CreditRisk$^+$; risk aggregation; partial internal model; mortality risk; longevity risk; Markov chain Monte Carlo

1. Introduction

As the current low interest rate environment forces insurers to put more focus on biometric risks, proper stochastic modelling of mortality has become increasingly important. New regulatory requirements such as Solvency II[1] allow the use of internal stochastic models which provide a more risk-sensitive evaluation of capital requirements and the ability to derive accurate profit and loss (P&L) attributions with respect to different sources of risk. Benefits for companies which make use of actuarial tools such as internal models depend crucially on the accuracy of predicted death probabilities and the ability to extract different sources of risk. So far, insurers often use deterministic modelling techniques and then add artificial risk margins to account for risks associated with longevity, size of the portfolio, selection phenomena, estimation and various other sources. Such approaches often lack a stochastic foundation and are certainly not consistently appropriate for all companies.

Deriving P&L distributions of large credit, life and pension portfolios typically is a very challenging task. In applications, Monte Carlo is the most commonly used approach as it is easy to implement for all different kinds of stochastic settings. However, it has shortcomings in finesse and speed, especially for calculation of model sensitivities. Motivated by numerical trials, we found

1 https://eiopa.europa.eu/regulation-supervision/insurance/solvency-ii, accessed on March 28, 2017.

that the credit risk model *extended CreditRisk*$^+$ (ECRP), as introduced in (Schmock 2017, section 6), is an exceptionally efficient as well as flexible alternative to Monte Carlo and, simultaneously, fits into life actuarial settings as well. Coming from credit risk, this model allows flexible handling of dependence structures within a portfolio via common stochastic risk factors. The ECRP model relies on Panjer recursion (cf. Sundt (1999)) which, unlike Monte Carlo, does not require simulation. It allows an efficient implementation to derive P&L distributions exactly given input data and chosen granularity associated with discretisation. The speed up for deriving sensitivities, i.e., derivatives, of risk measures with respect to model parameters using Panjer recursion will even be an order of magnitude larger as it is extremely difficult to calculate them via finite differencing using Monte Carlo. In addition, our proposed approach can enhance pricing of retirement income products and can be used for applications to partial internal models in the underwriting risk module.

In Section 2 we introduce an additive stochastic mortality model which is related to classical approaches such as the Lee-Carter model introduced in Lee and Carter (1992) or models discussed in Cairns et al. (2009). It allows joint modelling of underlying stochastic death causes based on Poisson assumptions where dependence is introduced via common stochastic risk factors. Note that forecasting of death causes in a disaggregated way can lead to problems with dominating causes in the long run, as argued in Wilmoth (1995) as well as Booth and Tickle (2008). However, joint modelling of death causes can yield computational issues due to high dimensionality which is why the literature is sparse in this matter. An extensive literature review and a multinomial logistic model for joint modelling of death causes is studied in Alai et al. (2015).

Given suitable mortality data, in Section 3 we provide several methods to estimate model parameters including matching of moments, a maximum a posteriori approach and maximum likelihood as well as Markov chain Monte Carlo (MCMC). Death and population data are usually freely available on governmental websites or at statistic bureaus. Due to the high dimensionality of our problem, we suggest the use of MCMC which is one of the few statistical approaches allowing joint parameter estimation in high-dimensions. MCMC can become time-consuming, in particular for settings with common stochastic risk factors. However, estimation of model parameters does usually not have to be done on a frequent basis. We propose a parameter family for mortality trends which makes our model a generalisation of the Lee–Carter approach. However, our approach allows the use of any other kind of parameter family as MCMC is very flexible.

In Section 4 we estimate model parameters for Australian death data in a setting with 362 model parameters, where trends, trend acceleration/reduction and cohort effects are estimated. Further applications include forecasting of central mortality rates and expected future life time.

In Section 5 we then introduce the ECRP model, see (Schmock 2017, section 6), which is a collective risk model corresponding one-to-one to our proposed stochastic mortality model. As the name suggests, it is a credit risk model used to derive loss distributions of credit portfolios and originates from the classical CreditRisk$^+$ model which was introduced by Credit Suisse First Boston (1997). Within credit risk models it is classified as a Poisson mixture model. Identifying default with death makes the model perfectly applicable for actuarial applications. Extended CreditRisk$^+$ provides a flexible basis for modelling multi-level dependencies and allows a fast and numerically stable algorithm for risk aggregation. In the ECRP model, deaths are driven by independent stochastic risk factors. The number of deaths of each policyholder is assumed to be Poisson distributed with stochastic intensity. Thus, serving as an approximation for the true case with single deaths, each person can die multiple times within a period. However, with proper parameter scaling, approximations are very good and final loss distributions are accurate due to Poisson approximation, as shown in Barbour et al. (1992) or Vellaisamy and Chaudhuri (1996) as well as the references therein. The close fit of the ECRP model with (mixed) Poisson distributed deaths to more realistic Bernoulli models is outlined in an introductory example. Another great advantage of the ECRP model is that it automatically incorporates many different sources of risks, such as trends, statistical volatility risk and parameter risk.

Section 6 briefly illustrates validation and model selection techniques. Model validation approaches are based on previously defined dependence and independence structures. All tests suggest that the model suitably fits Australian mortality data.

2. An Alternative Stochastic Mortality Model

2.1. Basic Definitions and Notation

Following standard actuarial notations and definitions, Pitacco et al. (2009) or Cairns et al. (2009), let $T_{a,g}(t)$ denote the random variable of remaining life time of a person aged $a \in \{0, 1, \ldots, A\}$, with maximum age $A \in \mathbb{N}$, and of gender $g \in \{\mathrm{m}, \mathrm{f}\}$ at time/year $t \in \mathbb{N}$. Survival and death probabilities over a time frame $\tau \geq 0$ are given by ${}_{\tau}p_{a,g}(t) = \mathbb{P}(T_{a,g}(t) > \tau)$ and ${}_{\tau}q_{a,g}(t) = \mathbb{P}(T_{a,g}(t) \leq \tau)$, respectively. For notational purposes we write $q_{a,g}(t) := {}_{1}q_{a,g}(t)$.

Deterministic force of mortality (theory for the stochastic case is also available) at age $a + \tau$ with gender g of a person aged a at time t is given by the derivative $\mu_{a+\tau,g}(t) := -\frac{\partial}{\partial \tau} \log {}_{\tau}p_{a,g}(t)$. Henceforth, the central death rate of a person aged a at time t and of gender g is given by a weighted average of the force of mortality

$$m_{a,g}(t) := \frac{\int_0^1 {}_{s}p_{a,g}(t+s)\mu_{a+s,g}(t+s)\,ds}{\int_0^1 {}_{s}p_{a,g}(t+s)\,ds} = \frac{q_{a,g}(t)}{\int_0^1 {}_{s}p_{a,g}(t+s)\,ds} \approx \frac{q_{a,g}(t)}{1 - q_{a,g}(t)/2}.$$

If $\mu_{a+s,g}(t+s) = \mu_{a,g}(t)$ for all $0 \leq s < 1$ and $a, t \in \mathbb{N}_0$ with $a \leq A$, i.e., under piecewise constant force of mortality, we have $m_{a,g}(t) = \mu_{a,g}(t)$ as well as $q_{a,g}(t) = 1 - \exp(-m_{a,g}(t))$.

Let $N_{a,g}(t)$ denote the number of recorded deaths in year t of people having age a and gender g, as well as define the exposure to risk $E_{a,g}(t)$ as the average number of people in year t having age a and gender g. The latter can often be retrieved from statistical bureaus or approximated by the age-dependent population in the middle of a calender year. Estimates for these data in Australia (with several adjustment components such as census undercount and immigration taken into account) are available at the website of the Australian Bureau of Statistics. Considering underlying death causes $k = 0, \ldots, K$, which are to be understood as diseases or injury that initiated the train of morbid events leading directly to death, let $N_{a,g,k}(t)$ denote the actual number of recorded deaths due to death cause k in year t of people having age a and gender g. Note that $N_{a,g}(t) = N_{a,g,0}(t) + \cdots + N_{a,g,K}(t)$. Data on ICD-classified (short for International Statistical Classification of Diseases and Related Health Problems) death counts can be found for many countries. For Australia these data can be found at the Australian Institute of Health and Welfare (AIHW), classified by ICD-9 and ICD-10.

2.2. Some Classical Stochastic Mortality Models

We start with a simple model and assume that deaths in year t of people having age a and gender g are Poisson distributed $N_{a,g}(t) \sim \mathrm{Poisson}(E_{a,g}(t)m_{a,g}(t))$. In this case the maximum likelihood estimate for the central death rate is given by $\widehat{m}_{a,g}(t) = \widehat{N}_{a,g}(t)/E_{a,g}(t)$, where $\widehat{N}_{a,g}(t)$ is the actual recorded number of deaths.

The benchmark stochastic mortality model considered in the literature is the traditional Lee–Carter model, Lee and Carter (1992), where the logarithmic central death rates are modelled in the form

$$\log \widehat{m}_{a,g}(t) = \alpha_{a,g} + \beta_{a,g}\kappa_t + \varepsilon_{a,g,t}$$

with independent normal error terms $\varepsilon_{a,g,t}$ with mean zero, common time-specific component κ_t, as well as age and gender specific parameters $\alpha_{a,g}$ and $\beta_{a,g}$. Using suitable normalisations, estimates for these parameters and κ_t can be derived via the method of moments and singular value decompositions, (Kainhofer et al. 2006, section 4.5.1). Forecasts may then be obtained by applying auto-regressive models to κ_t. Note that Fung et al. (2017) and Fung et al. (2015) provide joint estimation of parameters and latent factor κ_t in the Lee-Carter model via a state-space framework using MCMC. Various extensions of this classical approach with multiple time factors and cohort components have been proposed in the literature; for a review, see Cairns et al. (2009).

Instead of modelling central death rates with normal error terms as in the Lee–Carter approach, Brouhns et al. (2002) propose to model death counts via Poisson regression where error terms are replaced by Poison random variables. In this case $N_{a,g}(t) \sim \text{Poisson}(E_{a,g}(t)m_{a,g}(t))$ where, in the simplest case, $\log m_{a,g}(t) = \alpha_{a,g} + \beta_{a,g}\kappa_t$. Correspondingly, assuming that we want to forecast central death rates for different underlying death causes k, it is natural to assume $N_{a,g,k}(t) \sim \text{Poisson}(E_{a,g}(t)m_{a,g,k}(t))$ where $\log m_{a,g,k}(t) = \alpha_{a,g,k} + \beta_{a,g,k}\kappa_{k,t}$. However, in this case, it is not difficult to see that $m_{a,g,0}(t) + \cdots + m_{a,g,K}(t) \neq m_{a,g}(t)$, in general, and thus

$$\mathbb{E}[N_{a,g}(t)] \neq \sum_{k=0}^{K} \mathbb{E}[N_{a,g,k}(t)]$$

since $N_{a,g}(t) \sim \text{Poisson}\big(E_{a,g}(t)(m_{a,g,0}(t) + \cdots + m_{a,g,K}(t))\big)$. Moreover, as central death rates are increasing for selected underlying death cause (e.g., central death rates for 75–79 year olds in Australia have doubled from 1987 throughout 2011), forecasts increase exponentially, exceeding one in the future.

In light of this shortcoming, we will introduce an additive stochastic mortality model which fits into the risk aggregation framework of extended CredtRisk$^+$, see Schmock (2017).

2.3. An Additive Stochastic Mortality Model

To be able to model different underlying death causes or, more generally, different covariates which show some common death behaviour (however, we will restrict to the first case in this paper), let us assume common stochastic risk factors $\Lambda_1(t), \ldots, \Lambda_K(t)$ with corresponding age-dependent weights $w_{a,g,k}(t)$ which give the age-dependent susceptibility to the different risk factors and which satisfy

$$w_{a,g,0}(t) + \cdots + w_{a,g,K}(t) = 1\,.$$

Remark 1. *Risk factors introduce dependence amongst deaths of different policyholders. If risk factor $\Lambda_k(t)$ takes large or small values, then the likelihood of death due to k increases or decreases, respectively, simultaneously for all policyholders depending on the weight $w_{a,g,k}(t)$. Weights $w_{a,g,0}, \ldots, w_{a,g,K}$ indicate the vulnerability of people aged a with gender g to risk factors $\Lambda_1(t), \ldots, \Lambda_K(t)$. Risk factors are of particular importance to forecast death causes. For a practical example, assume that a new, very effective cancer treatment is available such that fewer people die from lung cancer. This situation would have a longevity effect on all policyholders. Such a scenario would then correspond to the case when the risk factor for neoplasms shows a small realisation.*

Definition 1 (Additive stochastic mortality model). *Given risk factors $\Lambda_1(t), \ldots, \Lambda_K(t)$ with unit mean and variances $\sigma_1^2(t), \ldots, \sigma_K^2(t)$, assume*

$$N_{a,g,k}(t) \sim \text{Poisson}\big(E_{a,g}(t)m_{a,g}(t)w_{a,g,k}(t)\Lambda_k(t)\big), \quad k = 1, \ldots, K,$$

being conditionally independent of all $N_{a,g,k'}(t)$ with $k \neq k'$. Idiosyncratic deaths $N_{a,g,0}(t)$ with $k = 0$ are assumed to be mutually independent and independent of all other random variables such that

$$N_{a,g,0}(t) \sim \text{Poisson}\big(E_{a,g}(t)m_{a,g}(t)w_{a,g,0}(t)\big)\,.$$

In this case, in expectation, deaths due to different underlying death causes add up correctly, i.e.,

$$\mathbb{E}[N_{a,g}(t)] = E_{a,g}(t)m_{a,g}(t) = E_{a,g}(t)m_{a,g}(t)\sum_{k=0}^{K} w_{a,g,k}(t) = \sum_{k=0}^{K} \mathbb{E}[N_{a,g,k}(t)]$$

as $\mathbb{E}[\Lambda_k(t)] = 1$ by assumption.

Remark 2. *In applications, if $K = 0$, it is feasible to replace the Poisson assumption by a more realistic Binomial assumption $N_{a,g,0}(t) \sim \text{Binomial}(E_{a,g}(t), m_{a,g}(t))$, as done in Section 4.2 for illustration purposes.*

Remark 3. *If risk factors are independent and gamma distributed (as in the case of classical CreditRisk$^+$), then, unconditionally, deaths $N_{a,g,k}(t)$ have a negative binomial distribution. Then, variance of deaths is given by $\text{Var}(N_{a,g,k}(t)) = E_{a,g}(t)m_{a,g}(t)w_{a,g,k}(t)(1 + E_{a,g}(t)m_{a,g}(t)w_{a,g,k}(t)\sigma_k^2(t))$ with $\sigma_k^2(t)$ denoting the variance of $\Lambda_k(t)$. Analogously, for all $a \neq a'$ or $g \neq g'$,*

$$\text{Cov}(N_{a,g,k}(t), N_{a',g',k}(t)) = E_{a,g}(t)E_{a',g'}(t)m_{a,g}(t)m_{a',g'}(t)w_{a,g,k}(t)w_{a',g',k}(t)\sigma_k^2(t). \tag{1}$$

This result will be used in Section 6 for model validation. A similar result also holds for the more general model with dependent risk factors, see (Schmock 2017, section 6.5).

To account for improvement in mortality and shifts in death causes over time, we introduce the following time-dependent parameter families for trends. Similar to the Lee–Carter model, we could simply consider a linear decrease in log mortality. However, since this yields diminishing or exploding mortality over time, we choose a more sophisticated class with trend reduction features. First, in order to guarantee that values lie in the unit interval, let F^{Lap} denote the Laplace distribution function with mean zero and variance two, i.e.,

$$F^{\text{Lap}}(x) = \frac{1}{2} + \frac{1}{2}\text{sign}(x)(1 - \exp(-|x|)), \quad x \in \mathbb{R},$$

such that, for $x < 0$, twice the expression becomes the exponential function.

To ensure that weights and death probabilities are strictly positive for $t \to \infty$, we use the trend reduction/acceleration technique

$$\mathcal{T}^*_{\zeta,\eta}(t) = \frac{1}{\eta}\arctan(\eta(t - \zeta)), \tag{2}$$

with parameters $(\zeta, \eta) \in \mathbb{R} \times (0, \infty)$ and $t \in \mathbb{R}$, which is motivated by (Kainhofer et al. 2006, section 4.6.2). In particular, Equation (2) roughly gives a linear function of t if parameter η is small which illustrates the close link to the Lee–Carter model. In order to make estimation more stable, we suggest the normalisation $\mathcal{T}_{\zeta,\eta}(t) = (\mathcal{T}^*_{\zeta,\eta}(t) - \mathcal{T}^*_{\zeta,\eta}(t_0))/(\mathcal{T}^*_{\zeta,\eta}(t_0) - \mathcal{T}^*_{\zeta,\eta}(t_0 - 1))$ with normalisation parameter $t_0 \in \mathbb{R}$. A clear trend reduction in mortality improvements can be observed in Japan since 1970, see (Pasdika and Wolff 2005, section 4.2), and also for females in Australia.

Definition 2 (Trend families for central death rates and weights)**.** *Central death rates for age a, gender g in year t are given by*

$$m_{a,g}(t) = F^{\text{Lap}}(\alpha_{a,g} + \beta_{a,g}\mathcal{T}_{\zeta_{a,g},\eta_{a,g}}(t) + \gamma_{t-a}), \tag{3}$$

with parameters $\alpha_{a,g}, \beta_{a,g}, \zeta_{a,g}, \gamma_{t-a} \in \mathbb{R}$ and $\eta_i \in (0, \infty)$, as well as where weights are given by

$$w_{a,g,k}(t) = \frac{\exp(u_{a,g,k} + v_{a,g,k}\mathcal{T}_{\phi_k,\psi_k}(t))}{\sum_{j=0}^{K}\exp(u_{a,g,j} + v_{a,g,j}\mathcal{T}_{\phi_j,\psi_j}(t))}, \quad k \in \{0, \ldots, K\}, \tag{4}$$

with parameters $u_{a,g,0}, v_{a,g,0}, \phi_0, \ldots, u_{a,g,K}, v_{a,g,K}, \phi_K \in \mathbb{R}$ and $\psi_0, \ldots, \psi_K \in (0, \infty)$.

The assumptions above yield an exponential evolution of central death rates over time, modulo trend reduction $\mathcal{T}_{\zeta,\eta}(t)$ and cohort effects γ_{t-a} ($t - a$ refers to the birth year). Vector α can be interpreted as intercept parameter for central death rates. Henceforth, β gives the speed of mortality improvement while η gives the speed of trend reduction and ζ gives the shift on the S-shaped arctangent curve, i.e., the location of trend acceleration and trend reduction. Parameter γ_{t-a} models cohort effects for groups with the same year of birth. This factor can also be understood as a categorical variate such as smoker/non-smoker, diabetic/non-diabetic or country of residence. The interpretation of model parameters for families of weights is similar.

Cohort effects are not used for modelling weights $w_{a,g,k}(t)$ as sparse data do not allow proper estimation. In applications, we suggest to fix ϕ and ψ in order to reduce dimensionality to suitable levels. Furthermore, fixing trend acceleration/reduction parameters $(\zeta, \eta, \phi, \psi)$ yields stable results over time, with similar behavior as in the Lee-Carter model. Including trend reduction parameters can lead to less stable results over time. However, our proposed model allows free adaption of parameter families for mortality and weights.

Remark 4 (Long-term projections). *Long-term projections of death probabilities using Equation (3) give*

$$\lim_{t\to\infty} m_{a,g}(t) = F^{\mathrm{Lap}}\left(\alpha_{a,g} + \beta_{a,g}\frac{\pi}{2\eta_{a,g}}\right).$$

Likewise, long-term projections for weights using Equation Equation (4) are given by

$$\lim_{t\to\infty} w_{a,g,k}(t) = \frac{\exp\left(u_{a,g,k} + v_{a,g,k}\frac{\pi}{2\psi_k}\right)}{\sum_{j=0}^{K}\exp\left(u_{a,g,j} + v_{a,g,j}\frac{\pi}{2\psi_j}\right)}.$$

Thus, given weak trend reduction, i.e., ψ_k close to zero, weights with the strongest trend will tend to dominate in the long term. If we a priori fix the parameter for trend reduction ψ_k at suitable values, this effect can be controlled. Alternatively, different parameter families for weights can be used, e.g., linear families. Note that our model ensures that weights across risk factors $k = 0, 1, \ldots, K$ always sum up to one which is why overall mortality $m_{a,g}(t)$ is not influenced by weights and their trends.

3. Parameter Estimation

In this section we provide several approaches for parameter estimation in our proposed model from Definitions 1 and 2. The approaches include maximum likelihood, maximum a posteriori, matching of moments and MCMC. Whilst matching of moments estimates are easy to derive but less accurate, maximum a posterior and maximum likelihood estimates cannot be calculated by deterministic numerical optimisation, in general. Thus, we suggest MCMC as a slower but very powerful alternative. Publicly available data based on the whole population of a country are used.

McNeil et al. (2005) in section 8.6 consider statistical inference for Poisson mixture models and Bernoulli mixture models. They briefly introduce moment estimators and maximum likelihood estimators for homogeneous groups in Bernoulli mixture models. Alternatively, they derive statistical inference via a generalised linear mixed model representation for mixture models which is distantly related to our setting. In their 'Notes and Comments' section the reader can find a comprehensive list of interesting references. Nevertheless, most of their results and arguments are not directly applicable to our case since we use a different parametrisation and since we usually have rich data of death counts compared to the sparse data on company defaults.

In order to be able to derive statistically sound estimates, we make the following simplifying assumption for time independence:

Definition 3 (Time independence and risk factors). *Given Definition 1, consider discrete-time periods $U := \{1, \ldots, T\}$ and assume that random variables are independent for different points in time $s \neq t$ in U. Moreover, for each $t \in U$, risk factors $\Lambda_1(t), \ldots, \Lambda_K(t)$ are assumed to be independent and, for each $k \in \{1, \ldots, K\}$, $\Lambda_k(1), \ldots, \Lambda_k(T)$ are identically gamma distributed with mean one and variance $\sigma_k^2 \geq 0$.*

The assumptions made above seem suitable for Austrian and Australian data, as shown in Section 6 via model validation. In particular, serial dependence is mainly captured by trend families in death probabilities and weights.

For estimation of life tables we usually assume $K = 0$ or $K = 1$ with $w_{a,g,1} = 1$ for all ages and genders. For estimation and forecasting of death causes, we identify risk factors with underlying death causes. Note that for fixed a and g, Equation (4) is invariant under a constant shift of parameters $(u_{a,g,k})_{k\in\{0,\dots,K\}}$ as well as $(v_{a,g,k})_{k\in\{0,\dots,K\}}$ if $\phi_0 = \cdots = \phi_K$ and $\psi_0 = \cdots = \psi_K$, respectively. Thus, for each a and g, we can always choose fixed and arbitrary values for $u_{a,g,0}$ and $v_{a,g,0}$.

3.1. Estimation via Maximum Likelihood

We start with the classical *maximum likelihood* approach. The likelihood function can be derived in closed form but, unfortunately, estimates have to be derived via MCMC as deterministic numerical optimisation quickly breaks down due to high dimensionality.

Lemma 1 (Likelihood function). *Given Definitions 1–3, define*

$$\widehat{N}_k(t) := \sum_{a=0}^{A} \sum_{g\in\{\mathrm{f,m}\}} \widehat{N}_{a,g,k}(t)\,, \quad k \in \{0,\dots,K\} \text{ and } t \in U\,,$$

as well as $\rho_{a,g,k}(t) := E_{a,g}(t) m_{a,g}(t) w_{a,g,k}(t)$ *for all age groups* a*, with maximum age group* A*, and gender* g *and*

$$\rho_k(t) := \sum_{a=0}^{A} \sum_{g\in\{\mathrm{f,m}\}} \rho_{a,g,k}(t)\,.$$

Then, the likelihood function $\ell(\widehat{N}|\theta_m,\theta_w,\sigma)$ *of parameters* $\theta_m := (\alpha,\beta,\zeta,\eta) \in E$*, as well as* $\theta_w := (u,v,\phi,\psi) \in F$ *and* $\sigma := (\sigma_k) \in [0,\infty)^K$ *given* $\widehat{N} := (\widehat{N}_{a,g,k}(t)) \in \mathbb{N}_0^{A\times 2\times(K+1)\times T}$ *is given by*

$$\begin{aligned}\ell(\widehat{N}|\theta_m,\theta_w,\sigma) = \prod_{t=1}^{T}\Bigg(\Bigg(\prod_{a=0}^{A}\prod_{g\in\{\mathrm{f,m}\}} \frac{e^{-\rho_{a,g,0}(t)}\rho_{a,g,0}(t)^{\widehat{N}_{a,g,0}(t)}}{\widehat{N}_{a,g,k}(t)!}\Bigg)\\ \times\prod_{k=1}^{K}\Bigg(\frac{\Gamma(\sigma_k^{-2}+\widehat{N}_k(t))}{\Gamma(\sigma_k^{-2})\sigma_k^{2\sigma_k^{-2}}(\sigma_k^{-2}+\rho_k(t))^{\sigma_k^{-2}+\widehat{N}_k(t)}}\prod_{a=0}^{A}\prod_{g\in\{\mathrm{f,m}\}}\frac{\rho_{a,g,k}(t)^{\widehat{N}_{a,g,k}(t)}}{\widehat{N}_{a,g,k}(t)!}\Bigg)\Bigg)\,.\end{aligned} \tag{5}$$

Proof. Following our assumptions, by straightforward computation we get

$$\begin{aligned}\ell(\widehat{N}|\theta_m,\theta_w,\sigma) = \prod_{t=1}^{T}\Bigg(\Bigg(\prod_{a=0}^{A}\prod_{g\in\{\mathrm{f,m}\}} \frac{e^{-\rho_{a,g,0}(t)}\rho_{a,g,0}(t)^{\widehat{N}_{a,g,0}(t)}}{\widehat{N}_{a,g,0}(t)!}\Bigg)\\ \times\prod_{k=1}^{K}\mathbb{E}\Bigg[\mathbb{P}\Bigg(\bigcap_{a=0}^{A}\bigcap_{g\in\{\mathrm{f,m}\}}\{N_{a,g,k}(t)=\widehat{N}_{a,g,k}(t)\}\,\Bigg|\,\Lambda_k(t)\Bigg)\Bigg]\Bigg)\,,\end{aligned}$$

where $\ell(\widehat{N}|\theta_m,\theta_w,\sigma) = \mathbb{P}(N = \widehat{N}|\theta_m,\theta_w,\sigma)$ denotes the probability of the event $\{N = \widehat{N}\}$ given parameters. Taking expectations in the equation above yields

$$\begin{aligned}&\mathbb{E}\Bigg[\mathbb{P}\Bigg(\bigcap_{a=0}^{A}\bigcap_{g\in\{\mathrm{f,m}\}}\{N_{a,g,k}(t)=\widehat{N}_{a,g,k}(t)\}\,\Bigg|\,\Lambda_k(t)\Bigg)\Bigg]\\ &= \Bigg(\prod_{a=0}^{A}\prod_{g\in\{\mathrm{f,m}\}}\frac{\rho_{a,g,k}(t)^{\widehat{N}_{a,g,k}(t)}}{\widehat{N}_{a,g,k}(t)!}\Bigg)\int_0^\infty e^{-\rho_k(t)x_t}x_t^{\widehat{N}_k(t)}\frac{x_t^{\sigma_k^{-2}-1}e^{-x_t\sigma_k^{-2}}}{\Gamma(\sigma_k^{-2})\sigma_k^{2\sigma_k^{-2}}}\,dx_t\,.\end{aligned}$$

The integrand above is a density of a gamma distribution—modulo the normalisation constant—with parameters $\sigma_k^{-2} + \widehat{N}_k(t)$ and $\sigma_k^{-2} + \rho_k(t)$. Therefore, the corresponding integral equals the multiplicative inverse of the normalisation constant, i.e.,

$$\left(\frac{(\sigma_k^{-2} + \rho_k(t))^{\sigma_k^{-2}+\widehat{N}_k(t)}}{\Gamma(\sigma_k^{-2} + \widehat{N}_k(t))}\right)^{-1}, \quad k \in \{1, \dots, K\} \text{ and } t \in \{1, \dots, T\}.$$

Putting all results together gives Equation (5). □

Since the products in Equation (5) can become small, we recommend to use the log-likelihood function instead. For implementations we recommend to use the log-gamma function, e.g., the lgamma function in 'R' see R Core Team (2013).

Definition 4 (Maximum likelihood estimates). *Recalling Equation (5), as well as given the assumptions of Lemma 1,* maximum likelihood estimates *for parameters θ_m, θ_w and σ are defined by*

$$(\hat{\theta}_m^{\mathrm{MLE}}, \hat{\theta}_w^{\mathrm{MLE}}, \hat{\sigma}^{\mathrm{MLE}}) := \underset{\theta_m, \theta_w, \sigma}{\arg\sup}\, \ell(\widehat{N}|\theta_m, \theta_w, \sigma) = \underset{\theta_m, \theta_w, \sigma}{\arg\sup} \log \ell(\widehat{N}|\theta_m, \theta_w, \sigma).$$

Deterministic optimisation of the likelihood function may quickly lead to numerical issues due to high dimensionality. In 'R' the deterministic optimisation routine nlminb, see R Core Team (2013), gives stable results in simple examples. Our proposed alternative is to switch to a Bayesian setting and use MCMC as described in Section 3.3.

3.2. Estimation via a Maximum a Posteriori Approach

Secondly we propose a variation of *maximum a posteriori estimation* based on Bayesian inference, (Shevchenko 2011, section 2.9). If risk factors are not integrated out in the likelihood function, we may also derive the posterior density of the risk factors as follows. One main advantage of this approach is that estimates for risk factors are obtained which is very useful for scenario analysis and model validation. Furthermore, handy approximations for estimates of risk factor realisations and variances are obtained.

Lemma 2 (Posterior density). *Given Definitions 1–3, consider parameters $\theta_m := (\alpha, \beta, \zeta, \eta) \in E$, $\theta_w := (u, v, \phi, \psi) \in F$, as well as realisations $\lambda := (\lambda_k(t)) \in (0, \infty)^{K \times T}$ of risk factors $\Lambda := (\Lambda_k(t)) \in (0, \infty)^{K \times T}$, as well as data $\widehat{N} := (\widehat{N}_{a,g,k}(t)) \in \mathbb{N}_0^{A \times 2 \times (K+1) \times T}$. Assume that their prior distribution is denoted by $\pi(\theta_m, \theta_w, \sigma)$. Then, the posterior density $\pi(\theta_m, \theta_w, \lambda, \sigma|\widehat{N})$ of parameters given data $\widehat{N}$ is up to constant given by*

$$\begin{aligned}
\pi(\theta_m, \theta_w, \lambda, \sigma|\widehat{N}) &\propto \pi(\theta_m, \theta_w, \sigma)\pi(\lambda|\theta_m, \theta_w, \sigma)\ell(\widehat{N}|\theta_m, \theta_w, \lambda, \sigma) \\
&= \prod_{t=1}^{T}\left(\left(\prod_{a=0}^{A}\prod_{g\in\{\mathrm{f,m}\}} \frac{e^{-\rho_{a,g,0}(t)}\rho_{a,g,0}(t)^{\widehat{N}_{a,g,0}(t)}}{\widehat{N}_{a,g,0}(t)!}\right)\prod_{k=1}^{K}\left(\frac{e^{-\lambda_k(t)\sigma_k^{-2}}\lambda_k(t)^{\sigma_k^{-2}-1}}{\Gamma(\sigma_k^{-2})\sigma_k^{2\sigma_k^{-2}}}\right.\right. \\
&\quad \left.\left.\times \prod_{a=0}^{A}\prod_{g\in\{\mathrm{f,m}\}} \frac{e^{-\rho_{a,g,k}(t)\lambda_k(t)}(\rho_{a,g,k}(t)\lambda_k(t))^{\widehat{N}_{a,g,k}(t)}}{\widehat{N}_{a,g,k}(t)!}\right)\right)\pi(\theta_m, \theta_w, \sigma),
\end{aligned} \tag{6}$$

where $\pi(\lambda|\theta_m, \theta_w, \sigma)$ denotes the prior distribution of risk factors at $\Lambda = \lambda$ given all other parameters, where $\ell(\widehat{N}|\theta_m, \theta_w, \lambda, \sigma)$ denotes the likelihood of $N = \widehat{N}$ given all parameters and where $\rho_{a,g,k}(t) = E_{a,g}(t)m_{a,g}(t)w_{a,g,k}(t)$.

Proof. The first proportional equality follows by Bayes' theorem which is also widely used in Bayesian inference, see, for example, (Shevchenko 2011, section 2.9). Moreover,

$$\pi(\lambda|\theta_m,\theta_w,\sigma) = \prod_{k=1}^{K}\prod_{t=1}^{T}\left(\frac{e^{-\lambda_k(t)\sigma_k^{-2}}\lambda_k(t)^{\sigma_k^{-2}-1}}{\Gamma(\sigma_k^{-2})\sigma_k^{2\sigma_k^{-2}}}\right).$$

If $\theta_m \in E, \theta_w \in F, \lambda \in (0,\infty)^{K\times T}$ and $\sigma \in [0,\infty)^K$, then note that

$$\ell(\widehat{N}|\theta_m,\theta_w,\lambda,\sigma) = \prod_{a=0}^{A}\prod_{g\in\{\mathrm{f,m}\}}\prod_{t=1}^{T}\Bigg(e^{-\rho_{a,g,0}(t)}\frac{\rho_{a,g,0}(t)^{\widehat{N}_{a,g,0}(t)}}{\widehat{N}_{a,g,0}(t)!} \times \prod_{k=1}^{K}\mathbb{P}(N_{a,g,k}(t) = \widehat{N}_{a,g,k}(t) \mid \Lambda_k(t) = \lambda_k(t))\Bigg),$$

which then gives Equation (6) by straightforward computation as in Lemma 1. □

The approach described above may look like a pure Bayesian inference approach but note that risk factors $\Lambda_k(t)$ are truly stochastic and, therefore, we refer to it as a maximum a posteriori estimation approach. There are many reasonable choices for prior distributions of parameters which include (improper) uniform priors $\pi(\theta_m,\theta_w,\sigma) := 1_E(\theta_m)1_F(\theta_w)1_{(0,\infty)^K}(\sigma)$ to smoothing priors as given in Section 4.2. Having derived the posterior density, we can now define corresponding maximum a posteriori estimates.

Definition 5 (Maximum a posteriori estimates). *Recalling Equation (6), as well as given the assumptions of Lemma 2,* maximum a posteriori estimates *for parameters $\theta_m,\theta_w,\lambda$ and σ, given uniqueness, are defined by*

$$(\hat{\theta}_m^{\mathrm{MAP}},\hat{\theta}_w^{\mathrm{MAP}},\hat{\lambda}^{\mathrm{MAP}},\hat{\sigma}^{\mathrm{MAP}}) := \underset{\theta_m,\theta_w,\lambda,\sigma}{\arg\sup}\,\pi(\theta_m,\theta_w,\lambda,\sigma|\widehat{N}) = \underset{\theta_m,\theta_w,\lambda,\sigma}{\arg\sup}\,\log\pi(\theta_m,\theta_w,\lambda,\sigma|\widehat{N}).$$

Again, deterministic optimisation of the posterior function may quickly lead to numerical issues due to high dimensionality of the posterior function which is why we recommend MCMC. However, we can provide handy approximations for risk factor and variance estimates.

Lemma 3 (Conditions for maximum a posteriori estimates). *Given Definition 5, estimates $\hat{\lambda}^{\mathrm{MAP}}$ and $\hat{\sigma}^{\mathrm{MAP}}$ satisfy, for every $k \in \{1,\ldots,K\}$ and $t \in U$,*

$$\hat{\lambda}_k^{\mathrm{MAP}}(t) = \frac{(\hat{\sigma}_k^{\mathrm{MAP}})^{-2} - 1 + \sum_{a=0}^{A}\sum_{g\in\{\mathrm{f,m}\}}\widehat{N}_{a,g,k}(t)}{(\hat{\sigma}_k^{\mathrm{MAP}})^{-2} + \sum_{a=0}^{A}\sum_{g\in\{\mathrm{f,m}\}}\rho_{a,g,k}(t)} \tag{7}$$

if $(\hat{\sigma}_k^{\mathrm{MAP}})^{-2} - 1 + \sum_{a=0}^{A}\sum_{g\in\{\mathrm{f,m}\}}\widehat{N}_{a,g,k}(t) > 0$, as well as

$$2\log\hat{\sigma}_k^{\mathrm{MAP}} + \frac{\Gamma'((\hat{\sigma}_k^{\mathrm{MAP}})^{-2})}{\Gamma((\hat{\sigma}_k^{\mathrm{MAP}})^{-2})} = \frac{1}{T}\sum_{t=1}^{T}\left(1 + \log\hat{\lambda}_k^{\mathrm{MAP}}(t) - \hat{\lambda}_k^{\mathrm{MAP}}(t)\right), \tag{8}$$

where, for given $\hat{\lambda}_k^{\mathrm{MAP}}(1),\ldots,\hat{\lambda}_k^{\mathrm{MAP}}(T) > 0$, Equation (8) has a unique solution which is strictly positive.

Proof. First, set $\pi^*(\widehat{N}) := \log\pi(\theta_m,\theta_w,\lambda,\sigma|\widehat{N})$. Then, for every $k \in \{1,\ldots,K\}$ and $t \in U$, differentiating $\pi^*(\widehat{N})$ gives

$$\frac{\partial\pi^*(\widehat{N})}{\partial\lambda_k(t)} = \frac{\sigma_k^{-2}-1}{\lambda_k(t)} - \frac{1}{\sigma_k^2} + \sum_{a=0}^{A}\sum_{g\in\{\mathrm{f,m}\}}\left(\frac{\widehat{N}_{a,g,k}(t)}{\lambda_k(t)} - \rho_{a,g,k}(t)\right).$$

Setting this term equal to zero and solving for $\Lambda_k(t)$ gives Equation (7). Similarly, for every $k \in \{1, \ldots, K\}$, we obtain

$$\frac{\partial \pi^*(\widehat{N})}{\partial \sigma_k^2} = \frac{1}{\sigma_k^4} \sum_{t=1}^{T} \left(\log \sigma_k^2 - 1 + \frac{\Gamma'(\sigma_k^{-2})}{\Gamma(\sigma_k^{-2})} - \log \lambda_k(t) + \lambda_k(t) \right).$$

Again, setting this term equal to zero and rearranging the terms gives Equation (8).

For existence and uniqueness of the solution in Equation (8), consider $\hat{\lambda}_k^{\text{MAP}}(1), \ldots, \hat{\lambda}_k^{\text{MAP}}(T) > 0$ and let $k \in \{1, \ldots, K\}$ be fixed. Then, note that the right side in Equation (8) is strictly negative unless $\hat{\lambda}_k^{\text{MAP}}(1) = \cdots = \hat{\lambda}_k^{\text{MAP}}(T) = 1$, as $\log x \leq x - 1$ for all $x > 0$ with equality for $x = 1$. If $\hat{\lambda}_k^{\text{MAP}}(1) = \cdots = \hat{\lambda}_k^{\text{MAP}}(T) = 1$, then there is no variability in the risk factor such that $\sigma_k^2 = 0$. Henceforth, note that $f(x) := \log x - \Gamma'(x)/\Gamma(x)$, for all $x > 0$, is continuous ($\Gamma'(x)/\Gamma(x)$ is known as digamma function or ψ-function) with

$$\frac{1}{2x} < f(x) < \frac{1}{2x} + \frac{1}{12x^2}, \quad x > 0, \tag{9}$$

which follows by (Qi et al. 2005, Corollary 1) and $f(x+1) = 1/x + f(x)$ for all $x > 0$. As we want to solve $-f(1/x) = -c$ for some given $c > 0$, note that $f(0+) = \infty$, as well as $\lim_{x \to \infty} f(x) = 0$. Thus, a solution has to exist as $f(1/x)$ is continuous on $x > 0$. Furthermore,

$$f'(x) = \frac{1}{x} - \sum_{i=0}^{\infty} \frac{1}{(x+i)^2} < \frac{1}{x} - \int_x^{\infty} \frac{1}{z^2}\, dz = 0, \quad x > 0,$$

where the first equality follows by Chaudhry and Zubair (2001). This implies that $f(x)$ and $(-f(1/x))$ are strictly decreasing. Thus, the solution in (8) is unique. □

Using Lemma 3, it is possible to derive handy approximations for risk factor and variance estimates, given estimates for weights and death probabilities which can be derived by matching of moments as given in Section 3.4 or other models such as Lee–Carter. If $\sum_{a=0}^{A} \sum_{g \in \{\text{f,m}\}} \widehat{N}_{a,g,k}(t)$ is large, it is reasonable to define

$$\hat{\lambda}_k^{\text{MAPappr}}(t) := \frac{-1 + \sum_{a=0}^{A} \sum_{g \in \{\text{f,m}\}} \widehat{N}_{a,g,k}(t)}{\sum_{a=0}^{A} \sum_{g \in \{\text{f,m}\}} \rho_{a,g,k}(t)} \tag{10}$$

as an approximative estimate for $\lambda_k(t)$ where $\rho_{a,g,k}(t) := E_{a,g}(t) m_{a,g}(t) w_{a,g,k}(t)$. Having derived approximations for λ, we can use Equation (8) to get estimates for σ. Alternatively, note that due to Equation (9), we get

$$-2 \log \hat{\sigma}_k^{\text{MAP}} - \frac{\Gamma'((\hat{\sigma}_k^{\text{MAP}})^{-2})}{\Gamma((\hat{\sigma}_k^{\text{MAP}})^{-2})} = \frac{(\hat{\sigma}_k^{\text{MAP}})^2}{2} + \mathcal{O}((\hat{\sigma}_k^{\text{MAP}})^4).$$

Furthermore, if we use second order Taylor expansion for the logarithm, then the right hand side of Equation (8) gets

$$\frac{1}{T} \sum_{t=1}^{T} (\hat{\lambda}_k^{\text{MAP}}(t) - 1 - \log \hat{\lambda}_k^{\text{MAP}}(t)) = \frac{1}{2T} \sum_{t=1}^{T} \left((\hat{\lambda}_k^{\text{MAP}}(t) - 1)^2 + \mathcal{O}((\hat{\lambda}_k^{\text{MAP}}(t) - 1)^3) \right).$$

This approximation is better the closer the values of λ are to one. Thus, using these observations, an approximation for risk factor variances σ^2 is given by

$$(\hat{\sigma}_k^{\text{MAPappr}})^2 := \frac{1}{T} \sum_{t=1}^{T} (\hat{\lambda}_k^{\text{MAPappr}}(t) - 1)^2, \tag{11}$$

which is simply the sample variance of $\hat{\lambda}^{\text{MAP}}$. Note that $|\hat{\lambda}_k^{\text{MAP}}(t) - 1| < |\hat{\lambda}_k^{\text{MAPappr}}(t) - 1|$, implying that Equation (11) will dominate solutions obtained by Equation (8) in most cases.

3.3. Estimation via MCMC

As we have already outlined in in the previous sections, deriving maximum a posteriori estimates and maximum likelihood estimates via deterministic numerical optimisation is mostly impossible due to high dimensionality (several hundred parameters). Alternatively, we can use MCMC under a Bayesian setting. Introductions to this topic can be found, for example, in Gilks (1995), Gamerman and Lopes (2006), as well as (Shevchenko 2011, section 2.11). We suggest to use the random walk Metropolis–Hastings within Gibbs algorithm which, given that the Markov chain is irreducible and aperiodic, generates sample chains that converge to the stationary distribution, Tierney (1994) and also (Robert and Casella 2004, sections 6–10). However, note that various MCMC algorithms are available.

MCMC requires a Bayesian setting which we automatically have in the maximum a posteriori approach, see Section 3.2. Similarly, we can switch to a Bayesian setting in the maximum likelihood approach, see Section 3.1, by simply multiplying the likelihood function with a prior distribution of parameters. MCMC generates Markov chains which provide samples from the posterior distribution where the mode of these samples then corresponds to an approximation for the maximum a posteriori estimate. More stable estimates in terms of mean squared error are obtained by taking the mean over all samples once MCMC chains sample from the stationary distribution, (Shevchenko 2011, section 2.10). Taking the mean over all samples as an estimate, of course, can lead to troubles if posterior distributions of parameters are, e.g., bimodal, such that we end up in a region which is highly unlikely. Furthermore, sampled posterior distribution can be used to estimate parameter uncertainty. The method requires a certain burn-in period until the generated chain becomes stationary. Typically, one tries to get average acceptance probabilities close to 0.234 which is asymptotically optimal for multivariate Gaussian proposals as shown in Roberts et al. (1997). To reduce long computational times, one can run several independent MCMC chains with different starting points on different CPUs in a parallel way. To prevent overfitting, it is possible to regularise, i.e., smooth, maximum a posteriori estimates via adjusting the prior distribution. This technique is particularly used in regression, as well as in many applications, such as signal processing. When forecasting death probabilities in Section 4.2, we use a Gaussian prior density with a certain correlation structure.

Also under MCMC, note that ultimately we are troubled with the curse of dimensionality as we will never be able to get an accurate approximation of the joint posterior distribution in a setting with several hundred parameters.

As MCMC samples yield confidence bands for parameter estimates, they can easily be checked for significance at every desired level, i.e., parameters are not significant if confidence bands cover the value zero. In our subsequent examples, almost all parameters are significant. Given internal mortality data, these confidence bands for parameter estimates can also be used to test whether parameters significantly deviate from officially published life tables. On the other hand, MCMC is perfectly applicable to sparse data as life tables can be used as prior distributions with confidence bands providing an estimate for parameter uncertainty which increase with fewer data points.

3.4. Estimation via Matching of Moments

Finally, we provide a *matching of moments* approach which allows easier estimation of parameters but which is less accurate. Therefore, we suggest this approach solely to be used to obtain starting values for the other, more sophisticated estimation procedures. In addition, matching of moments approach needs simplifying assumptions to guarantee independent and identical random variables over time.

Assumption 1 (i.i.d. setting). *Given Definitions 1–3, assume death counts* $(N_{a,g,k}(t))_{t \in U}$ *to be i.i.d. with* $E_{a,g} := E_{a,g}(1) = \cdots = E_{a,g}(T)$ *and* $m_{a,g} := m_{a,g}(1) = \cdots = m_{a,g}(T)$*, as well as* $w_{a,g,k} := w_{a,g,k}(1) = \cdots = w_{a,g,k}(T)$.

To achieve such an i.i.d. setting, transform deaths $N_{a,g,k}(t)$ such that Poisson mixture intensities are constant over time via

$$N'_{a,g,k}(t) := \left\lfloor \frac{E_{a,g}(T)m_{a,g}(T)w_{a,g,k}(T)}{E_{a,g}(t)m_{a,g}(t)w_{a,g,k}(t)} N_{a,g,k}(t) \right\rfloor, \quad t \in U,$$

and, correspondingly, define $E_{a,g} := E_{a,g}(T)$, as well as $m_{a,g} := m_{a,g}(T)$ and $w_{a,g,k} := w_{a,g,k}(T)$. Using this modification, we manage to remove long term trends and keep $E_{a,g}(t)$, $m_{a,g}(t)$ and $w_{a,g,k}(t)$ constant over time.

Estimates $\hat{m}^{\mathrm{MM}}_{a,g}(t)$ for central death rates $m_{a,g}(t)$ can be obtained via minimising mean squared error to crude death rates which, if parameters ζ, η and γ are previously fixed, can be obtained by regressing

$$(F^{\mathrm{Lap}})^{-1}\left(\frac{\sum_{k=0}^{K} \widehat{N}'_{a,g,k}(t)}{E_{a,g}}\right) - \gamma_{a-t}$$

on $\mathcal{T}_{\zeta_{a,g},\eta_{a,g}}(t)$. Estimates $\hat{u}^{\mathrm{MM}}_{a,g,k}, \hat{v}^{\mathrm{MM}}_{a,g,k}, \hat{\phi}^{\mathrm{MM}}_{k}, \hat{\psi}^{\mathrm{MM}}_{k}$ for parameters $u_{a,g,k}, v_{a,g,k}, \phi_k, \psi_k$ via minimising the mean squared error to crude death rates which again, if parameters ϕ and ψ are previously fixed, can be obtained by regressing $\log(\widehat{N}'_{a,g,k}(t)) - \log(E_{a,g}\hat{m}^{\mathrm{MM}}_{a,g}(t))$ on $\mathcal{T}_{\phi_k,\psi_k}(t)$. Estimates $\hat{w}^{\mathrm{MM}}_{a,g,k}(t)$ are then given by Equation (4).

Then, define unbiased estimators for weights $W^*_{a,g,k}(t) := N'_{a,g,k}(t)/E_{a,g}m_{a,g}$, as well as

$$\overline{W}^*_{a,g,k} := \frac{1}{T}\sum_{t=1}^{T} W^*_{a,g,k}(t).$$

In particular, we have $\mathbb{E}[\overline{W}^*_{a,g,k}] = \mathbb{E}[W^*_{a,g,k}(t)] = w_{a,g,k}$.

Lemma 4. *Given Assumptions 3, define*

$$\widehat{\Sigma}^2_{a,g,k} = \frac{1}{T-1}\sum_{t=1}^{T}\left(W^*_{a,g,k}(t) - \overline{W}^*_{a,g,k}\right)^2,$$

for all $a \in \{0,\dots,A\}$, $g \in \{\mathrm{f},\mathrm{m}\}$ *and* $k \in \{0,\dots,K\}$. *Then,*

$$\mathbb{E}[\widehat{\Sigma}^2_{a,g,k}] = \mathrm{Var}(W^*_{a,g,k}(1)) = \frac{w_{a,g,k}}{E_{a,g}m_{a,g}} + \sigma_k^2 w^2_{a,g,k}. \tag{12}$$

Proof. Note that $(W^*_{a,g,k}(t))_{t\in U}$ is assumed to be an i.i.d. sequence. Thus, since $\widehat{\Sigma}_{a,g,k}$ is an unbiased estimator for the standard deviation of $W^*_{a,g,k}(1)$ and $\overline{W}^*_{a,g,k}$, see (Lehmann and Romano 2005, Example 11.2.6), we immediately get

$$\mathbb{E}[\widehat{\Sigma}^2_{a,g,k}] = \mathrm{Var}(\overline{W}^*_{a,g,k}(1)) = \mathrm{Var}\left(\frac{N'_{a,g,k}(1)}{E_{a,g}m_{a,g}}\right).$$

Using the law of total variance as in (Schmock 2017, Lemma 3.48), as well as Definition 10 gives

$$E^2_{a,g}m^2_{a,g}\mathbb{E}[\widehat{\Sigma}^2_{a,g,k}] = \mathbb{E}[\mathrm{Var}(N'_{a,g,k}(1)|\Lambda_k)] + \mathrm{Var}(\mathbb{E}[N'_{a,g,k}(1)|\Lambda_k]).$$

Since $\mathrm{Var}(N'_{a,g,k}(1)|\Lambda_k) = \mathbb{E}[N'_{a,g,k}(1)|\Lambda_k] = E_{a,g}m_{a,g}w_{a,g,k}\Lambda_k$ a.s., the equation above gives the result. □

Having obtained Equation (12), we may define the following matching of moments estimates for risk factor variances.

Definition 6 (Matching of moments estimates for risk factor variances). *Given Assumption 3, the* matching of moments estimate *for σ_k for all $k \in \{1, \dots, K\}$ is defined as*

$$(\hat{\sigma}_k^{\mathrm{MM}})^2 := \max\left\{0, \frac{\sum_{a=0}^{A} \sum_{g \in \{\mathrm{f},\mathrm{m}\}} \left(\hat{\sigma}^2_{a,g,k} - \frac{w^{\mathrm{MM}}_{a,g,k}(T)}{E_{a,g} m^{\mathrm{MM}}_{a,g}(T)}\right)}{\sum_{a=0}^{A} \sum_{g \in \{\mathrm{f},\mathrm{m}\}} (w^{\mathrm{MM}}_{a,g,k}(T))^2}\right\},$$

where $\hat{\sigma}^2_{a,g,k}$ is the estimate corresponding to estimator $\widehat{\Sigma}^2_{a,g,k}$.

4. Applications

4.1. Prediction of Underlying Death Causes

As an applied example for our proposed stochastic mortality model, as well as for some further applications, we take annual death data from Australia for the period 1987 to 2011. We fit our model using the matching of moments approach, as well as the maximum-likelihood approach with Markov chain Monte Carlo (MCMC). Data source for historical Australian population, categorised by age and gender, is taken from the Australian Bureau of Statistics[2] and data for the number of deaths categorised by death cause and divided into eight age categories, i.e., 50–54 years, 55–59 years, 60–64 years, 65–69 years, 70–74 years, 75–79 years, 80–84 years and 85+ years, denoted by $a_1, \dots, a_8$, respectively, for each gender is taken from the AIHW[3]. The provided death data is divided into 19 different death causes—based on the ICD-9 or ICD-10 classification—where we identify the following ten of them with common non-idiosyncratic risk factors: *'certain infectious and parasitic diseases'*, *'neoplasms'*, *'endocrine, nutritional and metabolic diseases'*, *'mental and behavioural disorders'*, *'diseases of the nervous system'*, *'circulatory diseases'*, *'diseases of the respiratory system'*, *'diseases of the digestive system'*, *'external causes of injury and poisoning'*, *'diseases of the genitourinary system'*. We merge the remaining eight death causes to idiosyncratic risk as their individual contributions to overall death counts are small for all categories. Data handling needs some care as there was a change in classification of death data in 1997 as explained at the website of the Australian Bureau of Statistics[4]. Australia introduced the tenth revision of the International Classification of Diseases (ICD-10, following ICD-9) in 1997, with a transition period from 1997 to 1998. Within this period, comparability factors are given in Table 1. Thus, for the period 1987 to 1996, death counts have to be multiplied by corresponding comparability factors.

Table 1. Comparability factors for International Classification of Diseases (ICD)-9 to ICD-10.

Death Cause	Factor	Death Cause	Factor	Death Cause	Factor	Death Cause	
infectious	1.25	neoplasms	1.00	endocrine	1.01	mental	0.78
nervous	1.20	circulatory	1.00	respiratory	0.91	digestive	1.05
genitourinary	1.14	external	1.06	not elsewhere	1.00		

To reduce the number of parameters which have to be estimated, cohort effects are not considered, i.e., $\gamma = 0$, and trend reduction parameters are fixed with values $\zeta = \phi = 0$ and $\eta = \psi = \frac{1}{150}$. This corresponds to slow trend reduction over the data and forecasting period (no acceleration) which makes the setting similar to the Lee–Carter model. Moreover, we choose the arbitrary normalisation $t_0 = 1987$. Results for a more advanced modelling of trend reduction are shown later in Section 4.2. Thus, within the maximum-likelihood framework, we end up with 394 parameters, with 362 to be

---

2 http://www.abs.gov.au/AUSSTATS/abs@.nsf/DetailsPage/3101.0Jun%202013?OpenDocument, accessed on May 10, 2016.
3 http://www.aihw.gov.au/deaths/aihw-deaths-data/#nmd, accessed on May 10, 2016.
4 http://www.abs.gov.au/ausstats/abs@.nsf/Products/3303.0~2007~Appendix~Comparability+of+statistics+over+time+%28Appendix%29?OpenDocument, accessed on May 10, 2016.

optimised. For matching of moments we follow the approach given in Section 3.4. Risk factor variances are then estimated via Approximations (10) and (11) of the maximum a posteriori approach as they give more reliable results than matching of moments.

Based on 40,000 MCMC steps with burn-in period of 10,000 we are able to derive estimates of all parameters where starting values are taken from matching of moments, as well as (10) and (11). Tuning parameters are frequently re-evaluated in the burn-in period. The execution time of our algorithm is roughly seven hours on a standard computer in 'R'. Running several parallel MCMC chains reduces execution times to several minutes. However, note that a reduction in risk factors (e.g., one or zero risk factors for mortality modelling) makes estimation much quicker.

As an illustration, Figure 1 shows MCMC chains of the variance of risk factor for external causes of injury and poisoning σ_9^2, as well as of the parameter $\alpha_{2,f}$ for death probability intercept of females aged 55 to 59 years. We observe in Figure 1 that stationary distributions of MCMC chains for risk factor variances are typically right skewed. This indicates risk which is associated with underestimating variances due to limited observations of tail events.

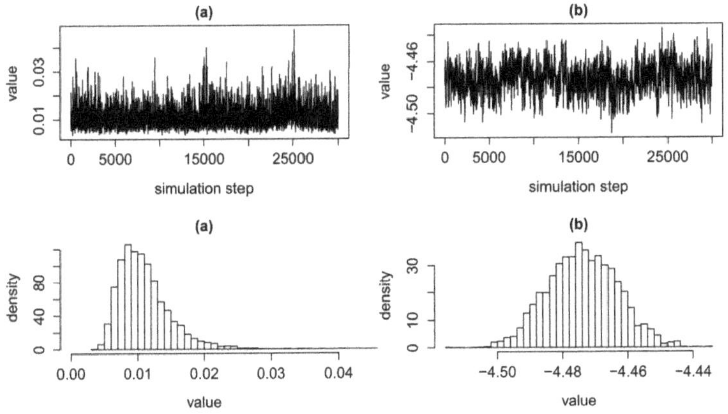

Figure 1. MCMC chains and corresponding density histograms for the variance of risk factor for deaths due to external causes of injury and poisoning σ_9^2 in subfigure (**a**) and for the death probability intercept parameter of females aged 55 to 59 years $\alpha_{2,f}$ in subfigure (**b**).

Table 2 shows estimates for risk factor standard deviations using matching of moments, Approximation (11), as well as mean estimates of MCMC with corresponding 5% and 95% quantiles, as well as standard errors. First, Table 2 illustrates that (10) and (11), as well as matching of moments estimates for risk factor standard deviations σ are close to mean MCMC estimates. Risk factor standard deviations are small but tend to be higher for death causes with just few deaths as statistical fluctuations in the data are higher compared to more frequent death causes. Solely estimates for the risk factor standard deviation of mental and behavioural disorders give higher values. Standard errors, as defined in (Shevchenko 2011, section 2.12.2) with block size 50, for corresponding risk factor variances are consistently less than 3%. We can use the approximation given in Equation (7) to derive risk factor estimates over previous years. For example, we observe increased risk factor realisations of diseases of the respiratory system over the years 2002 to 2004. This is mainly driven by many deaths due to influenza and pneumonia during that period.

Table 2. Estimates for selected risk factor standard deviations σ using matching of moments (MM), Approximation (11) (appr.) and MCMC mean estimates (mean), as well as corresponding standard deviations (stdev.) and 5% and 95% quantiles (5% and 95%).

	MM	Appr.	Mean	5%	95%	Stdev.
infectious	0.1932	0.0787	0.0812	0.0583	0.1063	0.0147
neoplasms	0.0198	0.0148	0.0173	0.0100	0.0200	0.0029
mental	0.1502	0.1357	0.1591	0.1200	0.2052	0.0265
circulatory	0.0377	0.0243	0.0300	0.0224	0.0387	0.0053
respiratory	0.0712	0.0612	0.0670	0.0510	0.0866	0.0110
external	0.1044	0.0912	0.1049	0.0787	0.1353	0.0176

Assumption Equation (4) provides a joint forecast of all death cause intensities, i.e., weights, simultaneously—in contrast to standard procedures where projections are made for each death cause separately. Throughout the past decades we have observed drastic shifts in crude death rates due to certain death causes over the past decades. This fact can be be illustrated by our model as shown in Table 3. This table lists weights $w_{\mathrm{a},g,k}(t)$ for all death causes estimated for 2011, as well as forecasted for 2031 using Equation (4) with MCMC mean estimates for males and females aged between 80 to 84 years. Model forecasts suggest that if these trends in weight changes persist, then the future gives a whole new picture of mortality. First, deaths due to circulatory diseases are expected to decrease whilst neoplasms will become the leading death cause over most age categories. Moreover, deaths due to mental and behavioural disorders are expected to rise considerably for older ages. High uncertainty in forecasted weights is reflected by wide confidence intervals (values in brackets) for the risk factor of mental and behavioural disorders. These confidence intervals are derived from corresponding MCMC chains and, therefore, solely reflect uncertainty associated with parameter estimation. Note that results for estimated trends depend on the length of the data period as short-term trends might not coincide with mid- to long-term trends. Further results can be found in Shevchenko et al. (2015).

Table 3. Selected estimated weights in years 2011 and 2031 for ages 80 to 84 years. 5 and 95% MCMC quantiles are given in brackets.

	2011, Male	2031, Male	2011, Female	2031, Female
neoplasms	0.327 $\binom{0.328}{0.319}$	0.385 $\binom{0.392}{0.363}$	0.263 $\binom{0.267}{0.258}$	0.295 $\binom{0.319}{0.287}$
circulatory	0.324 $\binom{0.330}{0.320}$	0.169 $\binom{0.181}{0.164}$	0.340 $\binom{0.348}{0.337}$	0.145 $\binom{0.158}{0.140}$
respiratory	0.106 $\binom{0.111}{0.102}$	0.090 $\binom{0.101}{0.083}$	0.101 $\binom{0.104}{0.096}$	0.129 $\binom{0.139}{0.113}$
endocrine	0.047 $\binom{0.049}{0.045}$	0.073 $\binom{0.085}{0.070}$	0.053 $\binom{0.053}{0.050}$	0.071 $\binom{0.074}{0.061}$
nervous	0.044 $\binom{0.047}{0.043}$	0.058 $\binom{0.068}{0.055}$	0.054 $\binom{0.057}{0.052}$	0.080 $\binom{0.089}{0.071}$
infectious	0.015 $\binom{0.016}{0.014}$	0.020 $\binom{0.027}{0.019}$	0.015 $\binom{0.018}{0.015}$	0.019 $\binom{0.028}{0.020}$
mental	0.042 $\binom{0.046}{0.037}$	0.115 $\binom{0.130}{0.078}$	0.063 $\binom{0.068}{0.055}$	0.168 $\binom{0.188}{0.118}$

4.2. Forecasting Death Probabilities

Forecasting death probabilities and central death rates within our proposed model is straight forward using Equation (3). In the special case with just idiosyncratic risk, i.e., $K = 0$, death indicators can be assumed to be Bernoulli distributed instead of being Poisson distributed in which case we may write the likelihood function in the form

$$\ell^{\mathrm{B}}(\widehat{N}|\alpha,\beta,\zeta,\eta,\gamma) = \prod_{t=1}^{T}\prod_{a=0}^{A}\prod_{g\in\{\mathrm{f},\mathrm{m}\}} \binom{E_{a,g}(t)}{\widehat{N}_{a,g,0}(t)} m_{a,g}(t)^{\widehat{N}_{a,g,0}(t)}\left(1-m_{a,g}(t)\right)^{E_{a,g}(t)-\widehat{N}_{a,g,0}(t)},$$

with $0 \le \widehat{N}_{a,g,0}(t) \le E_{a,g}(t)$. Due to possible overfitting, derived estimates may not be sufficiently smooth across age categories $a \in \{0,\ldots,A\}$. Therefore, if we switch to a Bayesian setting, we may use regularisation via prior distributions to obtain stabler results. To guarantee smooth results and a sufficient stochastic foundation, we suggest the usage of Gaussian priors with mean zero and a specific correlation structure, i.e., $\pi(\alpha,\beta,\zeta,\eta,\gamma) = \pi(\alpha)\pi(\beta)\pi(\zeta)\pi(\eta)\pi(\gamma)$ with

$$\log \pi(\alpha) := -c_\alpha \sum_{g\in\{\mathrm{f},\mathrm{m}\}} \left(\sum_{a=0}^{A-1} (\alpha_{a,g} - \alpha_{a+1,g})^2 + \varepsilon_\alpha \sum_{a=0}^{A} \alpha_{a,g}^2 \right) + \log(d_\alpha), \quad c_\alpha, d_\alpha, \varepsilon_\alpha > 0, \tag{13}$$

and correspondingly for β, ζ, η and γ. Parameters c_α (correspondingly for β, ζ, η and γ) is a scaling parameters and directly associated with the variance of Gaussian priors while normalisation-parameter d_α guarantees that $\pi(\alpha)$ is a proper Gaussian density. Penalty-parameter ε_α scales the correlation amongst neighbour parameters in the sense that the lower it gets, the higher the correlation. The more we increase c_α the stronger the influence of, or the believe in the prior distribution. This particular prior density penalises deviations from the ordinate which is a mild conceptual shortcoming as this does not accurately reflect our prior believes. Setting $\varepsilon_\alpha = 0$ gives an improper prior with uniformly distributed (on $\mathbb{R}$) marginals such that we gain that there is no prior believe in expectations of parameters but, simultaneously, lose the presence of variance-covariance-matrices and asymptotically get perfect positive correlation across parameters of different ages. Still, whilst lacking theoretical properties, better fits to data are obtained by setting $\varepsilon_\alpha = 0$. For example, setting $\varepsilon_\alpha = \varepsilon_\beta = 10^{-2}$ and $\varepsilon_\zeta = \varepsilon_\eta = \varepsilon_\gamma = 10^{-4}$ yields a prior correlation structure which decreases with higher age differences and which is always positive as given in subfigure (**a**) of Figure 2.

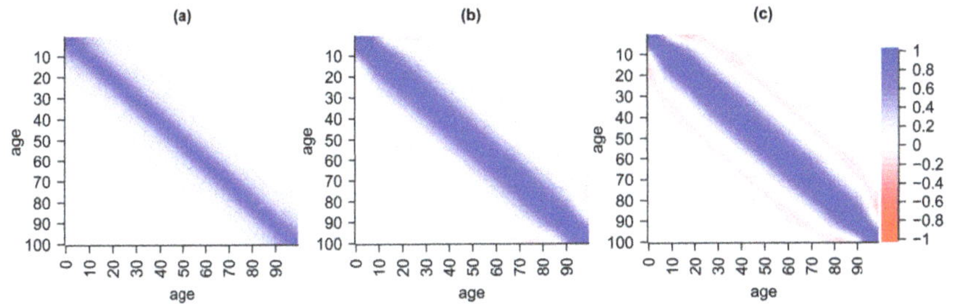

Figure 2. Correlation structure of Gaussian priors with penalisation for deviation from ordinate with $\varepsilon = 1/100$ in subfigure (**a**), straight line with $\varepsilon = 1/2000$ in subfigure (**b**), and parabola $\varepsilon = 1/50000$ in subfigure (**c**).

There exist many other reasonable choices for Gaussian prior densities. For example, replacing graduation terms $(\alpha_{a,g} - \alpha_{a+1,g})^2$ in Equation (13) by higher order differences of the form $\left(\sum_{v=0}^{k}(-1)^v \binom{k}{v} \alpha_{a,g+v}\right)^2$ yields a penalisation for deviations from a straight line with $k = 2$, see subfigure (**b**) in Figure 2, or from a parabola with $k = 3$, see subfigure (**c**) in Figure 2. The usage of higher order differences for graduation of statistical estimates goes back to the Whittaker–Henderson method. Taking $k = 2,3$ unfortunately yields negative prior correlations amongst certain parameters which is why we do not recommend their use. Of course, there exist many further possible choices for prior distributions. However, in our example, we set $\varepsilon_\alpha = \varepsilon_\beta = \varepsilon_\zeta = \varepsilon_\eta = \varepsilon_\gamma = 0$ as this yields accurate results whilst still being reasonably smooth.

An optimal choice of regularisation parameters $c_\alpha, c_\beta, c_\zeta, c_\eta$ and c_γ can be obtained by cross-validation.

Results for Australian data from 1971 to 2013 with $t_0 = 2013$ are given in Figure 3. Using MCMC we derive estimates for logarithmic central death rates $\log m_{a,g}(t)$ with corresponding forecasts, mortality trends $\beta_{a,g}$, as well as trend reduction parameters $\zeta_{a,g}, \eta_{a,g}$ and cohort effects γ_{a-t}. As we do not assume common stochastic risk factors, the MCMC algorithm we use can be implemented very efficiently such that 40 000 samples from the posterior distribution of all parameters are derived within a minute. We observe negligible parameter uncertainty due to a long period of data. Further, regularisation parameters obtained by cross-validation are given by $c_\alpha = 500$, $c_\beta = c_\eta = 30{,}000 c_\alpha$, $c_\zeta = c_\alpha/20$ and $c_\gamma = 1000 c_\alpha$.

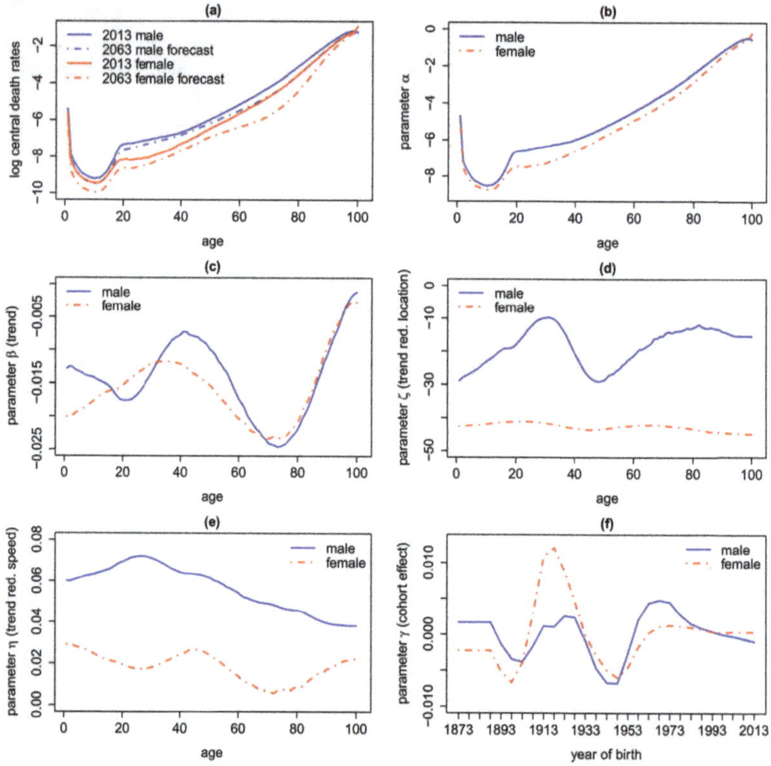

Figure 3. Logarithm of death central death rates (**a**) for 2013 and forecasts for 2063 in Australia as well as parameter values for $\alpha, \beta, \zeta, \eta$ and γ in subfigures (**b**), (**c**), (**d**), (**e**) and (**f**), respectively.

We can draw some immediate conclusions. Firstly, we see an overall improvement in mortality over all ages where the trend is particularly strong for young ages and ages between 60 and 80 whereas the trend vanishes towards the age of 100, maybe implying a natural barrier for life expectancy. Due to sparse data the latter conclusion should be treated with the utmost caution. Furthermore, we see the classical hump of increased mortality driven by accidents around the age of 20 which is more developed for males.

Secondly, estimates for $\zeta_{a,g}$ suggest that trend acceleration switched to trend reduction throughout the past 10 to 30 years for males while for females this transition already took place 45 years ago. However, note that parameter uncertainty (under MCMC) associated with $\zeta_{a,g}$ is high, particularly if estimates are not regularised. Estimates for $\eta_{a,g}$ show that the speed of trend reduction is much stronger for males than for females. Estimates for γ_{a-t} show that the cohort effect is particularly strong (in the sense of increased mortality) for the generation born between 1915 and 1930 (probably associated with World War II) and particularly weak for the generation born around 1945. However, considering cohort effects makes estimation and forecasts significantly less stable for the used data, which is why we recommend to set $\gamma_{a-t} = 0$.

Based on forecasts for death probabilities, expected future life time can be estimated. To be consistent concerning longevity risk, mortality trends have to be included as a 60-year-old today will probably not have as good medication as a 60-year-old in several decades. However, it seems that this is not the standard approach in the literature. Based on the definitions above, expected (curtate) future life time of a person at date T is given by $e_{a,g}(T) = \mathbb{E}[K_{a,g}(T)] = \sum_{k=1}^{\infty} {}_kp_{a,g}(T)$, where survival probabilities over $k \in \mathbb{N}$ years are given by ${}_kp_{a,g}(T) := \prod_{j=0}^{k-1}(1 - q_{a+j,g}(T+j))$ and where $K_{a,g}(T)$ denotes the number of completed future years lived by a person of particular age and gender at time T. Approximating death probabilities by central death rates, for newborns in Australia we get a life expectancy of roughly 83 years for males and 89.5 for females born in 2013, see Table 4. Thus, comparing these numbers to a press release from October 2014 from the Australian Bureau of Statistics[5] saying that 'Aussie men now expected to live past 80' and 'improvements in expected lifespan for women has since slowed down, increasing by around four years over the period—it's 84.3 now', our results show a much higher life expectancy due to the consideration of mortality trends.

Table 4. Curtate future life time $e_{a,g}(T)$ for males and females in 2013.

Age in 2013	0 (Newborn)	20	40	60	80
male	83.07	63.33	43.62	24.44	8.26
female	89.45	69.05	48.20	27.76	9.88

5. A Link to the Extended CreditRisk$^+$ Model and Applications

5.1. The ECRP Model

In this section we establish the connection from our proposed stochastic mortality model to the risk aggregation model extended CreditRisk$^+$ (abbreviated as ECRP), as given in (Schmock 2017, section 6).

Definition 7 (Policyholders and number of deaths). *Let* $\{1, \ldots, E\}$ *with* $E \in \mathbb{N}$ *denote the set of* people *(termed as policyholders in light of insurance applications) in the portfolio and let random variables* $N_1, \ldots, N_E : \Omega \to \mathbb{N}_0$ *indicate the* number of deaths *of each policyholder in the following period. The event* $\{N_i = 0\}$ *indicates survival of person i whilst* $\{N_i \geq 1\}$ *indicates death.*

Definition 8 (Portfolio quantities). *Given Definition 7, the independent random vectors* $Y_1, \ldots, Y_E : \Omega \to \mathbb{N}_0^d$ *with* $d \geq 1$ *dimensions denote* portfolio quantities *within the following period given deaths of policyholders, i.e., on* $\{N_i \geq 1\}$ *for all* $i \in \{1, \ldots, E\}$*, and are independent of* $N_1, \ldots, N_E$.

Remark 5. *(Portfolio quantities).*

(a) For applications in the context of internal models we may set Y_i *as the best estimate liability, i.e., discounted future cash flows, of policyholder i at the end of the period. Thus, when using stochastic discount factors or contracts with optionality, for example, portfolio quantities may be stochastic.*

5 http://www.abs.gov.au/ausstats/abs@.nsf/mediareleasesbyReleaseDate/51FD51C3FC56234DCA257EFA001AE940?OpenDocument, accessed on May 10, 2016.

(b) *In the context of portfolio payment analysis we may set Y_i as the payments (such as annuities) to i over the next period. We may include premiums in a second dimension in order to get joint distributions of premiums and payments.*
(c) *For applications in the context of mortality estimation and projection we set $Y_i = 1$.*
(d) *Using discretisation which preserves expectations (termed as stochastic rounding in (Schmock 2017, section 6.2.2), we may assume Y_i to be $[0,\infty)^d$-valued .*

Definition 9 (Aggregated portfolio quantities). *Given Definitions 7 and 8, aggregated portfolio quantities due to deaths are given by*

$$S := \sum_{i=1}^{E}\sum_{j=1}^{N_i} Y_{i,j}\,,$$

where $(Y_{i,j})_{j\in\mathbb{N}}$ for every $i \in \{1,\dots,E\}$ is an i.i.d. sequence of random variables with the same distributions as Y_i.

Remark 6. *In the context of term life insurance contracts, for example, S is the sum of best estimates of payments and premiums which are paid and received, respectively, due to deaths of policyholders, see Section 5.2. In the context of annuities, S is the sum of best estimates of payments and premiums which need not be paid and are received, respectively, due to deaths of policyholders. Then, small values of S, i.e., the left tail of its distribution, is the part of major interest and major risk.*

It is a demanding question how to choose the modelling setup such that the distribution of S can be derived efficiently and accurately. Assuming N_i to be Bernoulli distributed is not suitable for our intended applications as computational complexity explodes. Therefore, to make the modelling setup applicable in practical situations and to ensure a flexible handling in terms of multi-level dependence, we introduce the ECRP model which is based on extended CreditRisk$^+$, see (Schmock 2017, section 6).

Definition 10 (The ECRP model). *Given Definitions 7 and 8, the ECRP model satisfies the following additional assumptions:*

(a) *Consider independent random common risk factors $\Lambda_1,\dots,\Lambda_K : \Omega \to [0,\infty)$ which have a gamma distribution with mean $e_k = 1$ and variance $\sigma_k^2 > 0$, i.e., with shape and inverse scale parameter σ_k^{-2}. Also the degenerate case with $\sigma_k^2 = 0$ for $k \in \{1,\dots,K\}$ is allowed. Corresponding weights $w_{i,0},\dots,w_{i,K} \in [0,1]$ for every policyholder $i \in \{1,\dots,E\}$. Risk index zero represents idiosyncratic risk and we require $w_{i,0} + \dots + w_{i,K} = 1$.*
(b) *Deaths $N_{1,0},\dots,N_{E,0} : \Omega \to \mathbb{N}_0$ are independent from one another, as well as all other random variables and, for all $i \in \{1,\dots,E\}$, they are Poisson distributed with intensity $m_i w_{i,0}$, i.e.,*

$$\mathbb{P}\Big(\bigcap_{i=1}^{E}\{N_{i,0} = \widehat{N}_{i,0}\}\Big) = \prod_{i=1}^{E} e^{-m_i w_{i,0}} \frac{(m_i w_{i,0})^{\widehat{N}_{i,0}}}{\widehat{N}_{i,0}!}\,, \qquad \widehat{N}_{1,0},\dots,\widehat{N}_{E,0} \in \mathbb{N}_0\,.$$

(c) *Given risk factors, deaths $(N_{i,k})_{i\in\{1,\dots,E\},k\in\{1,\dots,K\}} : \Omega \to \mathbb{N}_0^{E\times K}$ are independent and, for every policyholder $i \in \{1,\dots,E\}$ and $k \in \{1,\dots,K\}$, they are Poisson distributed with random intensity $m_i w_{i,k}\Lambda_k$, i.e.,*

$$\mathbb{P}\Big(\bigcap_{i=1}^{E}\bigcap_{k=1}^{K}\{N_{i,k} = \widehat{N}_{i,k}\}\,\Big|\,\Lambda_1,\dots,\Lambda_K\Big) = \prod_{i=1}^{E}\prod_{k=1}^{K} e^{-m_i w_{i,k}\Lambda_k} \frac{(m_i w_{i,k}\Lambda_k)^{\widehat{N}_{i,k}}}{\widehat{N}_{i,k}!} \quad a.s.,$$

for all $n_{i,k} \in \mathbb{N}_0$.
(d) *For every policyholder $i \in \{1,\dots,E\}$, the total number of deaths N_i is split up additively according to risk factors as $N_i = N_{i,0} + \dots + N_{i,K}$. Thus, by model construction, $\mathbb{E}[N_i] = m_i(w_{i,0} + \dots + w_{i,K}) = m_i$.*

Given Definition 7, central death rates are given by $m_i = \mathbb{E}[N_i]$ and death probabilities, under piecewise constant death rates, are given by $q_i = 1 - \exp(-m_i)$.

Remark 7. *Assuming that central death rates and weights are equal for all policyholders for the same age and gender, it is obvious that the ECRP corresponds one-to-one to our proposed stochastic mortality model, as given in Definition 1, if risk factors are independent gamma distributed.*

In reality, number of deaths are Bernoulli random variables as each person can just die once. Unfortunately in practice, such an approach is not tractable for calculating P&L distributions of large portfolios as execution times explode if numerical errors should be small. Instead, we will assume the number of deaths of each policyholder to be compound Poisson distributed. However, for estimation of life tables we will assume the number of deaths to be Bernoulli distributed. Poisson distributed deaths give an efficient way for calculating P&L distributions using an algorithm based on Panjer's recursion, also for large portfolios, see (Schmock 2017, section 6.7). The algorithm is basically due to Giese (2003) for which Haaf et al. (2004) proved numerical stability. The relation to Panjer's recursion was first pointed out in (Gerhold et al. 2010, section 5.5). Schmock (2017) in section 5.1 generalised the algorithm to the multivariate case with dependent risk factors and risk groups, based on the multivariate extension of Panjer's algorithm given by Sundt (1999). The algorithm is numerically stable since just positive terms are added up. To avoid long execution times for implementations of extended CreditRisk$^+$ with large annuity portfolios, greater loss units and stochastic rounding, see (Schmock 2017, section 6.2.2), can be used.

However, the proposed model allows for multiple (Poisson) deaths of each policyholder and thus approximates the 'real world' with single (Bernoulli) deaths. From a theoretical point of view, this is justified by the Poisson approximation and generalisations of it, see for example Vellaisamy and Chaudhuri (1996). Since annual death probabilities for ages up to 85 are less than 10%, multiple deaths are relatively unlikely for all major ages. However, implementations of this algorithm are significantly faster than Monte Carlo approximations for comparable error (Poisson against Bernoulli) levels.

As an illustration we take a portfolio with $E = 10,000$ policyholders having central death rate $m := m_i = 0.05$ and payments $Y_i = 1$. We then derive the distribution of S using the ECRP model for the case with just idiosyncratic risk, i.e., $w_{i,0} = 1$ and Poisson distributed deaths, and for the case with just one common stochastic risk factor Λ_1 with variance $\sigma_1 = 0.1$ and no idiosyncratic risk, i.e., $w_{i,1} = 1$ with mixed Poisson distributed deaths. Then, using 50,000 simulations of the corresponding model where N_i is Bernoulli distributed or mixed Bernoulli distributed given truncated risk factor $\Lambda_1 | \Lambda_1 \leq \frac{1}{m}$, we compare the results of the ECRP model to Monte Carlo, respectively. Truncation of risk factors in the Bernoulli model is necessary as otherwise death probabilities may exceed one. We observe that the ECRP model drastically reduces execution times in 'R' at comparable error levels and leads to a speed up by the factor of 1000. Error levels in the purely idiosyncratic case are measured in terms of total variation distance between approximations and the binomial distribution with parameters $(10,000, 0.05)$ which arises as the independent sum of all Bernoulli random variables. Error levels in the purely non-idiosyncratic case are measured in terms of total variation distance between approximations and the mixed binomial distribution where for the ECRP model we use Poisson approximation to get an upper bound. the total variation between those distributions is 0.0159 in our simulation and, thus, dominates the Poisson approximation in terms of total variation. Results are summarised in Table 5.

Table 5. Quantiles, execution times (speed) and total variation distance (accuracy) of Monte Carlo with Bernoulli deaths and 50,000 simulations, as well as the *extended CreditRisk*$^+$ (ECRP) model with Poisson deaths, given a simple portfolio.

	Quantiles					Speed	Accuracy
	1%	10%	50%	90%	99%		
Bernoulli (MC), $w_{i,0} = 1$	450	472	500	528	552	22.99 s	0.0187
Poisson (ECRP), $w_{i,0} = 1$	449	471	500	529	553	0.01 s	0.0125
Bernoulli (MC), $w_{i,1} = 1$	202	310	483	711	936	23.07 s	0.0489
Poisson (ECRP), $w_{i,1} = 1$	204	309	483	712	944	0.02 s	$\leq$0.0500

5.2. Application I: Mortality Risk, Longevity Risk and Solvency II Application

In light of the previous section, life tables can be projected into the future and, thus, it is straightforward to derive best estimate liabilities (BEL) of annuities and life insurance contracts. The possibility that death probabilities differ from an expected curve, i.e., estimated parameters do no longer reflect the best estimate and have to be changed, contributes to mortality or longevity risk, when risk is measured over a one year time horizon as in Solvency II and the duration of in-force insurance contracts exceeds this time horizon. In our model, this risk can be captured by considering various MCMC samples $(\hat{\theta}^h)_{h=1,\ldots,m}$ (indexed by superscript h) of parameters $\theta = (\alpha, \beta, \zeta, \eta, \gamma)$ for death probabilities, yielding distributions of BELs. For example, taking $D(T, T+t)$ as the discount curve from time $T+t$ back to T and choosing an MCMC sample $\hat{\theta}^h$ of parameters to calculate death probabilities $q^h_{a,g}(T)$ and survival probabilities $p^h_{a,g}(T)$ at age a with gender g, the BEL for a term life insurance contract which pays 1 unit at the end of the year of death within the contract term of d years is given by

$$A^T_{a,g}(\hat{\theta}^h) = D(T, T+1)q^h_{a,g}(T) + \sum_{t=1}^{d} D(T, T+t+1) \cdot {}_tp^h_{a,g}(T)q^h_{a+t,g}(T+t). \tag{14}$$

In a next step, this approach can be used as a building block for (partial) internal models to calculate basic solvency capital requirements (BSCR) for biometric underwriting risk under Solvency II, as illustrated in the following example.

Consider an insurance portfolio at time 0 with $E \in \mathbb{N}$ whole life insurance policies with lump sum payments $C_i > 0$, for $i = 1, \ldots, E$, upon death at the end of the year. Assume that all assets are invested in an EU government bond (risk free under the standard model of the Solvency II directive) with maturity 1, nominal A_0 and coupon rate $c > -1$. Furthermore, assume that we are only considering mortality risk and ignore profit sharing, lapse, costs, reinsurance, deferred taxes, other assets and other liabilities, as well as the risk margin. Note that in this case, basic own funds, denoted by BOF_t, are given by market value of assets minus BEL at time t, respectively. Then, the BSCR at time 0 is given by the 99.5% quantile of the change in basic own funds over the period $[0, 1]$, denoted by $\Delta\mathrm{BOF}_1$, which can be derived by, see Equation (14),

$$\begin{aligned}\Delta\mathrm{BOF}_1 = \mathrm{BOF}_0 - D(0,1)\mathrm{BOF}_1 = A_0(1 - D(0,1)(1+c)) - \sum_{i=1}^{E} C_i A^0_{a,g}(\hat{\theta}) \\ + \frac{D(0,1)}{m} \sum_{h=1}^{m} \left(\sum_{i=1}^{E} C_i A^1_{a+1,g}(\hat{\theta}^h) + \sum_{i=1}^{E} \sum_{j=1}^{N^h_i} C_i(1 - A^1_{a+1,g}(\hat{\theta}^h)) \right).\end{aligned} \tag{15}$$

where $\hat{\theta} := \frac{1}{m}\sum_{h=1}^{m} \hat{\theta}^h$ and where $N^h_1, \ldots, N^h_E$ are independent and Poisson distributed with $\mathbb{E}[N^h_i] = q^h_{a_i,g_i}(0)$ with policyholder i belonging to age group a_i and of gender g_i. The distribution of the last sum above can be derived efficiently by Panjer recursion. This example does not require a consideration of market risk and it nicely illustrates how mortality risk splits into a part associated with statistical fluctuation (experience variance: Panjer recursion) and into a part with long-term impact (change in assumptions: MCMC). Note that by mixing N_i with common stochastic risk factors, we may include other biometric risks such as morbidity.

Consider a portfolio with 100 males and females at each age between 20 and 60 years, each having a 40-year term life insurance, issued in 2014, which provides a lump sum payment between 10,000 and 200,000 (randomly chosen for each policyholder) if death occurs within these 40 years. Using MCMC samples and estimates based on the Austrian data from 1965 to 2014 as given in the previous section, we may derive the change in basic own funds from 2014 to 2015 by Equation (15) using the extended CreditRisk$^+$ algorithm. The 99.5% quantile of change in BOFs, i.e., the SCR, is lying slightly above one million. If we did not consider parameter risk in the form of MCMC samples, the SCR would decrease by roughly 33%.

5.3. Application II: Impact of Certain Health Scenarios in Portfolios

Analysis of certain health scenarios and their impact on portfolio P&L distributions is straightforward As an explanatory example, assume $m = 1600$ policyholders which distribute uniformly over all age categories and genders, i.e., each age category contains 100 policyholders with corresponding death probabilities, as well as weights as previously estimated and forecasted for 2012. Annuities Y_i for all $i \in \{1, \ldots, E\}$ are paid annually and take deterministic values in $\{11, \ldots, 20\}$ such that ten policyholders in each age and gender category share equally high payments. We now analyse the effect on the total amount of annuity payments in the next period under the scenario, indexed by 'scen', that deaths due to neoplasms are reduced by 25% in 2012 over all ages. In that case, we can estimate the realisation of risk factor for neoplasms, see Equation (7), which takes an estimated value of 0.7991. Running the ECRP model with this risk factor realisation being fixed, we end up with a loss distribution L^{scen} where deaths due to neoplasms have decreased. Figure 4 then shows probability distributions of traditional loss L without scenario, as well as of scenario loss L^{neo} with corresponding 95% and 99% quantiles. We observe that a reduction of 25% in cancer crude death rates leads to a remarkable shift in quantiles of the loss distribution as fewer people die and, thus, more annuity payments have to be made.

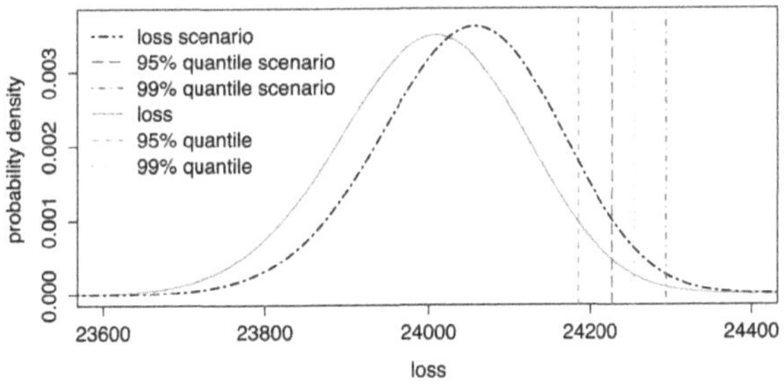

Figure 4. Loss distributions of L and L^{scen} with 95 and 99% quantiles.

5.4. Application III: Forecasting Central Death Rates and Comparison With the Lee–Carter Model

We can compare out-of-sample forecasts of death rates from our proposed model to forecasts obtained by other mortality models. Here, we choose the traditional Lee–Carter model as a proxy as our proposed model is conceptionally based on a similar idea. We make the simplifying assumption of a constant population for out-of-sample time points.

Using the ECRP model it is straight-forward to forecast central death rates and to give corresponding confidence intervals via setting $Y_j(t) := 1$. Then, for an estimate $\hat{\theta}$ of parameter vector θ run the ECRP model with parameters forecasted, see Equations (3) and (4). We then obtain the distribution of the total number of deaths $S_{a,g}(t)$ given $\hat{\theta}$ and, thus, forecasted death rate $\widehat{m}_{a,g}(t)$ is given by $\mathbb{P}(\widehat{m}_{a,g}(t) = N/E_{a,g}(T)) = \mathbb{P}(S_{a,g}(t) = N)$, for all $N \in \mathbb{N}_0$.

Uncertainty in the form of confidence intervals represent statistical fluctuations, as well as random changes in risk factors. Additionally, using results obtained by Markov chain Monte Carlo (MCMC) it is even possible to incorporate parameter uncertainty into predictions. To account for an increase in uncertainty for forecasts we suggest to assume increasing risk factor variances for forecasts, e.g., $\tilde{\sigma}_k^2(t) = \sigma_k^2(1 + d(t-T))^2$ with $d \geq 0$. A motivation for this approach with $k = 1$ is the following: A major source of uncertainty for forecasts lies in an unexpected deviation from the estimated trend for death probabilities. We may therefore assume that rather than being deterministic, forecasted values $m_{a,g}(t)$ are beta distributed (now denoted by $M_{a,g}(t)$) with $\mathbb{E}[M_{a,g}(t)] = m_{a,g}(t)$ and variance $\sigma_{a,g}^2(t)$ which is increasing in time. Then, given independence amongst risk factor Λ_1 and $M_{a,g}(t)$, we may assume that there exists a future point in time t_0 such that

$$\sigma_{a,g}^2(t_0) = \frac{m_{a,g}(t_0)(1 - m_{a,g}(t_0))}{\sigma_1^{-2} + 1}.$$

In that case, $M_{a,g}(t_0)\Lambda_1$ is again gamma distributed with mean one and increased variance $m_{a,g}(t_0)\sigma_1^2$ (instead of $m_{a,g}^2(t_0)\sigma_1^2$ for the deterministic case). Henceforth, it seems reasonable to stay within the family of gamma distributions for forecasts and just adapt variances over time. Of course, families for these variances for gamma distributions can be changed arbitrarily and may be selected via classical information criteria.

Using in-sample data, d can be estimated via Equation (5) with all other parameters being fixed. Using Australian death and population data for the years 1963 to 1997 we estimate model parameters via MCMC in the ECRP model with one common stochastic risk factor having constant weight one. In average, i.e., for various forecasting periods and starting at different dates, parameter d takes the value 0.22 in our example. Using fixed trend parameters as above, and using the mean of 30,000 MCMC samples, we forecast death rates and corresponding confidence intervals out of sample for the period 1998 to 2013. We can then compare these results to crude death rates within the stated period and to forecasts obtained by the Lee–Carter model which is shown in Figure 5 for females aged 50 to 54 years. We observe that crude death rates mostly fall in the 90% confidence band for both procedures. Moreover, Lee–Carter forecasts lead to wider spreads of quantiles in the future whilst the ECRP model suggests a more moderate increase in uncertainty. Taking various parameter samples from the MCMC chain and deriving quantiles for death rates, we can extract contributions of parameter uncertainty in the ECRP model coming from posterior distributions of parameters.

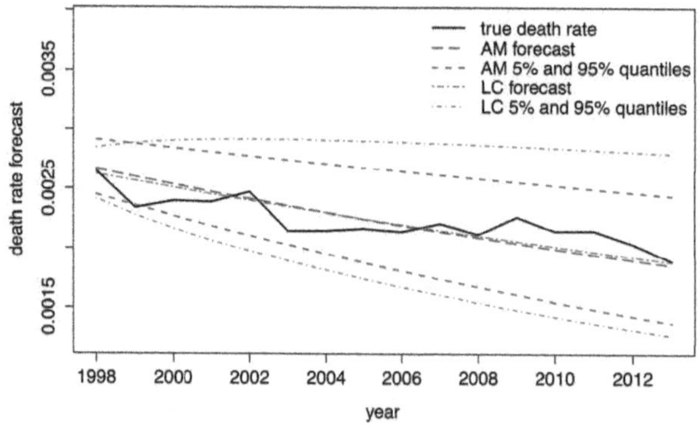

Figure 5. Forecasted and true death rates using the ECRP model (AM) and the Lee–Carter model (LC) for females aged 50 to 54 years.

Within our approach to forecast death rates, it is now possible to derive contributions of various sources of risk. If we set $\delta = 0$ we get forecasts where uncertainty solely comes from statistical fluctuations and random changes in risk factors. Using $\delta = 0.22$ this adds the uncertainty increase associated with uncertainty for forecasts. Finally, considering several MCMC samples this adds parameter risk. We observe that the contribution of statistical fluctuations and random changes in risk factors decreases from 63% in 1998 to 20% in 2013. Adding the increase in uncertainty for forecasts gives a roughly constant contribution of 72% which implies that δ becomes the main driver of risk in the long term. On top of that, parameter uncertainty leaves a constant contribution of 28%.

5.5. Considered Risks

Regulators often require security margins in life tables when modelling annuity or certain life insurance products and portfolios to account for different sources of risk, including trends, volatility risk, model risk and parameter risk, Kainhofer et al. (2006) as well as Pasdika and Wolff (2005).

In the ECRP model, mortality trends are incorporated via families for death probabilities which are motivated by the Lee–Carter model. It is straight forward to arbitrarily change parameter families such that it fits the data as in the case when trends change fundamentally. If other families for weights are used, one always has to check that they sum up to one over all death causes. Note that for certain alternative parameter families, mean estimates obtained from Markov chain Monte Carlo do not necessarily sum up to one anymore. Changing model parameter families may also be necessary when using long-term projections since long-term trends are fundamentally different from short-term trends. Further estimation and testing procedures for trends in composite Poisson models in the context of convertible bonds can be found in Schmock (1999). Trends for weights are particularly interesting insofar as the model becomes sensitive to the change in the vulnerability of policyholders to different death causes over time. Cross dependencies over different death causes and different ages can occur. Such an effect can arise as a reduction in deaths of a particular cause can lead to more deaths in another cause, several periods later, as people have to die at some point. Furthermore, the ECRP model captures unexpected, temporary deviations from a trend with the variability introduced by common stochastic risk factors which effect all policyholders according to weights simultaneously.

Assuming that the model choice is right and that estimated values are correct, life tables still just give mean values of death probabilities over a whole population. Therefore, in the case of German data it is suggested to add a non gender specific due to legal reasons and it is set to 7.4% to account for the risk of random fluctuations in deaths, approximately at a 95% quantile, see German Actuarial Association (DAV) (Todesfallrisiko 2009, section 4.1). In the ECRP model this risk is captured automatically by risk aggregation. As a reference to the suggested security margin of 7.4% on death probabilities, we can use the same approach as given in Section 5.4 to estimate quantiles for death rates via setting $Y_j = 1$. These quantiles then correspond to statistical fluctuations around death probabilities. We roughly observe an average deviation from death probability of 8.4% for the 5% quantile and of 8.7% for the 95% quantile of females aged 55 to 60 years in 2002, i.e., these values are in line with a security margin of 7.4%.

The risk of wrong parameter estimates, i.e., that realised death probabilities deviate from estimated values, can be captured using MCMC as described in Section 3.3 where we sample from the joint posterior distributions of the estimators. As our proposed extended CreditRisk$^+$ algorithm is numerically very efficient, we can easily run the ECRP model for several thousand samples from the MCMC chain to derive sensitivities of quantiles, for example. Note that parameter risk is closely linked to longevity risk. To cover the risk of fundamental changes in future death probabilities, Section 5.4 provides an approach where future risk factor variances increase over time.

Modelling is usually a projection of a sophisticated real world problem on a relatively simple subspace which cannot cover all facets and observations in the data. Therefore, when applying the ECRP model to a portfolio of policyholders, we usually find structural differences to the data which is used for estimation. There may also be a difference in mortality rates between individual companies or between portfolios within a company since different types of insurance products attract different types of policyholders with a different individual risk profile. In Germany, for these risks a minimal security margin of ten% is suggested, see (Pasdika and Wolff 2005, section 2.4.2). Within the ECRP model, this risk can be addressed by using individual portfolio data instead of the whole population. Estimates from the whole population or a different portfolio can be used as prior distributions under MCMC which, in case of sparse data, makes estimation more stable. Another possibility for introducing dependency amongst two portfolios is the introduction of a joint stochastic risk factor for both portfolios. In that case, estimation can be performed jointly with all remaining (except risk factors and their variances) parameters being individually estimated for both portfolios. In contrast to the whole population, observed mortality rates in insurance portfolios often show a completely different structure due to self-selection of policyholders. In particular, for ages around 60, this effect is very strong. In Germany, a security margin for death probabilities of 15% is suggested to cover selection effects, see DAV (Todesfallrisiko 2009, section 4.2). In the literature, this effect is also referred to as basis risk, Li and Hardy (2011). As already mentioned, instead of using a fixed security margin, this issue can be tackled by using portfolio data with estimates from the whole population serving as prior distribution. Again, dependence amongst a portfolio and the whole population can be introduced by a joint stochastic risk factor in the ECRP model.

Alternatively, in (Kainhofer et al. 2006, section 4.7.1) it is suggested that all these risks are addressed by adding a constant security margin on the trend. This approach has the great conceptional advantage that the security margin is increasing over time and does not diminish as in the case of direct security margins on death probabilities.

5.6. Generalised and Alternative Models

Up to now, we applied a simplified version of extended CreditRisk$^+$ to derive cumulative payments in annuity portfolios. A major shortcoming in this approach is the limited possibility of modelling dependencies amongst policyholders and death causes. In the most general form of extended CreditRisk$^+$ as described in (Schmock 2017, section 6), it is possible to introduce risk groups which enable us to model joint deaths of several policyholders and it is possible to model dependencies amongst death causes. Dependencies can take a linear dependence structure combined with dependence scenarios to model negative correlations as well. Risk factors may then be identified with statistical variates such as average blood pressure, average physical activity or the average of smoked cigarettes, etc., and not directly with death causes. Moreover, for each policyholder individually, the general model allows for losses which depend on the underlying cause of death. This gives scope to the possibility of modelling—possibly new—life insurance products with payoffs depending on the cause of death as, for example, in the case of accidental death benefits. Including all extensions mentioned above, a similar algorithm may still be applied to derive loss distributions, see (Schmock 2017, section 6.7).

Instead of using extended CreditRisk$^+$ to model annuity portfolios, i.e., an approach based on Poisson mixtures, we can assume a similar Bernoulli mixture model. In such a Bernoulli mixture model, conditionally Poisson distributed deaths are simply replaced by conditionally Bernoulli distributed deaths. In general, explicit and efficient derivation of loss distributions in the case of Bernoulli mixture models is not possible anymore. Thus, in this case, one has to rely on other methods such as Monte Carlo. Estimation of model parameters works similarly as discussed in Section 3. Poisson approximation suggests that loss distributions derived from Bernoulli and Poisson mixture models are similar in terms of total variation distance if death probabilities are small.

6. Model Validation and Model Selection

In this section we propose several validation techniques in order to check whether the ECRP model fits the given data or not. Results for Australian data, see Section 4.1, strongly suggest that the proposed model is suitable. If any of the following validation approaches suggested misspecification in the model or if parameter estimation did not seem to be accurate, one possibility to tackle these problems would be to reduce risk factors.

6.1. Validation via Cross-Covariance

For the first procedure, we transform deaths $N_{a,g,k}(t)$ to $N'_{a,g,k}(t)$, see Section 3.4, such that this sequence has constant expectation and can thus be assumed to be i.i.d. Then, sample variances of transformed death counts, cumulated across age and gender groups, can be compared to MCMC confidence bounds from the model. In the death-cause-example all observed sample variances of $N_k(t)$ lie within 5%- and 95%-quantiles.

6.2. Validation via Independence

Number of deaths for different death causes are independent within the ECRP model as independent risk factors are assumed. Thus, for all $a, a' \in \{1, \dots, A\}$ and $g, g' \in \{\mathrm{f}, \mathrm{m}\}$, as well as $k, k' \in \{0, \dots, K\}$ with $k \neq k'$ and $t \in U$, we have $\mathrm{Cov}(N_{a,g,k}(t), N_{a',g',k'}(t)) = 0$. Again, transform the data as above and subsequently normalise the transformed data, given $\mathrm{Var}(N'_{a,g,k}(t)|\Lambda_k(t)) > 0$ a.s., as follows:

$$N^*_{a,g,k}(t) := \frac{N'_{a,g,k}(t) - \mathbb{E}[N'_{a,g,k}(t)|\Lambda_k(t)]}{\sqrt{\mathrm{Var}(N'_{a,g,k}(t)|\Lambda_k(t))}} = \frac{N'_{a,g,k}(t) - E_{a,g} m_{a,g} w_{a,g,k} \Lambda_k(t)}{\sqrt{E_{a,g} m_{a,g} w_{a,g,k} \Lambda_k(t)}}.$$

Using the conditional central limit theorem as in Grzenda and Zieba (2008), we have $N^*_{a,g,k}(t) \to N(0,1)$ in distribution as $E_{a,g}(t) \to \infty$ where $N(0,1)$ denotes the standard normal distribution. Thus, normalised death counts $n^*_{a,g,k}(t)$ are given by

$$n^*_{a,g,k}(t) = \frac{n'_{a,g,k}(t) - E_{a,g} \hat{m}_{a,g} \hat{w}_{a,g,k} \hat{\lambda}_k(t)}{\sqrt{E_{a,g} \hat{m}_{a,g} \hat{w}_{a,g,k} \hat{\lambda}_k(t)}}.$$

with $\hat{\lambda}_0(t) := 1$. Then, assuming that each pair $(N^*_{a,g,k}(t), N^*_{a',g',k'}(t))$, for $a, a' \in \{1, \dots, A\}$ and $g, g' \in \{\mathrm{f}, \mathrm{m}\}$, as well as $k, k' \in \{0, \dots, K\}$ with $k \neq k'$ and $t \in U$, has a joint normal distribution with some correlation coefficient ρ and standard normal marginals, we may derive the sample correlation coefficient

$$R_{a,g,a',g',k,k'} := \frac{\sum_{t=1}^{T} (N^*_{a,g,k}(t) - \overline{N}^*_{a,g,k})(N^*_{a',g',k'}(t) - \overline{N}^*_{a',g',k'})}{\sqrt{\sum_{t=1}^{T} (N^*_{a,g,k}(t) - \overline{N}^*_{a,g,k})^2 \sum_{t=1}^{T} (N^*_{a',g',k'}(t) - \overline{N}^*_{a',g',k'})^2}},$$

where $\overline{N}^*_{a,g,k} := \frac{1}{T} \sum_{s=1}^{T} N^*_{a,g,k}(s)$. Then, the test of the null hypothesis $\rho = 0$ against the alternative hypothesis $\rho \neq 0$ rejects the null hypothesis at an δ-percent level, see (Lehmann and Romano 2005, section 5.13), when

$$\frac{|R_{a,g,a',g',k,k'}|}{\sqrt{(1 - R^2_{a,g,a',g',k,k'})/(T-2)}} > K_{\delta,T}, \tag{16}$$

with $K_{\delta,T}$ such that $\int_{K_{\delta,T}}^{\infty} t_{T-2}(y)\, dy = \delta/2$ where t_{T-2} denotes the density of a t-distribution with $(T-2)$ degrees of freedom.

Applying this validation procedure on Australian data with ten death causes shows that 88.9% of all independence tests, see Equation (16), are accepted at a 5% significance level. Thus, we may assume that the ECRP model fits the data suitably with respect to independence amongst death counts due to different causes.

6.3. Validation via Serial Correlation

Using the same data transformation and normalisation as in Section 6.2, we may assume that random variables $(N^*_{a,g,k}(t))_{t\in U}$ are identically and standard normally distributed. Then, we can check for serial dependence and autocorrelation in the data such as causalities between a reduction in deaths due to certain death causes and a possibly lagged increase in different ones. Note that we already remove a lot of dependence via time-dependent weights and death probabilities. Such serial effects are, for example, visible in the case of mental and behavioural disorders and circulatory diseases.

Many tests are available most of which assume an autoregressive model with normal errors such as the Breusch–Godfrey test, see Godfrey (1978). For the Breusch–Godfrey test a linear model is fitted to the data where the residuals are assumed to follow an autoregressive process of length $p \in \mathbb{N}$. Then, $(T-p)R^2$ asymptotically follows a χ^2 distribution with p degrees of freedom under the null hypothesis that there is no autocorrelation. In 'R', an implementation of the Breusch–Godfrey is available within the function bgtest in the 'lmtest' package, see Zeileis and Hothorn (2002).

Applying this validation procedure to Australian data given in Section 4.1, the null hypothesis, i.e., that there is no serial correlation of order $1, 2, \ldots, 10$, is not rejected at a 5% level in 93.8% of all cases. Again, this is an indicator that the ECRP model with trends for weights and death probabilities fits the data suitably

6.4. Validation via Risk Factor Realisations

In the ECRP model, risk factors Λ are assumed to be independent and identically gamma distributed with mean one and variance σ_k^2. Based on these assumptions, we can use estimates for risk factor realisations λ to judge whether the ECRP model adequately fits the data. These estimates can either be obtained via MCMC based on the maximum a posteriori setting or by Equations (7) or (10).

For each $k \in \{1, \ldots, K\}$, we may check whether estimates $\hat{\lambda}_k(1), \ldots, \hat{\lambda}_k(T)$ suggest a rejection of the null hypothesis that they are sampled from a gamma distribution with mean one and variance σ_k^2. The classical way is to use the Kolmogorov–Smirnov test, see e.g., (Lehmann and Romano 2005, section 6.13) and the references therein. In 'R' an implementation of this test is provided by the ks.test function, see R Core Team (2013). The null hypotheses is rejected as soon as the test statistic $\sup_{x\in\mathbb{R}} |F_T(x) - F(x)|$ exceeds the corresponding critical value where F_T denotes the empirical distribution function of samples $\hat{\lambda}_k(1), \ldots, \hat{\lambda}_k(T)$ and where F denotes the gamma distribution function with mean one and variance σ_k^2.

Testing whether risk factor realisations are sampled from a gamma distribution via the Kolmogorov–Smirnov test as described above gives acceptance of the null hypothesis for all ten risk factors on all suitable levels of significance.

6.5. Model Selection

For choosing a suitable family for mortality trends, information criteria such as AIC, BIC, or DIC can be applied straight away. The decision how many risk factors to use cannot be answered by traditional information criteria since a reduction in risk factors leads to a different data structure. It also depends on the ultimate goal. For example, if the development of all death causes is of interest, then a reduction of risk factors is not wanted. On the contrary, in the context of annuity portfolios several risk factors may be merged to one risk factor as their contributions to the risk of the total portfolio are small.

7. Conclusions

We introduce an additive stochastic mortality model which is closely related to classical approaches such as the Lee–Carter model but allows for joint modelling of underlying death causes and improves models using disaggregated death cause forecasts. Model parameters can be jointly estimated using MCMC based on publicly available data. We give a link to extended CreditRisk$^+$ which provides a useful actuarial tool with numerous portfolio applications such as P&L derivation in annuity and life insurance portfolios or (partial) internal model applications. Yet, there exists a fast and numerically stable algorithm to derive loss distributions exactly, instead of Monte Carlo, even for large portfolios. Our proposed model directly incorporates various sources of risk including trends, longevity, mortality risk, statistical volatility and estimation risk. In particular, it is possible to quantify the risk of statistical fluctuations within the next period (experience variance) and parameter uncertainty over a longer time horizon (change in assumptions). Compared to the Lee–Carter model, we have a more flexible framework and can directly extract several sources of uncertainty. Straightforward model validation techniques are available.

Acknowledgments: J. Hirz acknowledges financial support from the Australian Government via the 2014 Endeavour Research Fellowship, as well as from the Oesterreichische Nationalbank (Anniversary Fund, project number: 14977) and Arithmetica. P. V. Shevchenko acknowledges support from CSIRO Australia, CSIRO-Monash Superannuation Research Cluster, and Australian Research Council's Discovery Projects funding scheme (project number DP160103489).

Author Contributions: All authors contributed equally to this research work by providing new ideas, writing the paper, discussing existing results and sharing their knowledge in this field. Implementation and numerical calculations were performed by Jonas Hirz.

Conflicts of Interest: The authors declare no conflict of interest.

References

Alai, Daniel H., Séverine Arnold, and Michael Sherris. 2015. Modelling cause-of-death mortality and the impact of cause-elimination. *Annals of Actuarial Science* 9:167–86.

Barbour, Andrew D., Lars Holst, and Svante Janson. 1992. *Poisson Approximation*. Oxford Studies in Probability. Oxford: Oxford University Press, vol. 2.

Booth, Heather, and Leonie Tickle. 2008. Mortality modelling and forecasting: A review of methods. *Annals of Actuarial Science* 3: 3–43.

Brouhns, Natacha, Michel Denuit, and Jeroen K. Vermunt. 2002. A Poisson log-bilinear regression approach to the construction of projected lifetables. *Insurance: Mathematics and Economics* 31: 373–93.

Cairns, Andrew J. G., David Blake, Kevin Dowd, Guy D. Coughlan, David Epstein, Alen Ong, and Igor Balevich. 2009. A quantitative comparison of stochastic mortality models using data from England and Wales and the United States. *North American Actuarial Journal* 13: 1–35.

Chaudhry, M. Aslam, and Syed M. Zubair. 2001. *On a Class of Incomplete Gamma Functions with Applications*. Abingdon: Taylor & Francis.

Credit Suisse First Boston. 1997. *Creditrisk$^+$: A Credit Risk Management Framework*. Technical Report. New York: CSFB.

Fung, Man Chung, Gareth W. Peters, and Pavel V. Shevchenko. 2017. A unified approach to mortality modelling using state-space framework: Characterization, identification, estimation and forecasting. To appear in *Annals of Actuarial Science*.

Fung, Man Chung, Gareth W. Peters, and Pavel V. Shevchenko. 29 November–4 December 2015. A state-space estimation of the Lee–Carter mortality model and implications for annuity pricing. Paper presented at 21st International Congress on Modelling and Simulation, Modelling and Simulation Society of Australia and New Zealand (MODSIM2015), Broadbeach, Australia. Edited by T. Weber, M.J. McPhee and R.S. Anderssen, pp. 952–58.

Gamerman, Dani, and Hedibert F. Lopes. 2006. *Markov chain Monte Carlo: Stochastic Simulation for Bayesian Inference*, 2nd ed. Texts in Statistical Science Series. Boca Raton: Chapman & Hall/CRC.

Gerhold, Stefan, Uwe Schmock, and Richard Warnung. 2010. A generalization of Panjer's recursion and numerically stable risk aggregation. *Finance and Stochastics* 14: 81–128.

Giese, Gotz. 2003. Enhancing CreditRisk$^+$. *Risk* 16: 73–77.

Gilks, Walter R., Sylvia Richardson, and David Spiegelhalter. 1995. *Markov Chain Monte Carlo in Practice*. Boca Raton: Chapman & Hall/CRC Interdisciplinary Statistics, Taylor & Francis.

Godfrey, Leslie G. 1978. Testing against general autoregressive and moving average error models when the regressors include lagged dependent variables. *Econometrica* 46: 1293–301.

Grzenda, Wioletta, and Wieslaw Zieba. 2008. Conditional central limit theorem. *International Mathematical Forum* 3: 1521–28.

Haaf, Hermann, Oliver Reiss, and John Schoenmakers. 2004. Numerically stable computation of CreditRisk$^+$. In *CreditRisk$^+$ in the Banking Industry*. Edited by Matthias Gundlach and Frank Lehrbass. Berlin: Springer Finance, pp. 69–77.

Kainhofer, Reinhold, Martin Predota, and Uwe Schmock. 2006. The new Austrian annuity valuation table AVÖ 2005R. *Mitteilungen der Aktuarvereinigung Österreichs* 13: 55–135.

Lee, Ronald D., and Lawrence R. Carter. 1992. Modeling and forecasting U.S. mortality. *Journal of the American Statistical Association* 87: 659–71.

Lehmann, Erich L., and Joseph P. Romano. 2005. *Testing Statistical Hypotheses*, 3rd ed. Springer Texts in Statistics. Berlin: Springer-Verlag.

Li, Johnny Siu-Hang, and Mary R. Hardy. 2011. Measuring basis risk in longevity hedges. *North American Actuarial Journal* 15: 177–200.

McNeil, Alexander J., Rüdiger Frey, and Paul Embrechts. 2005. *Quantitative Risk Management: Concepts, Techniques and Tools*. Princeton Series in Finance. Princeton: Princeton University Press.

Pasdika, Ulrich and Jürgen Wolff. 12–14 January 2005. Coping with longvity: The new German annuity valuation table DAV 2004 R. Paper presented at the Living to 100 and beyond Symposium, Orlando, FL, USA.

Pitacco, Ermanno, Michel Denuit, and Steven Haberman. 2009. *Modelling Dynamics for Pensions and Annuity Business*. Oxford: Oxford University Press.

Qi, Feng, Run-Qing Cui, Chao-Ping Chen, and Bai-Ni Guo. 2005. Some completely monotonic functions involving polygamma functions and an application. *Journal of Mathematical Analysis and Applications* 310: 303–8.

R Core Team. 2013. *R: A Language and Environment for Statistical Computing*. Vienna: R Foundation for Statistical Computing.

Robert, Christian P., and George Casella. 2004. *Monte Carlo Statistical Methods*, 2nd ed. Springer Texts in Statistics. New York: Springer-Verlag.

Roberts, Gareth O., Andrew Gelman, and Walter R. Gilks. 1997. Weak convergence and optimal scaling of random walk Metropolis algorithms. *The Annals of Applied Probability* 7: 110–20.

Schmock, Uwe. 1999. Estimating the value of the WinCAT coupons of the Winterthur insurance convertible bond: A study of the model risk. *Astin Bulletin* 29: 101–63.

Schmock, Uwe. 2017. Modelling Dependent Credit Risks with Extensions of Credit Risk+ and Application to Operational Risk. Lecture Notes, Version March 28, 2017. Available online: http://www.fam.tuwien.ac.at/~schmock/notes/ExtensionsCreditRiskPlus.png (accessed on 28 March 2017).

Shevchenko, Pavel V., Jonas Hirz, and Uwe Schmock. 29 November–4 December 2015. Forecasting leading death causes in Australia using extended CreditRisk+. Paper presented at 21st International Congress on Modelling and Simulation, Modelling and Simulation Society of Australia and New Zealand (MODSIM2015), Broadbeach, Australia. Edited by T. Weber, M. J. McPhee, and R. S. Anderssen (Eds.), pp. 966–72.

Shevchenko, Pavel V. 2011. *Modelling Operational Risk Using Bayesian Inference*. Berlin: Springer-Verlag.

Sundt, Bjørn. 1999. On multivariate Panjer recursions. *Astin Bulletin* 29: 29–45.

Tierney, Luke. 1994. Markov chains for exploring posterior distributions. *The Annals of Statistics* 22: 1701–62.

Todesfallrisiko, DAV-Unterarbeitsgruppe. 2009. Herleitung der Sterbetafel DAV 2008 T für Lebensversicherungen mit Todesfallcharakter. *Blätter der DGVFM* 30: 189–224. (In German)

Vellaisamy P., and B. Chaudhuri. 1996. Poisson and compound Poisson approximations for random sums of random variables. *Journal of Applied Probability* 33: 127–37.

Wilmoth, John R. 1995. Are mortality projections always more pessimistic when disaggregated by cause of death? *Mathematical Population Studies* 5: 293–319.

Zeileis, Achim, and Torsten Hothorn. 2002. Diagnostic checking in regression relationships. *R News* 2: 7–10.

risks

Article

Stochastic Period and Cohort Effect State-Space Mortality Models Incorporating Demographic Factors via Probabilistic Robust Principal Components

Dorota Toczydlowska [1,*], Gareth W. Peters [1,2], Man Chung Fung [3] and Pavel V. Shevchenko [4]

1. Department of Statistical Science, University College London, 1-19 Torrington Place, London WC1E 7HB, UK; garethpeters78@gmail.com
2. Man Institute of Quantitative Finance, University of Oxford, Oxford OX1 3BD, UK
3. Data61, CSIRO, Sydney, NSW 2022, Australia; simon.fung@csiro.au
4. Department of Applied Finance and Actuarial Studies, Macquarie University, Sydney, NSW 2109, Australia; pavel.shevchenko@mq.edu.au

* Correspondence: dtoczydlowska@gmail.com; Tel.: +44-207-679-1238

Academic Editor: Mogens Steffensen
Received: 31 May 2017; Accepted: 17 July 2017; Published: 27 July 2017

Abstract: In this study we develop a multi-factor extension of the family of Lee-Carter stochastic mortality models. We build upon the time, period and cohort stochastic model structure to extend it to include exogenous observable demographic features that can be used as additional factors to improve model fit and forecasting accuracy. We develop a dimension reduction feature extraction framework which (a) employs projection based techniques of dimensionality reduction; in doing this we also develop (b) a robust feature extraction framework that is amenable to different structures of demographic data; (c) we analyse demographic data sets from the patterns of missingness and the impact of such missingness on the feature extraction, and (d) introduce a class of multi-factor stochastic mortality models incorporating time, period, cohort and demographic features, which we develop within a Bayesian state-space estimation framework; finally (e) we develop an efficient combined Markov chain and filtering framework for sampling the posterior and forecasting. We undertake a detailed case study on the Human Mortality Database demographic data from European countries and we use the extracted features to better explain the term structure of mortality in the UK over time for male and female populations when compared to a pure Lee-Carter stochastic mortality model, demonstrating our feature extraction framework and consequent multi-factor mortality model improves both in sample fit and importantly out-off sample mortality forecasts by a non-trivial gain in performance.

Keywords: mortality modelling; cohort models; factor models; state-space models; Bayesian inference; Markov chain Monte Carlo; features extraction; robust dimensionality reduction

---

1. Introduction

Modelling the "term-structure" of age specific mortality rates by gender and country has enjoyed a growing resurgence in the actuarial and statistics literature. This is primarily driven by the importance of better understanding and forecasting age specific mortality rates for purposes of understanding longevity risk, pension design, annuities pricing and population studies.

The most widely utilised class of stochastic mortality models in actuarial science and statistics arise from the class of regression or state-space models that incorporate explanatory factors which correspond to stylised latent stochastic factors representing structural features in the evolution of the age specific mortality rates. Typically these latent stochastic features are interpreted as either temporal effects, period effects and cohort effects. The most famous class of such models is the Lee-Carter type models, see a summary recently in Fung et al. (2017) and references therein.

In this paper we aim to combine these classes of stochastic mortality model with other observable exogenous features obtained from a range of demographic data sets. The purpose being that they offer two advantages to standard Lee-Carter models, firstly they may improve predictive power of the models, secondly they may improve the interpretation of behaviour of the dynamic of the "term-structure" of age specific mortality rates.

We expect the mortality experience and demographic data to be characterised by a strong causal and time-varying interaction. There is an existing literature on incorporation of demographic data in stochastic mortality models. However, unlike the state space mortality age-term structure dynamic factor model approach we develop in this manuscript, the existing works have been primarily focused on regression type structures that consider single age group models. Furthermore, there is limited work on feature extraction methods in this space. We highlight a few related approaches that have considered demographic data to study single age group mortality. We comment on some of the widely used exogenous factors in such studies, which include for instance macroeconomic variables, as well as demographic variables. In (Hanewald 2011) and (Niu and Melenberg 2014), the authors investigate the links between the economic growth and morality trends through a class of single age group regression models which are estimated in a frequentist estimation framework. In addition to the period effect in the standard Lee-Carter mode, the authors incorporate gross domestic product (GDP) as an observable factor what improves the in-sample and out-of-sample performance of the model.

Other classes of factors that have been explored in such settings also include cause-of-death categorical variables, what has been also partly investigated in (Hanewald 2011). The relation between causes of death and their influence on mortality has started to be more detailed explore since the accessibility of the data improved. In Murray and Lopez (1997), the authors develop the scenarios of future mortality based on a multi factor linear regression model where the logarithm of the rate of mortality per age group, sex and clustered cause of death is regressed against the socio-economic, educational, technological and cause-of-death related predictors. The Bayesian inference has been adopted in (Girosi and King 2008) to build a regression framework for forecasting mortality rates which are age, sex, country and case of death specific. The work is mostly focused on the methodological side of the forecasting but uses as examples the applications of demography and macro-epidemiology data as explanatory variables for the regression-type model of mortality. Moreover, the dependency structures between cause-specific death rates are studied in (Gaille and Sherris 2015). The authors use Vector Error Correction Models to examine such causal relations within the countries.

The usage of principal components of the mortality curves as linear regressors has been examined in (Hyndman and Yasmeen 2012). The authors explored the common features of the data applying the functional version of Principal Component Analysis. The concept is further developed in (Erbas et al. 2010), where the cause-of-death-specific smoothed mortality curves are treated as functional data. The obtained principal components serve as basis functions in functional data analysis.

In the following study, we aim to broaden these concepts and investigate the impact of global mortality trends given by various sets of international demographic data, and their potential influence on the mortality experience in one country, in our case study the United Kingdom. To achieve this in a manner suitable for incorporation in multi-age stochastic mortality models we need to perform a parsimonious feature extraction method in order to reduce the large dimensional sets of data to a form suitable for inclusion in such a mortality model. Therefore, we introduce a methodology which is not exclusive to one type of demographic data and is capable of handling the analysis jointly over many different exogenous variables.

To achieve this we must undertake several tasks: the first is to explain a canonical and principled approach to combining of such demographic time series data into the stochastic mortality models, for which there is a number of structural approaches we develop and present.

The second aspect is that large demographic data sets are now available, but a naive incorporation of such features into a stochastic mortality model would result in far too many parameters to perform estimation, the models would be overfit and would not provide good generalisation properties for out-off-sample forecast performance. Therefore, we introduce a class of probabilistic, statistically robust feature extraction approaches to reduce dimensionality and capture core information present in the demographic data that can be more parsimoniously included in the stochastic mortality models. The standard concept of robust Principal Component Analysis by means of M- and S-estimators cannot be easily utilized since the demographic data is not equal length and contains missing values across different age groups. Hence, we adopt a probabilistic formulation of Principal Component Analysis which additionally allows to model the hidden process of missing values.

Another challenge is the issue of parameters uncertainty in mortality modelling which we address by adopting the Bayesian Inference framework based on efficient Markov Chain Monte Carlo as in Fung et al. (2017). The estimation of the model is achieved via a Rao-Blackwellised Gibbs sampler. We sample the static parameters via conjugate Gibbs sampling steps which are followed by Forward Backward filtering sampler for state variables to inference from the resulting posteriors.

The contributions of each part of the paper are as follows. Firstly, we briefly overview the concept of the mortality modelling and discuss the state-space formulation of the Lee-Carter model with cohort effects and impose identification contains. Section 3 provides with several illustrations of how to incorporate observable factors into Lee- Carter models. The discussion is followed by an introduction to features extraction by means of Principal Component Analysis. Section 5 extends the standard Principal Component Analysis terminology to the probabilistic setting and derives the steps of its estimation via Expectation-Maximisation Algorithm in order to combine Principal Component with missingness. An overview of the data is given in Section 7 whereas numerical illustrations of empirical studies are presented in Section 8. Finally, Section 11 concludes.

2. Period and Cohort Effect Stochastic Mortality Models: State-Space Formulation

We begin this section by briefly recalling the classical two factor period effect and cohort effect models that have been proposed in Renshaw and Haberman (2006); Pedroza (2006) and Kogure and Kurachi (2010). This includes in particular the state-space formulation of such models which was developed in Fung et al. (2016) and Fung et al. (2017).

Extension of Lee-Carter model to cohort features proposed in (Renshaw and Haberman 2006) introduces the concept of the stochastic cohort factor, denoted by γ_{t-x}, is incorporated into the one factor stochastic Lee-Carter (Lee and Carter 1992) stochastic period effect, denoted κ_t to produce a two factor stochastic model. This second cohort factor, like the period effect factor, can also have an age-modulating coefficient, denoted by β_x^γ. In this work we adopt the recommendations discussed in (Cairns et al. 2009); (Haberman and Renshaw 2011) and (Hunt and Villegas 2015), where it is proposed to simplify this feature to be a constant age-modulating coefficient accross all age groups, given by:

$$\log m_{x,t} = \alpha_x + \beta_x \kappa_t + \gamma_{t-x}, \tag{1}$$

where $x \in \{x_1, \dots, x_p\}$ and $t \in \{1, \dots, T\}$ represent age and year respectively. $m_{x,t}$ denotes the mortality rate in age group x and time t. α_x and β_x are the age specific static parameters of the model. This simplifying assumption that $\beta_x^\gamma = 1$ (or generally any constant other than one) is supposed to improve estimation performance when fitting the model in practice. Furthermore, there is discussion in the literature to argue that it may also be justified based on empirical findings. By studying the mortality experience of England and Wales males, the study of (Willets 2004) finds that the cohort effect is not "wearing off" with increasing ages and the mortality improvement rates, defined as $1 - m_{x,t}/m_{x,t-1}$, of different cohorts seem to be rather stable. Together with the consideration of the convergence problem, one may argue that it is indeed reasonable to assume that $\beta_x^\gamma = 1$ to ensure estimation can be successfully performed for a range of mortality data while the explanatory power of the simplified model is comparable to the full model.

Next we recall the two-factor state-space formulation of the Lee-Carter type period-cohort models for stochastic mortality, see derivations and properties in Fung et al. (2016) and Fung et al. (2017). Note, we adopt the same standard notation as proposed in these papers to present the models in this manuscript.

The formulation of stochastic period-cohort models in state-space form is given by specification of both an observation equation and a state equation. Let $y_{x,t} = \log \hat{m}_{x,t}$ where $x = x_1, \ldots, x_p$ and $t = 1, \ldots, T$. The general form of the observation equation (when β_x^γ is flexible) of the cohort model Equation (1) is given in matrix form by (recall that $\gamma_t^x := \gamma_{t-x}$):

$$\begin{pmatrix} y_{x_1,t} \\ y_{x_2,t} \\ \vdots \\ y_{x_p,t} \end{pmatrix} = \begin{pmatrix} \alpha_{x_1} \\ \alpha_{x_2} \\ \vdots \\ \alpha_{x_p} \end{pmatrix} + \begin{pmatrix} \beta_{x_1} & \beta_{x_1}^\gamma & 0 & \cdots & 0 \\ \beta_{x_2} & 0 & \beta_{x_2}^\gamma & \cdots & 0 \\ \vdots & \vdots & \vdots & \ddots & \vdots \\ \beta_{x_p} & 0 & 0 & \cdots & \beta_{x_p}^\gamma \end{pmatrix} \begin{pmatrix} \kappa_t \\ \gamma_t^{x_1} \\ \gamma_t^{x_2} \\ \vdots \\ \gamma_t^{x_p} \end{pmatrix} + \begin{pmatrix} \varepsilon_{x_1,t} \\ \varepsilon_{x_2,t} \\ \vdots \\ \varepsilon_{x_p,t} \end{pmatrix}, \tag{2}$$

where iid noise terms $\varepsilon_{x,t}$ are included as we aim to model the crude death rates. In a given year t, we identify in this model the state vector as $(\kappa_t, \gamma_t^{x_1}, \ldots, \gamma_t^{x_p})^\top$ which represents the $p+1$ dimensional latent unobserved stochastic factor driving the observed log-mortality rates. The dynamic of this stochastic state vector is then specified in the state equation. In this work, we consider the state-space model given in matrix form as follows:

$$\begin{pmatrix} \kappa_t \\ \gamma_t^{x_1} \\ \gamma_t^{x_2} \\ \vdots \\ \gamma_t^{x_{p-1}} \\ \gamma_t^{x_p} \end{pmatrix} = \begin{pmatrix} 1 & 0 & 0 & \cdots & 0 & 0 \\ 0 & \lambda & 0 & \cdots & 0 & 0 \\ 0 & 1 & 0 & \cdots & 0 & 0 \\ 0 & 0 & 1 & \cdots & 0 & 0 \\ \vdots & \vdots & \vdots & \ddots & \vdots & \vdots \\ 0 & 0 & 0 & \cdots & 1 & 0 \end{pmatrix} \begin{pmatrix} \kappa_{t-1} \\ \gamma_{t-1}^{x_1} \\ \gamma_{t-1}^{x_2} \\ \vdots \\ \gamma_{t-1}^{x_{p-1}} \\ \gamma_{t-1}^{x_p} \end{pmatrix} + \begin{pmatrix} \theta \\ \eta \\ 0 \\ \vdots \\ 0 \\ 0 \end{pmatrix} + \begin{pmatrix} \omega_t^\kappa \\ \omega_t^\gamma \\ 0 \\ \vdots \\ 0 \\ 0 \end{pmatrix}. \tag{3}$$

In this particular instance, we assume κ_t is a random walk with drift process (ARIMA(0,1,0) with a constant) and the dynamics of $\gamma_t^{x_1}$ are described by a stationary AR(1) process with drift (ARIMA(1,0,0) with a constant) where $|\lambda| < 1$. One may consider other dynamics for $\gamma_t^{x_1}$ by specifying the second row of the $p+1$ by $p+1$ matrix in Equation (3). For example, an ARIMA(2,0,0) process for $\gamma_t^{x_1}$ can be assumed if one fixes

$$\begin{pmatrix} \kappa_t \\ \gamma_t^{x_1} \\ \gamma_t^{x_2} \\ \vdots \\ \gamma_t^{x_{p-1}} \\ \gamma_t^{x_p} \end{pmatrix} = \begin{pmatrix} 1 & 0 & 0 & \cdots & 0 & 0 \\ 0 & \lambda_1 & \lambda_2 & \cdots & 0 & 0 \\ 0 & 1 & 0 & \cdots & 0 & 0 \\ 0 & 0 & 1 & \cdots & 0 & 0 \\ \vdots & \vdots & \vdots & \ddots & \vdots & \vdots \\ 0 & 0 & 0 & \cdots & 1 & 0 \end{pmatrix} \begin{pmatrix} \kappa_{t-1} \\ \gamma_{t-1}^{x_1} \\ \gamma_{t-1}^{x_2} \\ \vdots \\ \gamma_{t-1}^{x_{p-1}} \\ \gamma_{t-1}^{x_p} \end{pmatrix} + \begin{pmatrix} \theta \\ \eta \\ 0 \\ \vdots \\ 0 \\ 0 \end{pmatrix} + \begin{pmatrix} \omega_t^\kappa \\ \omega_t^\gamma \\ 0 \\ \vdots \\ 0 \\ 0 \end{pmatrix}, \tag{4}$$

The matrix form of Equations (2) and (3) can be expressed succinctly as

$$\mathbf{y}_t = \boldsymbol{\alpha} + \mathbf{B}\boldsymbol{\varphi}_t + \boldsymbol{\varepsilon}_t, \quad \boldsymbol{\varepsilon}_t \overset{iid}{\sim} \mathcal{N}(0, \sigma_\varepsilon^2 \mathbb{I}_p), \tag{5a}$$

$$\boldsymbol{\varphi}_t = \boldsymbol{\Lambda}\boldsymbol{\varphi}_{t-1} + \boldsymbol{\Theta} + \boldsymbol{\omega}_t, \quad \boldsymbol{\omega}_t \overset{iid}{\sim} \mathcal{N}(0, \Upsilon), \tag{5b}$$

where $\boldsymbol{\varphi}_t = (\kappa_t, \gamma_t^{x_1}, \ldots, \gamma_t^{x_p})^\top$, $\mathbb{I}_p$ the p-dimensional identity matrix and Υ is a $p+1$ by $p+1$ diagonal matrix with diagonal $(\sigma_\kappa^2, \sigma_\gamma^2, 0, \ldots, 0)$. The matrices $\boldsymbol{\alpha}$, $\mathbf{B}$, $\boldsymbol{\Lambda}$ and $\boldsymbol{\Theta}$ can be easily identified in Equations (2) and (3). For simplicity we assume homoscedasticity in the observation equation; heteroscedasticity can be incorporated straightforwardly as developed in Fung et al. (2016).

We adopt the identification constraints which are based on Hunt and Villegas (2015) and are broadly discussed and examined in Fung et al. (2017). These are given by

$$\sum_x \beta_x = 1, \sum_x \beta_x^\gamma = 1, \sum_t \kappa_t = 0, \sum_{c=t_1-x_p}^{t_N-x_1} \gamma_c = 0. \tag{6}$$

3. Demographic Factor Model Extension to the Period-Cohort Stochastic Mortality State-Space Models

In this section we demonstrate several approaches one may adopt to extend the state-space model formulations presented previously for the Period-Cohort stochastic mortality models to allow for incorporation of additional observable covariate factors. The form of factor model we develop here is generic and in future sections we will develop a framework for factor extraction from demographic data that can be used in the models developed in this section.

We note that there are two fundamental ways to develop a factor time series based regression structure for incorporation of demographic data to a stochastic mortality model. We advocate in this paper an approach which is specifically developed to work with data which may be high dimensional in nature, structured but be represented by short time series lengths. This type of data is particularly prevalent in demographic studies. The main concept here is that the feature extraction is performed over the entire available time series of observable demographic data. The resultant features extracted are then added to the stochastic mortality model in a static form but with dynamic latent state processes for the factor loadings over time. That is the effect of the factor incorporated will be allowed to time vary through the factor loading. This approach has the advantage of not having to model explicitly the demographic data which may have a complex structure and furthermore, only requires forecasting components of the latent factor loading process. This is often significantly easier to perform since one may use for instance a standard parametric time series model such as a VAR model for their temporal evolution. Note, such approaches as this are also utilised in other financial term-structure state-space models for instance in the context of yield curve modelling, such as the dynamic Nelson-Siegel model of Diebold and Li (2006). However, we believe to the best of our knowledge we are the first to propose this type of factor model framework for incorporating demographic factors into stochastic mortality models.

We assume that we have an available set of factors that can be country, population, gender or age specific features. We wish to incorporate these age-specific and country-specific demographic/population information into the cohort state-space model described by Equations (5a) and (5b).

We will denote by $\mathbf{F}_t$ the $p \times k$ factors matrix where p may represent number of age groups and k may represent number of age specific factors. As in any feature based regression factor analysis such as PCA Regression (Jolliffe (2002)), we treat $\mathbf{F}_t$ as extracted via feature extraction methods from an exogenous observable input that is believed to have potential influence on the age specific mortality rates under study in the responses, over time. Then for each feature vector regressor, extracted from the exogenous demographic data, we will add this feature to the state-space model.

There are numerous structural ways to achieve this in a state-space model. For instance, the factor may either influence all age groups equally by entering the factor into the state equation, or it may influence each age specific mortality rate differently by adding it in the observation equation. Of course, there may also be a combination of such approaches, dependent on which demographic data the feature was extracted from the context of the model construction.

The influence of the feature on the log mortality is reasonable to assume it varies over time, so to achieve this we will specify a time dynamic for the regression factor loading. This requires that we specify an additional latent variable, a pk dimensional vector ϱ_t which denotes the vector of factor loading for year t. We assume ϱ_t to be modelled by VAR(1) process given by

$$\varrho_t = \boldsymbol{\Omega}\varrho_{t-1} + \boldsymbol{\Upsilon} + \omega_t^{\varrho}, \quad \omega_t^{\varrho} \overset{iid}{\sim} \mathcal{N}(0, \sigma_{\varrho}^2 \mathbb{I}_{pk}) \tag{7}$$

with homogeneous variant for covariance matrix of error term ω_t^{ϱ}. ϱ_t is a dynamic regression parameter for the factors matrix $\mathbf{F}_t$ which specifies the impact of $x_i \in \{x_1, \ldots, x_p\}$ age group and $m \in \{1, \ldots, k\}$ component corresponding to $[\mathbf{F}_t]_{i,m}$ by $\varrho_t^{i,m}$ element.

As noted, depending on the interpretability of the desired model, one may incorporate $\mathbf{F}_t$ into observation Equation (5a) (**Case 1**) or into the latent dynamic of either calendar year factor period effect κ_t (**Case 2**) or cohort factors vector γ_t (**Case 3**) from the state Equation (5b).

Next we develop the extended model of Equations (5a) and (5b), which incorporates information $\mathbf{F}_t$. The general notation of the model is as follows

$$y_t = \boldsymbol{\alpha} + \tilde{\mathbf{B}}_t \tilde{\boldsymbol{\varphi}}_t + \varepsilon_t, \quad \varepsilon_t \overset{iid}{\sim} \mathcal{N}(0, \sigma_{\varepsilon}^2 \mathbb{I}_p), \tag{8a}$$

$$\tilde{\boldsymbol{\varphi}}_t = \tilde{\boldsymbol{\Lambda}} \tilde{\boldsymbol{\varphi}}_{t-1} + \tilde{\boldsymbol{\Theta}} + \tilde{\omega}_t, \quad \tilde{\kappa}_t \overset{iid}{\sim} \mathcal{N}(0, \tilde{\Upsilon}) \tag{8b}$$

where $\tilde{\boldsymbol{\varphi}}_t = (\boldsymbol{\varphi}_t, \varrho_t)$ is a $(p + pk + 1) \times 1$ latent process vector and

$$\tilde{\boldsymbol{\Theta}} = \begin{pmatrix} \boldsymbol{\Theta}_{(p+1)\times 1} \\ \boldsymbol{\Upsilon}_{pk\times 1} \end{pmatrix}_{(p+pk+1)\times 1} \tag{9}$$

is a vector of drift parameters for state equations, where $\boldsymbol{\Upsilon}$ corresponds to the model Equation (7) of ϱ_t. We assume independence of error terms in latent variables what gives the following structure of a covariance matrix for the state equation error term $\tilde{\omega}_t$

$$\tilde{\Upsilon} = \left(\begin{array}{c|c} \Upsilon_{(p+1)\times(p+1)} & 0 \\ \hline 0 & \sigma_{\varrho}^2 \mathbb{I}_{pk} \end{array}\right)_{(p+pk+1)\times(p+pk+1)} \tag{10}$$

Let us specify the following two objects, $\tilde{\mathbf{F}}_t = \bigoplus_{j=1}^{k} [\mathbf{F}_t]_{j,\cdot}$, for $\bigoplus$ being a direct sum operator, and $\tilde{\mathbf{f}}_t = vec\left(\mathbf{F}_t^T\right)$, that is

$$\tilde{\mathbf{F}}_t = \begin{pmatrix} [\mathbf{F}_t]_{1,\cdot} & 0 & 0 & \cdots & 0 \\ 0 & [\mathbf{F}_t]_{2,\cdot} & 0 & \cdots & 0 \\ \vdots & & \ddots & & \vdots \\ 0 & \cdots & & & [\mathbf{F}_t]_{p,\cdot} \end{pmatrix}_{p\times pk} \quad \text{and } \tilde{\mathbf{f}}_t = \begin{pmatrix} [\mathbf{F}_t]_{1,1} \\ [\mathbf{F}_t]_{1,2} \\ \vdots \\ [\mathbf{F}_t]_{p,k} \end{pmatrix}_{pk\times 1} \tag{11}$$

where $[\mathbf{F}_t]_{j,\cdot}$ and $[\mathbf{F}_t]_{j,m}$ represent the vector of the jth row of the matrix $\mathbf{F}_t$ and the element corresponding to jth row and mth column, respectively. The structures of the other matrices and vectors for extended model Equations (8a) and (8b) depend on the introduced cases, that is

$$\tilde{\mathbf{B}}_{t\ p\times(p+pk+1)} = \begin{cases} \left(\mathbf{B}_{p\times(p+1)} \,\middle|\, \tilde{\mathbf{F}}_t \right) & \text{for } \textbf{Case 1}, \\ \left(\mathbf{B}_{p\times(p+1)} \,\middle|\, \mathbf{0}_{p\times pk} \right) & \text{otherwise,} \end{cases}$$

$$\tilde{\mathbf{\Lambda}}_{(p+pk+1)\times(p+pk+1)} = \begin{cases} \left(\begin{array}{c|c} \mathbf{\Lambda}_{(p+1)\times(p+1)} & \mathbf{0}_{(p+1)\times pk} \\ \hline \mathbf{0}_{pk\times(p+1)} & \mathbf{\Omega}_{pk\times pk} \end{array} \right) & \text{for } \textbf{Case 1}, \\ \left(\begin{array}{c|c} \mathbf{\Lambda}_{(p+1)\times(p+1)} & \begin{array}{c} \tilde{\mathbf{f}}_t^T \\ \mathbf{0}_{p\times pk} \end{array} \\ \hline \mathbf{0}_{pk\times(p+1)} & \mathbf{\Omega}_{pk\times pk} \end{array} \right) & \text{for } \textbf{Case 2}, \\ \left(\begin{array}{c|c} \mathbf{\Lambda}_{(p+1)\times(p+1)} & \begin{array}{c} \mathbf{0}_{1\times pk} \\ \tilde{\mathbf{F}}_t \end{array} \\ \hline \mathbf{0}_{pk\times(p+1)} & \mathbf{\Omega}_{pk\times pk} \end{array} \right) & \text{for } \textbf{Case 3}. \end{cases} \tag{12}$$

Given the formulated demographic factor model of the period-cohort stochastic mortality state-space models, we will denote this class of model by notation (DFM-PC). The estimation of this model will be achieved through a Bayesian model formulation and a specialised Markov chain Monte Carlo sampling framework based on Forward-Backward sampler for the latent state components and block-Gibbs conjugate sampling for the static model parameters. This follows closely the detailed framework developed extensively in Fung et al. (2016) and Fung et al. (2017), therefore, we repeat this only in relevant details in the Appendix A.

Remark 1. *The matrix $\tilde{\mathbf{F}}_t$ contains the observed (feature extracted) with exogenous factors and is a component of the model which is conditioned. Therefore it does not require to be estimated and, at this point, represents a known deterministic constant. As such $\tilde{\mathbf{F}}_t$ is fixed and held constant for the time period which the factor model is run. Hence, it is not a parameter but a covariate which is observed and deterministic. Therefore, the identifications constraints given by Equation* (6) *are valid for the new model.*

Remark 2. *Time series in the study undertaken are typically of the length less than* 100. *Compared to the number of available samples, the classical Lee-Carter model with cohort effect requires large number of parameters and has been already reported to be prone to overfitting as noted in (Cairns et al. 2009); (Haberman and Renshaw 2011) and (Hunt and Villegas 2015). The new model with the latent process introduced in Equation* (7) *provides with additional number of parameters. Therefore to decrease the risk of overfitting we choose to stay with the assumption of VAR(1) process for ϱ_t. We believe that the parsimony argument to keep the autoregressive structure without too many additional parameters was more important that adding more lags in this study.*

4. Approaches to Demographic Feature Extraction via Robust Probabilistic Principal Components

As we will demonstrate in the application in this paper there is a variety of issues to consider when undertaking feature extraction in demographic population data of relevance to modelling in stochastic mortality models such as those presented previously. In addition, we would like to make sure we achieve a parsimonious model presentation, where we extract features from the demographic data that are the most informative.

For instance, if we have d countries demographic data to consider where p denotes the number of different demographic attributes observed that can be considered, then the $p \times d$ matrix of this data in year t will be denoted by $\mathbf{Y}_t$. We assume that $\mathbf{Y}_t$ is observed (or partially observed) over periods $t \in \{1, \ldots, T\}$. We do not wish to utilise the raw demographic data $\mathbf{Y}_t$ as in general it will produce a model with too many parameters, therefore we resort to feature extraction methods based on minimizing some pre-specified projection pursuit index.

Our attention is placed to linear methods of dimensionality reduction, more precisely, those expressible as linear projections as defined in (Friedman and Tukey 1974) which includes Principal Component Analysis (PCA) and its extensions and robust alternatives. In this paper, we have focussed on the use of Principal Component Analysis, hence, we incorporate the basis vectors of the projected lower rank space as the most meaningful factors in terms of variation.

In this regard we consider obtaining the column wise pre-whitened $\mathbf{Y}_t$ which we can then estimate the sample mean and sample covariance matrix for demographic time series data $\mathbf{Y}_1, \ldots, \mathbf{Y}_T$, which will be achieved robustly in this paper. This approach then produces a lower rank matrix which is obtained by projection according to

$$\mathbf{X}_t = \mathbf{Y}_t\mathbf{F}$$

for $\mathbf{F}$ being the first k selected eigenvectors of the covariance matrix robustly estimated from sample demographic date $\mathbf{Y}_1, \ldots, \mathbf{Y}_T$. These factors are then entered into the state-space model as presented previously.

In the following subsections we introduce progressively the feature extraction methods that should be considered for demographic data, which have been developed to deal with real data issues such as missing data and outliers which may effect the feature extraction process.

4.1. Non-Stochastic Principal Component Analysis

Let us denote $N \times d$ matrix $\mathbf{Y}$ as original data set, where a row of the matrix is a single d-dimensional observation in a given moment of time. The goal of Principal Component Analysis is to identify the most meaningful unit length basis to re-express a data set $\mathbf{Y}$. The purpose of a new basis is to better filter out the noise and reveal hidden structure. Therefore, PCA looks for the given projection of the observation data

$$\mathbf{Y}_{N\times d}\mathbf{W}_{d\times d} = \mathbf{X}_{N\times d} \tag{13}$$

where $\mathbf{W}$ is a $d \times d$ matrix denotes a linear projection. The columns of $\mathbf{W}$ are the new basis vectors, that is $\mathbf{W}^T\mathbf{W} = \mathbb{I}_d$, and express rows of $\mathbf{X}$.

The goal of re-expressing $\mathbf{Y}$ in meaningful way means that PCA aims to lower a redundancy in data set, i.e., leads to removing the linear dependencies which provide measurements with additional noise. In mathematical terms, the goal can be written for i, j columns of $\mathbf{X}$

$$[\mathbf{X}]_{\cdot,i}^T [\mathbf{X}]_{\cdot,i} = [\mathbf{W}]_{\cdot,i}^T \mathbf{C}_Y [\mathbf{W}]_{\cdot,i}, \tag{14}$$

and

$$[\mathbf{X}]_{\cdot,i}^T [\mathbf{X}]_{\cdot,j} = [\mathbf{W}]_{\cdot,i}^T \mathbf{C}_Y [\mathbf{W}]_{\cdot,j} = 0, \tag{15}$$

where $\mathbf{C}_Y = \mathbf{Y}^T\mathbf{Y}$. We seek a linear combination given by Equation (13) that maximizes the overall variance of $\mathbf{X}$, $\mathbf{C}_X = \mathbf{X}^T\mathbf{X}$. The solution to the problem is found by a maximiser of the following Lagrangian expression.

$$Q(\mathbf{W}) = \mathbf{W}^T\mathbf{C}_Y\mathbf{W} - \mathbf{\Lambda}\left(\mathbf{W}^T\mathbf{W} - \mathbb{I}_d\right). \tag{16}$$

for $\mathbf{\Lambda}_{d\times d}$ being a diagonal $d \times d$ matrix with Lagrangian coefficients. The roots of a quadratic form are found by setting partial derivatives to zero

$$\frac{\partial Q}{\partial \mathbf{W}} = 2\mathbf{C}_Y\mathbf{W} - 2\mathbf{\Lambda}\mathbf{W} = 0 \Rightarrow \mathbf{C}_Y\mathbf{W} = \mathbf{\Lambda}\mathbf{W} \tag{17}$$

We see that $\mathbf{W}$ is a matrix which columns are eigenvectors of $\mathbf{C}_Y$ whereas $\mathbf{\Lambda}$ is a matrix of corresponding eigenvalues with the number of non-zero elements equal to the rank of $\mathbf{C}_Y$. The columns of $\mathbf{X}$ indeed are orthogonal since

$$[\mathbf{X}]_{\cdot,i}^T [\mathbf{X}]_{\cdot,j} = [\mathbf{W}]_{\cdot,i}^T \mathbf{C}_Y [\mathbf{W}]_{\cdot,j} = [\mathbf{W}]_{\cdot,i}^T \lambda_j [\mathbf{W}]_{\cdot,j} = \lambda_j [\mathbf{W}]_{\cdot,i}^T [\mathbf{W}]_{\cdot,j} = \mathbf{0} \tag{18}$$

and correspond to unequal eigenvalues. It is easily proven that $\mathbf{X}$, defined by $\mathbf{W}$ - the eigenvectors of $\mathbf{C}_Y$, maximizes the total trace of $\mathbf{C}_X$, its determinant and maximizes the Euclidean distance between the columns of $\mathbf{X}$, see (Basilevsky 1994). Also, the representation minimizes the mean square error between the observation and its projection as it is equivalent problem to maximizing the variance of $\mathbf{X}$.

We wish to find estimates of $\mathbf{W}$ and $\mathbf{X}$ which minimizes sum of squares, $\boldsymbol{\epsilon} = \mathbf{Y} - \mathbf{X}\mathbf{W}^T$, both of $\boldsymbol{\epsilon}^T\boldsymbol{\epsilon}$ and $\boldsymbol{\epsilon}\boldsymbol{\epsilon}^T$. Assuming that the residuals have homogeneous covariance matrix, that is $\boldsymbol{\epsilon}^T\boldsymbol{\epsilon} = \sigma^2\mathbb{I}_d$ we have

$$\begin{aligned} Q(\mathbf{W},\mathbf{X}) &= \boldsymbol{\epsilon}^T\boldsymbol{\epsilon} = \sigma^2\mathbb{I}_d = \left(\mathbf{Y} - \mathbf{X}\mathbf{W}^T\right)^T\left(\mathbf{Y} - \mathbf{X}\mathbf{W}^T\right) \\ &= \mathbf{Y}^T\mathbf{Y} + \mathbf{W}\mathbf{X}^T\mathbf{X}\mathbf{W}^T - \mathbf{W}\mathbf{X}^T\mathbf{Y} - \mathbf{Y}^T\mathbf{X}\mathbf{W}^T. \end{aligned} \tag{19}$$

Since both $\mathbf{W}$ and $\mathbf{X}$ are treated as parameters to be estimated, we minimize Equation (19) by computing partial derivatives of function Q with respect to them and setting them to zero

$$\frac{\partial Q}{\partial \mathbf{W}} = -2\mathbf{Y}^T\mathbf{X} + 2\mathbf{W}\mathbf{X}^T\mathbf{X} = 0 \tag{20}$$

and since $\mathbf{Y}\mathbf{W} = \mathbf{X}$

$$\begin{aligned} \mathbf{Y}\mathbf{Y}^T\mathbf{X} &= \mathbf{Y}\mathbf{W}\mathbf{X}^T\mathbf{X} \\ \mathbf{Y}\mathbf{Y}^T\mathbf{X} &= \mathbf{X}\mathbf{X}^T\mathbf{X} \end{aligned} \tag{21}$$

As we are looking for uncorrelated explanatory variables, for $\mathbf{\Lambda} = \mathbf{X}^T\mathbf{X}$ we get

$$\mathbf{Y}\mathbf{Y}^T\mathbf{X} = \mathbf{X}\mathbf{\Lambda} \tag{22}$$

which shows that $\mathbf{X}$ and $\mathbf{\Lambda}$ are eigenvectors and eigenvalues of the $N \times N$ matrix $\mathbf{Y}\mathbf{Y}^T$. What is more, differentiating Q with respect to $\mathbf{X}$ gives

$$\frac{\partial Q}{\partial \mathbf{X}} = -2\mathbf{Y}\mathbf{W} + 2\mathbf{X}\mathbf{W}^T\mathbf{W} = 0, \tag{23}$$

what using similar arguments as above provides with

$$\mathbf{Y}^T\mathbf{Y}\mathbf{W} = \mathbf{W}\mathbf{\Lambda}, \tag{24}$$

showing that $\mathbf{W}$ and $\mathbf{\Lambda}$ are eigenvectors and eigenvalues of the $d \times d$ covariance matrix of $\mathbf{Y}$, $\mathbf{C}_Y = \mathbf{Y}^T\mathbf{Y}$.

4.2. *Stochastic Principal Component Analysis*

In the following part we consider PCA from the population distribution point of view, i.e., instead of the matrix $\mathbf{Y}$, we have a d-dimensional random variable $\mathbf{y}_t$ which is linearly transformed into uncorrelated d-dimensional random variable $\mathbf{x}_t$. **At this stage the Principal Component Analysis does not require any assumption about the distribution of a random vector $\mathbf{y}_t$.** The only assumption we make refers to the projection matrix $\mathbf{W}$ and demands its orthonormality. If the random vector $\mathbf{y}_t$ has a known mean equal to zero and covariance matrix $\mathbf{C}_Y$, the model transforms to

$$\mathbf{y}_t\mathbf{W} = \mathbf{x}_t \tag{25}$$

and implies $\mathbf{x}_t$ is a d-dimensional multivariate random variable with a diagonal covariance matrix $\mathbf{\Lambda}$. If in addition we assume $\mathbf{y}_t$ to be normally distributed, the lack of correlation imposes independence.

If we consider N realisations of the random variable $\mathbf{y}_t$ which are placed in rows of the $N \times d$ matrix $\mathbf{Y}$, we have an algebraic problem as introduced in Section 4.1. The conceptual difference is that in the case of stochastic PCA we work with an estimator of covariance matrix, e.g., a sample estimator $\mathbf{S}_Y = \frac{1}{N}\mathbf{Y}^T\mathbf{Y}$.

4.2.1. Extending Stochastic Principal Component Analysis to Factor Analysis

In this section we no longer assume the underlying process to be perfectly observed as would be the assumption typically made in the stochastic version of PCA above. The implication of this can be interpreted as follows: we no longer assume that the underlying time series of demographic data is perfectly observed with no observation error. Instead there is an observation error present and the covariance matrix used in the PCA (deterministic or stochastic-population estimator based analysis) no longer explains all variation in the response or the time series demographic data. This is practically important to consider in feature extraction in practice. In this section we briefly introduce this relaxation and show its relationship to stochastic PCA above.

To discuss the PCA by means of Factor Analysis we need to introduce an additional notation and variable to our model, that is, an d-dimensional error term, ϵ_t, and rewrite Equation (25) as

$$\mathbf{y}_t = \mathbf{x}_t\mathbf{W}^T + \epsilon_t, \tag{26}$$

where $\mathbf{y}_t$, $\mathbf{x}_t$ and ϵ_t are d-dimensional random vectors. Given N realisations of the random vector, which are placed in the rows of the matrices $\mathbf{Y}$, $\mathbf{X}$, ϵ respectively, the above problem has the following matrix form

$$\mathbf{Y}_{n\times d} = \mathbf{X}_{n\times d}\mathbf{W}^T_{d\times d} + \epsilon_{n\times d}. \tag{27}$$

Factor analysis assumes the diagonal covariance structure of ϵ_t. It differs from the PCA model discussion from the previous subsections as the components given by $\mathbf{x}_t$ and $\mathbf{W}$ accounts for correlation between elements of $\mathbf{y}_t$ and only part of the variation (in standard PCA $\mathbf{x}_t$ and $\mathbf{W}$ account for the entire variance) since

$$\mathbb{E}\mathbf{y}_t^T\mathbf{y}_t = \mathbb{E}\left[\left(\mathbf{x}_t\mathbf{W}^T + \epsilon_t\right)^T\left(\mathbf{x}_t\mathbf{W}^T + \epsilon_t\right)\right] = \mathbf{W}\mathbf{\Lambda}\mathbf{W}^T + \mathbf{\Psi}. \tag{28}$$

If we assume multivariate distribution of $\mathbf{x}_t \sim \mathcal{N}(\mathbf{0}, \mathbb{I}_d)$ and $\mathbf{e}_t \sim \mathcal{N}(\mathbf{0}, \mathbf{\Psi})$ we obtain conditional independence of $\mathbf{y}_t$ given latent variable $\mathbf{x}_t$, i.e.,

$$\mathbf{y}_t|\mathbf{x}_t, \mathbf{W}, \mathbf{\Psi} \sim \mathcal{N}\left(\mathbf{x}_t\mathbf{W}^T, \mathbf{\Psi}\right). \tag{29}$$

as $\mathbf{\Psi}$ is diagonal. Recall that the variable $\mathbf{x}_t$ reproduces all correlations between components of $\mathbf{y}_t$. Imposing normality assumptions on $\mathbf{y}_t$ and $\mathbf{x}_t$ enables performing ML estimation of $\mathbf{x}_t$, $\mathbf{W}$ and $\mathbf{\Psi}$ with optimality properties.

The marginal distribution of $\mathbf{y}_t$ is then calculated by the integration of the joint distribution of $\mathbf{y}_t$ and $\mathbf{x}_t$ (which is given via chain rule)

$$\begin{aligned}\pi(\mathbf{y}_t, \mathbf{x}_t|\mathbf{W}, \mathbf{\Psi}) &= \pi(\mathbf{y}_t|\mathbf{x}_t, \mathbf{W}, \mathbf{\Psi})\pi(\mathbf{x}_t|\mathbf{W}, \mathbf{\Psi}) \\ &= (2\pi|\mathbf{\Psi}|)^{-\frac{d}{2}} \exp\{-\frac{1}{2}\left[\mathbf{y}_t - \mathbf{x}_t\mathbf{W}^T\right]\mathbf{\Psi}^{-1}\left[\mathbf{y}_t - \mathbf{x}_t\mathbf{W}^T\right]^T\} (2\pi)^{-\frac{d}{2}} \exp\{-\frac{1}{2}\mathbf{x}_t\mathbf{x}_t^T\}\end{aligned} \tag{30}$$

with respect to the random variable $\mathbf{x}_t$, that is

$$\pi(\mathbf{y}_t|\mathbf{W}, \mathbf{\Psi}) = \int_{\mathbb{R}^d} \pi(\mathbf{y}_t, \mathbf{x}_t|\mathbf{W}, \mathbf{\Psi})d\mathbf{x}_t = (2\pi)^{-\frac{d}{2}}|\mathbf{C}|^{-1}\exp\{-\frac{1}{2}\mathbf{y}_t\mathbf{C}^{-1}\mathbf{y}_t^T\} \tag{31}$$

for $\mathbf{C} = \mathbf{W}\mathbf{W}^T + \mathbf{\Psi}$ where $|\mathbf{C}|$ denotes the determinant of the matrix. Hence, $\mathbf{y}_t|\mathbf{W},\mathbf{\Psi} \sim \mathcal{N}\left(\mathbf{0}, \mathbf{W}\mathbf{W}^T + \mathbf{\Psi}\right)$. Notice that since $\mathbf{\Psi}$ is diagonal, the correlation structure between components $\mathbf{y}_t$ is specified by the matrix $\mathbf{W}$.

Link to Principal Component Analysis

If we assume that the error term ϵ_t is homogeneous, that is $\mathbf{\Psi} = \sigma^2\mathbb{I}_d$ for $\sigma^2 > 0$, then the problem of finding $\mathbf{W}$ by means of PCA given $\mathbf{C} = \mathbf{W}\mathbf{W}^T + \sigma^2\mathbb{I}_d$ is identifiable (see further discussions in (Tipping and Bishop 1999))

Having the eigendecomposition of the covariance matrix, $\mathbf{C} = \mathbf{U}_{d\times d}\mathbf{L}_{d\times d}\mathbf{U}^T$, for diagonal matrix $\mathbf{L}$ and orthonormal matrix $\mathbf{U}$, we have

$$\mathbf{0} = (\mathbf{C}-\mathbf{L})\mathbf{U} = \left(\mathbf{W}^T\mathbf{W} + \sigma^2\mathbb{I}_d - \mathbf{L}\right)\mathbf{U} = \left(\mathbf{W}\mathbf{W}^T - \left(\mathbf{L} - \sigma^2\mathbb{I}_d\right)\right)\mathbf{U}. \tag{32}$$

Thus, the matrix $\mathbf{\Lambda} = \left(\mathbf{L} - \sigma^2\mathbb{I}_d\right)$ and $\mathbf{U}$ are matrices of eigenvalues and corresponding eigenvectors of $\mathbf{W}\mathbf{W}^T$. Since $\lambda_i = l_i - \sigma^2 \geq 0$, the scalar σ^2 can be chosen as the smallest diagonal element of $\mathbf{\Lambda}$. Then the factors loadings are given by $\mathbf{P} = \mathbf{U}\mathbf{\Lambda}^{\frac{1}{2}}$.

PCA as a Limiting Case of Factor Analysis

The assumption of the isotropic error term is crucial in order to establish the link between Factor Analysis and PCA. Standard derivation of PCA does not account for any error term. However, we can perceive PCA as a limiting case for $\sigma^2 \to 0$. Then, as noted in (Roweis 1998), PCA is a limiting case of the linear Gaussian model as the covariance matrix becomes infinitesimally small and equal in all directions. This has an effect that the likelihood of a point $\mathbf{y}_t$ is dominated by the squared residuals between the observation and its projection $\mathbf{x}_t\mathbf{W}^T$. As the σ^2 tends to zero, the posteriori over states $\mathbf{x}_t$ collapses to a single point and its covariance becomes zero since

$$\begin{aligned} \mathbf{x}_t|\mathbf{y}_t,\mathbf{W},\sigma^2 &\sim \mathcal{N}\left(\mathbf{y}_t\mathbf{W}\left(\mathbf{W}^T\mathbf{W} + \sigma^2\mathbb{I}_d\right)^{-1}, \sigma^2\mathbf{M}^{-1}\right) \\ &\xrightarrow{\sigma^2\to 0} \delta\left(\mathbf{x}_t - \mathbf{y}_t\mathbf{W}\left(\mathbf{W}^T\mathbf{W}\right)^{-1}\right). \end{aligned} \tag{33}$$

The form of conditional probability $\mathbf{x}_t|\mathbf{y}_t,\mathbf{W},\sigma^2$ is justified in Section 5.1.

4.2.2. Missing Values

Until now, we assumed the data did not contain any missing observations. However, in many demographic time series there are numerous types of missing data. This is therefore an important aspect to address in the feature extraction.

When considering missing values we need to incorporate additional variables which describe a distribution of missing observations. Let us denote $\mathbf{y}_t = (\mathbf{y}_t^o, \mathbf{y}_t^m)$ to be a real valued d-dimensional random vector, where $\mathbf{y}_t^o$ is a sub-vector of observed entries of $\mathbf{y}_t$ and $\mathbf{y}_t^m$ is a sub-vector of unobserved entries, i.e., missing. The indicator random variable $\mathbf{r}_t$ decides which entries of $\mathbf{y}_t$ are missing denoting them by 1, otherwise 0. Recall, that a single observation consists of the pair $(\mathbf{y}_t^o, \mathbf{r}_t)$ with distribution parameters (Θ, Θ^r) respectively. We assume the parameters to be distinct. The likelihood of parameters is proportional to the conditional probability $\mathbf{y}_t^o, \mathbf{r}_t|\Theta,\Theta^r$ that is

$$\pi\left(\mathbf{y}_t^o, \mathbf{r}_t|\Theta,\Theta^r\right) = \int \pi\left(\mathbf{y}_t^o, \mathbf{y}_t^m, \mathbf{r}_t|\Theta,\Theta^r\right) d\mathbf{y}_t^m = \int \pi\left(\mathbf{r}_t|\mathbf{y}_t,\Theta,\Theta^r\right)\pi\left(\mathbf{y}_t|\Theta,\Theta^r\right) d\mathbf{y}_t^m \tag{34}$$

In our study, we assume the pattern of missing data to be MAR-missing at random as defined in (Little and Rubin 2002). The assumptions imposes the indicator variable $\mathbf{r}_t$ to be independent of of the value of missing data. Then the vector $\mathbf{y}_t$ which is MAR satisfies

$$\pi(\mathbf{r}_t|\mathbf{y}_t,\Theta) = \pi(\mathbf{r}_t|\mathbf{y}_t^o,\Theta). \tag{35}$$

what results in

$$\pi\left(\mathbf{y}_t^o,\mathbf{r}_t|\Theta,\Theta^r\right) = \pi\left(\mathbf{r}_t|\mathbf{y}_t^o,\Theta^r\right)\int \pi\left(\mathbf{y}_t|\Theta\right) d\mathbf{y}_t^m = \pi\left(\mathbf{r}_t|\mathbf{y}_t^o,\Theta^r\right)\pi\left(\mathbf{y}_t^o|\Theta\right) \tag{36}$$

Under the MAR assumption, the estimation of Θ via maximum likelihood of the joint distribution $\mathbf{y}_t^o,\mathbf{r}_t|\Theta,\Theta^r$ is equivalent to the maximisation of the likelihood of the marginal distribution $\mathbf{y}_t^o|\Theta$. Hence, we do not worry about the distribution of the indicator random variable $\mathbf{r}_t$ and the joint distribution of $\mathbf{y}_t^o$ and $\mathbf{r}_t$. If the assumption about MAR does not hold, one needs to solve the integral from Equation (34) in order to maximize the joint likelihood.

5. Efficient Probabilisitic PCA Feature Extraction in the Presence of Missingness via EM Algorithm

The combination of PCA with missingness and the Factor Analysis leads us to the "Probabilistic PCA" which can be estimated via Expectation Maximisation framework as described below. This is an exceptionally efficient and numerically stable approach to apply in practice.

Let us consider $d \times 1$ vector of observable demographic data that we wish to extract features from, where it is denoted at time t by vector $\mathbf{y}_t$. We seek k-dimensional uncorrelated latent vector $\mathbf{x}_t$ which provides the most meaningful model of $\mathbf{y}_t$,

$$\mathbf{y}_t = \mathbf{x}_t\mathbf{W}_{d\times k}^T + \epsilon_t \tag{37}$$

We aim for $\mathbf{W}^T\mathbf{W} = \mathbb{I}_k$ (i.e., orthonormality of the projection matrix), however it is not assumed in the estimation process. We assume the multivariate normal priori distributions of the k dimensional latent variable $\mathbf{x}_t \sim \mathcal{N}\left(0,\mathbb{I}_k\right)$ and the error term $\epsilon_t \sim \mathcal{N}\left(0,\sigma^2\mathbb{I}_d\right)$. Given N realisations of observable variable $\mathbf{y}_t$, the sample model has a form

$$\mathbf{Y}_{N\times d} = \mathbf{X}_{N\times k}\mathbf{W}_{d\times k}^T + \epsilon_{N\times d} \tag{38}$$

where single realisations are placed in rows of $\mathbf{Y},\mathbf{X}$ and ϵ, respectively.

Our goal is to estimate coefficient matrix $\mathbf{W}$, scalar σ^2 and filter realisations of latent variable $\mathbf{x}_t$ employing Expectation-Maximisation (EM) algorithm. The steps and derivation of the algorithm have been described in (Rubin and Thayer 1982) where no missigness in assumed. The authors use the results introduced by (Dempster et al. 1977) for factors treated as missing data. The EM algorithm uses the complete data logliklehood, i.e., the logarithm of the likelihood of $\mathbf{y}_t,\mathbf{x}_t|\mathbf{W},\sigma^2$ Equation (30) given by

$$\mathcal{L}_{\mathbf{y}_t,\mathbf{x}_t|\mathbf{W},\sigma^2}(\sigma^2,\mathbf{W};\mathbf{y}_{1:N},\mathbf{x}_{1:N}) = \prod_{n=1}^{N}\pi\left(\mathbf{y}_n,\mathbf{x}_n|\mathbf{W},\sigma^2\right) \tag{39}$$

for $\mathbf{y}_n = [\mathbf{Y}]_{n,\cdot}$, and maximizes the expression Equation (39) which is integrated with respect to the unobserved values of $\mathbf{x}_t$. The algorithm is summarized by the following two steps

1. **Expectation step:** Expectation of the loglikelihood function of the join distribution of $\mathbf{y}_t,\mathbf{x}_t$ given by Equation (30) with respect to the conditional distribution $\mathbf{x}_t|\mathbf{y}_t,\mathbf{W},\sigma^2$

$$Q\left(\mathbf{W},\sigma^2|\mathbf{W}^*,\sigma^{*2}\right) = \mathbb{E}_{\mathbf{x}_t|\mathbf{y}_t,\mathbf{W},\sigma^2}\log\left[\mathcal{L}_{\mathbf{y}_t,\mathbf{x}_t|\mathbf{W},\sigma^2}(\sigma^{*2},\mathbf{W}^*;\mathbf{y}_{1:n},\mathbf{x}_{1:n})\right] \tag{40}$$

2. Maximisation step: Finding $\mathbf{W}^*$ and σ^{*2} that maximize $Q\left(\mathbf{W},\sigma^2|\mathbf{W}^*,\sigma^{*2}\right)$

$$\left(\mathbf{W}^*,\sigma^{*2}\right) = \underset{\mathbf{W}^*\in\mathbb{R}^{d\times k},\sigma^{*2}>0}{\text{argmax}} \quad Q\left(\mathbf{W},\ \sigma^2|\mathbf{W}^*,\sigma^{*2}\right) \tag{41}$$

The Expectation step (E-step) provides with the expectation Equation (40) of complete data likelihood Equation (39) based on $\mathbf{y}_{1:N}$ and assumes $\mathbf{W}$ and σ^2 to be known. It uses the observed data, current estimates of parameters and the distribution of missing values conditioned on these elements. The Maximisation step (M-step) maximizes the expectation Equation (40) with respect to $\mathbf{W}^*$ and σ^{*2} as if it was based on complete data information. In the paper (Dempster et al. 1977), the author proofs that the loglikelihood Equation (39) is non-decreasing on each iteration of the algorithm and provides with conditions that ensure its convergence (Theorem 1 and Theorem 2 in paper (Dempster et al. 1977), respectively).

We derive the steps of the algorithm using the assumptions of the normality of $\mathbf{y}_t$ and $\mathbf{x}_t$ given at the beginning of the section. As mentioned in (Dempster et al. 1977), the convexity of regular exponential families (where normal distribution belongs to) ensures the uniqueness of the maximizers computed in the M-step. Also, the normal distribution provides us with the closed forms of the moments used in subsequent steps of the algorithm. Hence, it simplifies the computations.

5.1. Expectation Step and Its Maximum

Finding the expectation Equation (40) requires specifying the conditional distribution of $\mathbf{x}_t$ given observations $\mathbf{y}_t$ and parameters. It is given via Bayes' rule as

$$\pi(\mathbf{x}_t|\mathbf{y}_t,\mathbf{W},\sigma^2) = \frac{\pi(\mathbf{y}_t|\mathbf{x}_t,\mathbf{W},\sigma^2)\pi(\mathbf{x}_t|\mathbf{W},\sigma^2)}{\pi(\mathbf{y}_t|\mathbf{W},\sigma^2)} \tag{42}$$

and results in $\mathbf{x}_t|\mathbf{y}_t,\mathbf{W},\sigma^2 \sim \mathcal{N}\left(\mathbf{y}_t\mathbf{W}\mathbf{M}^{-1},\sigma^2\mathbf{M}^{-1}\right)$ for $\mathbf{M} = \mathbf{W}^T\mathbf{W} + \sigma^2\mathbb{I}_k$. Given N realisations of $\mathbf{y}_t$, the expectation of the logliklihood with respect to the conditional distribution of $\mathbf{x}_t$ is equal to

Theorem 1. *The expectation of the E-step,* $\mathbb{E}_{\mathbf{x}_t|\mathbf{y}_t,\mathbf{W},\sigma^2}\log\left[\mathcal{L}_{\mathbf{y}_t,\mathbf{x}_t|\mathbf{W},\sigma^2}(\sigma^{*2},\mathbf{W}^*;\mathbf{y}_{1:N},\mathbf{x}_{1:N})\right]$, *is given by*

$$\begin{aligned} Q\left(\mathbf{W},\sigma^2|\mathbf{W}^*,\sigma^{*2}\right) &= \int_{\mathbb{R}^k}\pi(\mathbf{x}_t|\mathbf{y}_t,\mathbf{W},\sigma^2)\log\left[\prod_{n=1}^{N}\pi\left(\mathbf{y}_n,\mathbf{x}_n|\mathbf{W}^*,\sigma^{*2}\right)\right]d\mathbf{x}_t \\ &= -\sum_{n=1}^{N}\left\{\frac{d}{2}\log\sigma^2 + \frac{1}{2}tr\left(\mathbb{E}\left[\mathbf{x}_n^T\mathbf{x}_n|\mathbf{y}_t,\mathbf{W},\sigma^2\right]\right) + \frac{1}{2\sigma^2}\mathbf{y}_n\mathbf{y}_n^T\right. \\ &\left. - \frac{1}{\sigma^2}\mathbb{E}\left[\mathbf{x}_n|\mathbf{y}_t,\mathbf{W},\sigma^2\right]\mathbf{W}^{*T}\mathbf{y}_n^T + \frac{1}{2\sigma^2}tr\left(\mathbf{W}^{*T}\mathbf{W}^*\mathbb{E}\left[\mathbf{x}_n^T\mathbf{x}_n|\mathbf{y}_t,\mathbf{W},\sigma^2\right]\right)\right\} \end{aligned} \tag{43}$$

for the corresponding moments of the conditional distribution $\mathbf{x}_n|\mathbf{y}_t,\mathbf{W},\sigma^2$

$$\begin{aligned} \mathbb{E}\left[\mathbf{x}_n|\mathbf{y}_t,\mathbf{W},\sigma^2\right]_{1\times k} &= \mathbf{y}_n\mathbf{W}\mathbf{M}^{-1} \\ \mathbb{E}\left[\mathbf{x}_n^T\mathbf{x}_n|\mathbf{y}_t,\mathbf{W},\sigma^2\right]_{k\times k} &= \sigma^2\mathbf{M}^{-1} + \mathbb{E}\left[\mathbf{x}_n|\mathbf{y}_t,\mathbf{W},\sigma^2\right]^T\mathbb{E}\left[\mathbf{x}_n|\mathbf{y}_t,\mathbf{W},\sigma^2\right] \end{aligned} \tag{44}$$

Proof. Please refer to the results of (Rubin and Thayer 1982). □

The M-step of EM algorithm uses the computed expectation and maximizes it with respect to the static parameters $\mathbf{W}^*$ and σ^{*2}. The maximizes are given by

Theorem 2. *The maximizers of* $Q\left(\mathbf{W}, \sigma^2 | \mathbf{W}^*, \sigma^{*2}\right)$ *are the solution to the set of the problems* $\frac{\partial Q}{\partial \mathbf{W}^*} = 0$ *and* $\frac{\partial Q}{\partial \sigma^{*2}} =$ *and are given by*

$$\begin{aligned} \mathbf{W}^*_{d\times k} &= \left[\sum_{n=1}^{N} \mathbf{y}_n^T \mathbb{E}\left[\mathbf{x}_n | \mathbf{y}_t, \mathbf{W}, \sigma^2\right]\right] \left[\sum_{n=1}^{N} \mathbb{E}\left[\mathbf{x}_n | \mathbf{y}_t, \mathbf{W}, \sigma^2\right]^T \mathbb{E}\left[\mathbf{x}_n | \mathbf{y}_t, \mathbf{W}, \sigma^2\right]\right]^{-1} \\ \sigma^{*2} &= \frac{1}{Nd} \sum_{n=1}^{N} \left\{ \mathbf{y}_n \mathbf{y}_n^T - 2\mathbf{y}_t \mathbf{W}^* \mathbb{E}\left[\mathbf{x}_n | \mathbf{y}_t, \mathbf{W}, \sigma^2\right]^T \right. \\ &\left. + tr\left(\mathbb{E}\left[\mathbf{x}_n | \mathbf{y}_t, \mathbf{W}, \sigma^2\right]^T \mathbb{E}\left[\mathbf{x}_n | \mathbf{y}_t, \mathbf{W}, \sigma^2\right] \mathbf{W}^{*T} \mathbf{W}^*\right) \right\}. \end{aligned} \tag{45}$$

The iteration over E-step and M-step provided by Theorem 1 and 2 can be replaced by iterations over one combined step, as noted in (Tipping and Bishop 1999), which for iterations i and $i+1$ is given by

$$\begin{aligned} 1&: \mathbf{W}^{(i+1)} = \mathbf{S}\mathbf{W}^{(i)} \left(\sigma^{(i)2} \mathbb{I}_k + \mathbf{M}^{-1} \mathbf{W}^{(i)T} \mathbf{S} \mathbf{W}^{(i)}\right)^{-1} \\ 2&: \sigma^{(i+1)2} = \frac{1}{d} tr\left(\mathbf{S} - \mathbf{S}\mathbf{W}^{(i)} \mathbf{M}^{-1} \mathbf{W}^{(i+1)T}\right) \end{aligned} \tag{46}$$

until the convergence of $Q\left(\mathbf{W}^{(i)}, \sigma^{(i)2} | \mathbf{W}^{(i+1)}, \sigma^{(i+1)2}\right)$ when $\mathbf{M} = \mathbf{W}^{(i)T}\mathbf{W}^{(i)} + \sigma^{(i)2}\mathbb{I}_k$ and $\mathbf{S} = \frac{1}{N}\mathbf{Y}^T\mathbf{Y}$.

5.2. The Maximum Likelihood Estimation—The Convergence of EM Algorithm

The work of (Dempster et al. 1977) proves that EM algorithm for the normal distribution always converges to local maximum. Recall that the solution provided by EM algorithm converges to the solution obtained by maximizing the likelihood of marginal distribution $\mathbf{y}_t | \mathbf{W}, \sigma^2$, given by

$$\mathcal{L}_{\mathbf{y}_t|\mathbf{W},\sigma^2}\left(\mathbf{W}, \sigma^2; \mathbf{y}_{1:n}\right) = -\frac{N}{2}\left[d\log(2\pi) + \log|\mathbf{C}| + tr\left(\mathbf{C}^{-1}\mathbf{S}\right)\right] \tag{47}$$

where $\mathbf{S}_{d\times d} = \frac{1}{N}\sum_{n=1}^{N} \mathbf{y}_n^T \mathbf{y}_n$ and $\mathbf{C} = \mathbf{W}\mathbf{W}^T + \sigma^2\mathbb{I}_d$. The MLE estimator of $\mathbf{W}$ given by the likelihood Equation (47) is a solution to the following fix point equation

$$\frac{\partial \mathcal{L}_{\mathbf{y}_t|\mathbf{W},\sigma^2}}{\partial \mathbf{W}} = N\left(\mathbf{C}^{-1}\mathbf{S}\mathbf{C}^{-1}\mathbf{W} - \mathbf{C}^{-1}\mathbf{W}\right) = 0 \Rightarrow \mathbf{W} = \mathbf{S}\mathbf{C}^{-1}\mathbf{W} \tag{48}$$

We may distinguish tree possible cases to the above solution:

Case 1: $\mathbf{W} = 0$

The solution to this case is treated as a minimum of the log-likelihood.

Case 2: $\mathbf{S} = \mathbf{C}$

The equality implies that $d-k$ smallest eigenvalues of $\mathbf{S}$ be equal to σ^2 and the problem is indefinable since $\mathbf{W}\mathbf{W}^T = \mathbf{S} - \sigma^2\mathbb{I}_d$. Given the eigendecomposition of $\mathbf{S}$, that is

$$\mathbf{S} = \mathbf{U}_{d\times d}\mathbf{\Lambda}_{d\times d}\mathbf{U}^T_{d\times d} \tag{49}$$

for orthonormal matrix $\mathbf{U}$ such that $\mathbf{U}^T\mathbf{U} = \mathbb{I}_d$ and diagonal matrix $\mathbf{\Lambda}$ with non-negative entries, the matrix $\mathbf{W}$ is equal to $\mathbf{W} = \mathbf{U}\left(\mathbf{\Lambda} - \sigma^2\mathbb{I}_d\right)^{\frac{1}{2}}\mathbf{R}^T$ where $\mathbf{R}_{k\times d}$ is an arbitrary rotation matrix. The case is proven in Section 4.2.1.

Case 3: $\mathbf{W} \neq 0$ and $\mathbf{S} \neq \mathbf{C}$

In order to compute the solution to Equation (48) we use the singular value decomposition of $\mathbf{W}$, that is

$$\mathbf{W} = \mathbf{V}_{d\times k}\mathbf{L}_{k\times k}\mathbf{R}^T_{k\times k} \tag{50}$$

where $\mathbf{V}$ and $\mathbf{R}$ are real valued orthogonal matrix by columns, and $\mathbf{L}$ is non-negative diagonal matrix. Using $\mathbf{C} = \mathbf{W}\mathbf{W}^T + \sigma^2\mathbb{I}_d$ we apply the above facts to the problem defined by the fix point equation

$$\begin{aligned}
\mathbf{W}_{d\times k} &= \mathbf{S}\mathbf{C}^{-1}\mathbf{W} \\
\mathbf{V}\mathbf{L}\mathbf{R}^T &= \mathbf{S}\left(\mathbf{V}\mathbf{L}\mathbf{R}^T\mathbf{R}\mathbf{L}\mathbf{V}^T + \sigma^2\mathbb{I}_d\right)^{-1}\mathbf{V}\mathbf{L}\mathbf{R}^T \\
\mathbf{V}\mathbf{L}\mathbf{R}^T &= \mathbf{S}\left(\mathbf{V}\mathbf{L}^2\mathbf{V}^T + \sigma^2\mathbb{I}_d\right)^{-1}\mathbf{V}\mathbf{L}\mathbf{R}^T \\
\mathbf{V}\mathbf{L}^2\mathbf{V}^T + \sigma^2\mathbb{I}_d &= \mathbf{S} \\
\mathbf{U}\mathbf{L}^2\mathbf{L} + \sigma^2\mathbb{I}_d\mathbf{V}\mathbf{L} &= \mathbf{S}\mathbf{V}\mathbf{L} \\
\mathbf{V}\left(\mathbf{L}^2 + \sigma^2\mathbb{I}_k\right)\mathbf{L} &= \mathbf{S}\mathbf{V}\mathbf{L}
\end{aligned} \tag{51}$$

Notice that

$$\mathbf{S}\mathbf{v}_j = (\sigma^2 + l_j^2)\mathbf{v}_j \tag{52}$$

where $\mathbf{v}_j = [\mathbf{V}]_{,j}$ and $l_j = [\mathbf{L}]_{j,j}$. Hence, the vectors $\mathbf{v}_j$ are eigenvectors of the estimated covariance matrix $\mathbf{S}$. Using the eigendecomposition of $\mathbf{S}$ given by Equation (49), we see that $\mathbf{v}_j$ corresponds to the eigenvectors of $\mathbf{S}$, $\mathbf{u}_j$ with eigenvalues $\lambda_j = l_j^2 + \sigma^2$. Since $\mathbf{L}$ has a different dimension than $\mathbf{\Lambda}$, we express it as

$$\mathbf{L} = (\mathbf{K} - \sigma^2\mathbb{I}_k)^{\frac{1}{2}} \tag{53}$$

where $[\mathbf{K}]_{j,j} = \lambda_j$ is an j eigenvalue of $\mathbf{S}$ and corresponds to the j eigenvector of $\mathbf{S}$, $\mathbf{u}_j$. In a case when $l_j = 0$, the eigenvector $\mathbf{v}_j$ is arbitrary and $[\mathbf{K}]_{j,j} = \sigma^2$. The scalar σ^2 is estimated as average of $i > k$ eigenvalues of $\mathbf{S}$.

The remaining question is if the EM algorithm converges to the global maximum. If the stationary points of the likelihood with respect to $\mathbf{W}$ which are spanned by minor eigenvectors (the eigenvectors with corresponding negligible eigenvalues), are stable, then the convergence is not guaranteed. However, we can show that any eigenvectors which does not correspond the highest eigenvalues of $\mathbf{S}$ is a saddle point of the logliklihood and does not provide stable solutions. For the detailed discussion please refer to (Tipping and Bishop 1999). The authors highlight the case when all $d - k$ discarded eigenvalues are equal to the smallest major principal eigenvalue(s). They show that such a situation provides with maximum spanned by principal eigenvectors and noise distribution (corresponding to the smallest principal eigenvalue(s), which become(s) zero).

5.3. The EM Algorithm for Incomplete Data

Until now, we developed the EM algorithm for Probabilistic PCA under the assumption that the data does not contain any missing values. In Section 4.2.2 we introduced the background of how we are going to treat missing entries of the observation. We assume them to be Missing-At-Random what allows us to ignore the existence of indicator variable $\mathbf{r}_t$ while estimating $\mathbf{W}$ and σ^2. Given the vector of an observation with missing entries $\mathbf{y}_t = (\mathbf{y}_t^o, \mathbf{y}_t^m)$, EM algorithms treats $\mathbf{y}_t^m$ as an additional latent variable to $\mathbf{x}_t$ in the model Equation (37). The expectation of the joint logliklihod Equation (30) is computed with respect to the conditional distribution of $\mathbf{x}_t, \mathbf{y}_t^m|\mathbf{y}_t^o, \mathbf{W}, \sigma^2$ and provides with the two following steps:

1. **Expectation step:** Expectation of loglikelihood function of join distribution of $\mathbf{y}_t, \mathbf{x}_t|\mathbf{W}, \sigma^2$ given by Equation (30) with respect to conditional distribution $\mathbf{x}_t, \mathbf{y}_t^m|\mathbf{y}_t^o, \mathbf{W}, \sigma^2$

$$Q^m\left(\mathbf{W}, \sigma^2|\mathbf{W}^*, \sigma^{*2}\right) = \mathbb{E}_{\mathbf{x}_t, \mathbf{y}_t^m|\mathbf{y}_t^o, \mathbf{W}, \sigma^2}\left\{\log\left[\mathcal{L}_{\mathbf{y}_t, \mathbf{x}_t|\mathbf{W}, \sigma^2}(\sigma^{*2}, \mathbf{W}^*; \mathbf{y}_{1:n}, \mathbf{x}_{1:n})\right]\right\} \tag{54}$$

2. Maximisation step: Finding $\mathbf{W}^*$ and σ^{*2} that maximize $Q^m\left(\mathbf{W},\sigma^2|\mathbf{W}^*,\sigma^{*2}\right)$

$$\left(\mathbf{W}^*,\sigma^{*2}\right) = \underset{\mathbf{W}^*\in\mathbb{R}^{d\times k},\sigma^{*2}>0}{\operatorname{argmax}} \quad Q^m\left(\mathbf{W},\sigma^2|\mathbf{W}^*,\sigma^{*2}\right) \tag{55}$$

We need to specify the moments of a conditional distribution of latent variables given the observation vector, when we include the latent variable $\mathbf{y}_t^m$. The conditional distribution $\mathbf{x}_t, \mathbf{y}_t^m|\mathbf{y}_t^o, \mathbf{W}, \sigma^2$ is obtained via Bayes' rule as

$$\pi\left(\mathbf{x}_t, \mathbf{y}_t^m|\mathbf{y}_t^o, \mathbf{W}, \sigma^2\right) = \pi\left(\mathbf{x}_t|\mathbf{y}_t, \mathbf{W}, \sigma^2\right)\pi\left(\mathbf{y}_t^m|\mathbf{y}_t^o, \mathbf{W}, \sigma^2\right) \tag{56}$$

Given N realisation of $\mathbf{y}_t$ with arbitrary missing entries, the expectation step has a form

$$\begin{aligned}
Q^m\left(\mathbf{W},\sigma^2|\mathbf{W}^*,\sigma^{*2}\right) &= \mathbb{E}_{\mathbf{x}_t,\mathbf{y}_t^m|\mathbf{y}_t^o,\mathbf{W},\sigma^2}\left\{\log\left[\mathcal{L}_{\mathbf{y}_t,\mathbf{x}_t|\mathbf{W},\sigma^2}(\sigma^{*2},\mathbf{W}^*;\mathbf{y}_{1:N},\mathbf{x}_{1:N})\right]\right\} \\
&= \int_{\mathbb{R}^k\times\mathbb{R}^d} \pi(\mathbf{x}_t,\mathbf{y}_t|\mathbf{y}_t^o,\mathbf{W},\sigma^2)\log\left[\prod_{n=1}^{N}\pi\left(\mathbf{y}_n,\mathbf{x}_n|\mathbf{W}^*,\sigma^{*2}\right)\right]d\mathbf{x}_t d\mathbf{y}_t \\
&= -\sum_{n=1}^{N}\left\{\frac{d}{2}\log\sigma^{*2} + \frac{1}{2}tr\left(\mathbb{E}\left[\mathbf{x}_n^T\mathbf{x}_n|\mathbf{y}_t^o,\mathbf{W},\sigma^2\right]\right) + \frac{1}{2\sigma^{*2}}tr\left(\mathbb{E}\left[\mathbf{y}_n^T\mathbf{y}_n|\mathbf{y}_t^o,\mathbf{W},\sigma^2\right]\right)\right. \\
&\left. - \frac{1}{\sigma^{*2}}tr\left(\mathbf{W}^*\mathbb{E}\left[\mathbf{x}_n^T\mathbf{y}_n|\mathbf{y}_t^o,\mathbf{W},\sigma^2\right]\right) + \frac{1}{2\sigma^{*2}}tr\left(\mathbf{W}^{*T}\mathbf{W}^*\mathbb{E}\left[\mathbf{x}_n^T\mathbf{x}_n|\mathbf{y}_t^o,\mathbf{W},\sigma^2\right]\right)\right\}
\end{aligned} \tag{57}$$

where $\mathbb{E}\left[\mathbf{x}_n^T\mathbf{x}_n|\mathbf{y}_t^o,\mathbf{W},\sigma^2\right]$ are derived in Equation (44) and need adjustment for missing data. The other moments of the conditional distribution $\mathbf{x}_t, \mathbf{y}_t|\mathbf{y}_t^o, \mathbf{W}, \sigma^2$ need to calculated.

5.3.1. The Moments of Joint Distribution $\mathbf{x}_t, \mathbf{y}_t^m|\mathbf{y}_t^o, \mathbf{W}, \sigma^2$.

The first component of the conditional probability Equation (56) is given by Equation (42). For simplicity assume for a moment $\mathbf{y}_t = (\mathbf{y}_t^o, \mathbf{y}_t^m) \sim \mathcal{N}(\mathbf{0}_d, \mathbf{C}_{d\times d})$ for a covariance matrix

$$\mathbf{C}_{d\times d} = \begin{bmatrix}\mathbf{C}_{oo} & \mathbf{C}_{om}\\ \mathbf{C}_{mo} & \mathbf{C}_{mm}\end{bmatrix} \tag{58}$$

where indexes o and m correspond to the locations of observed and missing entries of the random vector $\mathbf{y}_t$. As shown in (Little and Rubin 2002), the joint distribution $\mathbf{y}_t|\mathbf{y}_t^o$ under MAR assumption is multivariate normal, that is

$$\mathbf{y}_t|\mathbf{y}_t^o \sim \mathcal{N}\left(\begin{bmatrix}\mathbf{y}_t^o\\ \mathbf{y}_t^o\mathbf{C}_{oo}^{-1}\mathbf{C}_{om}\end{bmatrix}, \begin{bmatrix}\mathbf{0} & \mathbf{0}\\ \mathbf{0} & \mathbf{C}_{mm} - \mathbf{C}_{mo}\mathbf{C}_{oo}^{-1}\mathbf{C}_{om}\end{bmatrix}\right). \tag{59}$$

since

$$\pi\left(\mathbf{y}_t^m|\mathbf{y}_t^o\right) = \frac{\pi\left(\mathbf{y}_t^m, \mathbf{y}_t^o\right)}{\pi\left(\mathbf{y}_t^o\right)} \tag{60}$$

As derived in (Jamshidian 1997), the covariance matrix of the marginal distribution $\mathbf{y}_t|\mathbf{W}, \sigma^2$ is equal to

$$\mathbf{C} = \begin{bmatrix}\mathbf{W}_o\mathbf{W}_o^T + \sigma^2\mathbb{I}_{d_o} & \mathbf{W}_o\mathbf{W}_m^T\\ \mathbf{W}_m\mathbf{W}_o^T & \mathbf{W}_m\mathbf{W}_m^T + \sigma^2\mathbb{I}_{d_m}\end{bmatrix} \tag{61}$$

where d_o and d_m such that $d_o + d_m = d$ are numbers of elements observed and missing (which can be zero) respectively, m and o are the indexes of matrices denote sets of rows which correspond to missing and observed values of $\mathbf{y}_t$, respectively (recall that columns of matrix $\mathbf{W}$ correspond to values of $\mathbf{x}_t$).

Having above in mind, we can compute the following moments of the conditional distribution $\mathbf{x}_t, \mathbf{y}_t | \mathbf{y}_t^o, \mathbf{W}, \sigma^2$ are given by an alternative theorem to the Theorem 1 which accounts for the incomplete data case.

Theorem 3. *The expectation of the E-step,* $\mathbb{E}_{\mathbf{x}_t|\mathbf{y}_t,\mathbf{W},\sigma^2} \log \left[\mathcal{L}_{\mathbf{y}_t,\mathbf{x}_t|\mathbf{W},\sigma^2}(\sigma^{*2}, \mathbf{W}^*; \mathbf{y}_{1:n}, \mathbf{x}_{1:n})\right]$, *where* $\mathbf{y}_t = (\mathbf{y}_t^o, \mathbf{y}_t^m)$, *is given by*

$$
\begin{aligned}
Q^m\left(\mathbf{W}, \sigma^2 | \mathbf{W}^*, \sigma^{*2}\right) &= \int_{\mathbb{R}^k \times \mathbb{R}^d} \pi(\mathbf{x}_t, \mathbf{y}_t | \mathbf{y}_t^o, \mathbf{W}, \sigma^2) \log \left[\prod_{n=1}^{N} \pi\left(\mathbf{y}_n, \mathbf{x}_n | \mathbf{W}^*, \sigma^{*2}\right)\right] d\mathbf{x}_t d\mathbf{y}_t \\
&= -\sum_{n=1}^{N} \left\{ \frac{d}{2} \log \sigma^{*2} + \frac{1}{2} tr\left(\mathbb{E}\left[\mathbf{x}_n^T \mathbf{x}_n | \mathbf{y}_t^o, \mathbf{W}, \sigma^2\right]\right) + \frac{1}{2\sigma^{*2}} tr\left(\mathbb{E}\left[\mathbf{y}_n^T \mathbf{y}_n | \mathbf{y}_t^o, \mathbf{W}, \sigma^2\right]\right) \right. \\
&\left. - \frac{1}{\sigma^{*2}} tr\left(\mathbf{W}^* \mathbb{E}\left[\mathbf{x}_n^T \mathbf{y}_n | \mathbf{y}_t^o, \mathbf{W}, \sigma^2\right]\right) + \frac{1}{2\sigma^{*2}} tr\left(\mathbf{W}^{*T} \mathbf{W}^* \mathbb{E}\left[\mathbf{x}_n^T \mathbf{x}_n | \mathbf{y}_t^o, \mathbf{W}, \sigma^2\right]\right) \right\}
\end{aligned}
\tag{62}
$$

for the corresponding moments of the conditional distribution $\mathbf{x}_n | \mathbf{y}_t^o, \mathbf{W}, \sigma^2$

$$
\begin{aligned}
\mathbb{E}\left[\mathbf{y}_n | \mathbf{y}_t^o, \mathbf{W}, \sigma^2\right]_{1 \times d} &= \begin{bmatrix} \mathbf{y}_n^o \\ \mathbb{E}\left[\mathbf{y}_n^m | \mathbf{y}_t^o, \mathbf{W}, \sigma^2\right] \end{bmatrix} \\
\mathbb{E}\left[\mathbf{y}_n^T \mathbf{y}_n | \mathbf{y}_t^o, \mathbf{W}, \sigma^2\right]_{d \times d} &= \begin{bmatrix} \mathbf{0} & \mathbf{0} \\ \mathbf{0} & \mathbf{C}_{mm} - \mathbf{W}_m \mathbf{W}_o^T \mathbf{C}_{oo}^{-1} \mathbf{W}_o \mathbf{W}_m^T \end{bmatrix} + \mathbb{E}\left[\mathbf{y}_n | \mathbf{y}_t^o, \mathbf{W}, \sigma^2\right]^T \mathbb{E}\left[\mathbf{y}_n | \mathbf{y}_t^o, \mathbf{W}, \sigma^2\right] \\
\mathbb{E}\left[\mathbf{x}_n | \mathbf{y}_t^o, \mathbf{W}, \sigma^2\right]_{1 \times k} &= \mathbb{E}\left[\mathbf{y}_n | \mathbf{y}_t^o, \mathbf{W}, \sigma^2\right] \mathbf{W} \left(\mathbf{W}^T \mathbf{W} + \sigma^2 \mathbb{I}_d\right)^{-1} \\
\mathbb{E}\left[\mathbf{x}_n^T \mathbf{x}_n | \mathbf{y}_t^o, \mathbf{W}, \sigma^2\right]_{k \times k} &= \sigma^2 \left(\mathbf{W}^T \mathbf{W} + \sigma^2 \mathbb{I}_d\right)^{-1} + \mathbb{E}\left[\mathbf{x}_n | \mathbf{y}_t^o, \mathbf{W}, \sigma^2\right]^T \mathbb{E}\left[\mathbf{x}_n | \mathbf{y}_t^o, \mathbf{W}, \sigma^2\right] \\
\mathbb{E}\left[\mathbf{x}_n^T \mathbf{y}_n | \mathbf{y}_t^o, \mathbf{W}, \sigma^2\right]_{k \times d} &= \begin{bmatrix} \mathbf{0} \\ \mathbf{W}_m - \mathbf{W}_m \mathbf{W}_o^T \mathbf{C}_{oo}^{-1} \mathbf{W}_o \end{bmatrix} + \mathbb{E}\left[\mathbf{x}_n | \mathbf{y}_t^o, \mathbf{W}, \sigma^2\right]^T \mathbb{E}\left[\mathbf{y}_n | \mathbf{y}_t^o, \mathbf{W}, \sigma^2\right]
\end{aligned}
\tag{63}
$$

Proof. We can find the corresponding steps of calculation in (Jamshidian 1997). □

5.3.2. The Maximizers of $Q^m\left(\mathbf{W}, \sigma^2 | \mathbf{W}^*, \sigma^{*2}\right)$

The M-step of EM algorithm uses the computed expectation defined in Theorem 3 and maximizes it with respect to the static parameters $\mathbf{W}^*$ and σ^{*2}. The corresponding values of the maximizes are given by

Theorem 4. *The maximizers of* $Q^m\left(\mathbf{W}, \sigma^2 | \mathbf{W}^*, \sigma^{*2}\right)$ *are the solution to the set of the problems* $\frac{\partial Q^m}{\partial \mathbf{W}^*} = 0$ *and* $\frac{\partial Q^m}{\partial \sigma^{*2}} =$ *and are given by*

$$
\begin{aligned}
\mathbf{W}_{d \times k}^* &= \left(\sum_{n=1}^{N} \mathbb{E}\left[\mathbf{x}_n^T \mathbf{y}_n | \mathbf{y}_t^o, \mathbf{W}, \sigma^2\right]^T\right) \left[\left(\sum_{n=1}^{N} \mathbb{E}\left[\mathbf{x}_n | \mathbf{y}_t^o, \mathbf{W}, \sigma^2\right]^T \mathbb{E}\left[\mathbf{x}_n | \mathbf{y}_t^o, \mathbf{W}, \sigma^2\right)\right)\right]^{-1} \\
\sigma^{*2} &= \frac{1}{Nd} \sum_{n=1}^{N} tr\left(\mathbb{E}\left[\mathbf{y}_n^T \mathbf{y}_n | \mathbf{y}_t^o, \mathbf{W}, \sigma^2\right] - 2\mathbf{W}^* \mathbb{E}\left[\mathbf{x}_n^T \mathbf{y}_n | \mathbf{y}_t^o, \mathbf{W}, \sigma^2\right]\right. \\
&\left. + \mathbb{E}\left[\mathbf{x}_n | \mathbf{y}_t^o, \mathbf{W}, \sigma^2\right]^T \mathbb{E}\left[\mathbf{x}_n | \mathbf{y}_t^o, \mathbf{W}, \sigma^2\right] \mathbf{W}^{*T} \mathbf{W}^*\right)
\end{aligned}
\tag{64}
$$

Proof. We need to replace the moments of conditional distribution $\mathbf{x}_t | \mathbf{y}_t, \mathbf{W}, \sigma^2$ in the proof of the Theorem 2 with the corresponding moments of $\mathbf{x}_t | \mathbf{y}_t^o, \mathbf{W}, \sigma^2$ derived in Theorem 3. Also, we need to replace terms of $\mathbf{y}_t$ by its moments related to the joint distribution $\mathbf{x}_t, \mathbf{y}_t | \mathbf{y}_t^o, \mathbf{W}, \sigma^2$ also given in Theorem 3. □

5.4. The Algorithm

The steps of computing eigenvectors and corresponding loadings are summarized in the following algorithm. Firstly, we standardized data using information from observed values stored in $\mathbf{Y}_{N \times d}$. The estimator of location and variance, $\Theta_N = (\hat{\mu}, \hat{\sigma}^2)$ is a function of the non missing values of observation vector $\mathbf{y}$ among its N realisations. We execute PPCA on standardized data following two steps: the expectation and maximisation step.

Algorithm 1 Probabilistic Principal Component Analysis with missing values

for $j = 1, \ldots, d$ **do**

  Compute $\Theta_N\left([\mathbf{Y}^o]_{\cdot,j}\right) = (\hat{\mu}_j, \hat{\sigma}_j^2)$

  Standardize data $\left[\tilde{\mathbf{Y}}^o\right]_{\cdot,j} = \frac{[\mathbf{Y}^o]_{\cdot,j} - \hat{\mu}_j}{\sigma_j}$

end for

$\tilde{\mathbf{Y}}^m = \mathbf{0}$ and $\tilde{\mathbf{Y}} = (\tilde{\mathbf{Y}}^o, \tilde{\mathbf{Y}}^m)$

Initialise: ε, $i = 0$, $\mathbf{W}^{(0)} = \mathbf{W}_0$, $\sigma^{2(0)} = \sigma_0^2$,

repeat

  E-step: Compute corresponding moments from Equation (62) for

$$Q^m\left(\mathbf{W}^{(i)},\, \sigma^{2(i)} | \mathbf{W}^{(i)},\, \sigma^{2(i)}\right)$$

  M-step: Compute maxima of $Q^m\left(\mathbf{W}^{(i)},\, \sigma^{2(i)} | \mathbf{W},\, \sigma^2\right)$ from Equation (64):

$$\mathbf{W}^{(i+1)}, \sigma^{2(i+1)} = \operatorname{argmax}_{\mathbf{W} \in \mathbb{R}^{d \times k}, \sigma^2 > 0}\, Q^m\left(\mathbf{W}^{(i)},\, \sigma^{2(i)} | \mathbf{W},\, \sigma^2\right)$$

  $i = i + 1$

until a convergence criterion is satisfied

6. Statistically Robust Feature Extraction for Stochastic Principal Component Analysis

Until this point, we have assumed that any stochastic noise or observation errors in the demographic data is in some sense "well behaved", for instance: additive, light tailed, symmetric and zero mean. In this section we relax this inherent assumption by developing a class of robust estimators that can withstand violations of such assumptions which routinely arise in real data observations, especially as we will demonstrate in demographic data. Furthermore, we have assumed that the data is generally temporally stationary over the time period of study. If any of these assumptions does not hold then this has an influence from a statistical perspective for the real data analysis. In such cases we recommend to resort to implementation of feature extraction methods which are more robust (in a statistical sense) to violations of such features.

When non-robust feature extraction methods are naively utilised in the presence of violations of these implicit statistical assumptions it can lead to misleading feature extraction and falsify the information content of these features, leading to bias or variance enhancements in the forecast from stochastic mortality models incorporating such features.

Therefore, it is critical to ensure that the feature extraction is appropriately performed. To avoid or to robustify the feature extraction techniques presented previously against violations of such statistical features such as non-stationarity, heavy tails, hetroskedascity, non-Gaussianity one can turn to robust statistical methods. This can strongly influence the findings based on such demographic feature extractions. Therefore, in this section we demonstrate a statistically rigorous approach to perform feature extractions as detailed previously in a robust estimation and feature extraction extended framework.

To achieve this, we first recall some basics of robust statistical inference, primarily targeting the robust estimation of location and scale or mean and covariance, as will be directly relevant in the stochastic PCA based methods proposed above.

Regardless if we work with standard or probabilistic PCA, the most straightforward method to improve its statistical robustness, is to employ estimators of the covariance matrix which are less sensitive to outlying data points.

6.1. Robust Estimators of Mean and Covariance Matrix

To introduce the concept of statistically robust estimation for feature extraction in demographic data, we first introduce what exactly we mean by statistical robustness of feature extraction. This requires a short set of formal definitions.

Let us define an estimator Θ as a functional on the domain of distribution functions. We exchangeable use the definition of an estimator as a function of the d-dimensional sample $\mathbf{y}_1, \ldots, \mathbf{y}_N$, denoted by Θ_N. In the following part we drop the time related index of the random variable and denote it by the $\mathbf{y}$. The empirical distribution defined by sample is denoted by F_N. The true population distribution and density functions of $\mathbf{y}$ are denoted by capital letter F and f.

6.1.1. Concept of Robustness

We consider robustness according to two measures: a measure of local robustness and secondly a measure of global robustness. The two measures are defined by a ϵ-contamination set of a distribution functions, that is

Definition 1. *$\mathcal{F}_\epsilon$ is a contamination neighbourhood of distribution F defined as*

$$\mathcal{F}_\epsilon = \{G : G = (1-\epsilon)F + \epsilon H, \textit{ for } H \textit{ any distribution } \} \tag{65}$$

given fraction of contamination $0 \leq \epsilon \leq 1$.

One can then define the local robustness of an estimator Θ as measured by influence function given in Definition 2.

Definition 2 (Influence function). *The influence function of an estimator Θ on the domain of distribution function is defined as*

$$IF(\mathbf{x}_0, \Theta, F) = \lim_{\epsilon \to 0} \frac{\Theta\left((1-\epsilon)F + \epsilon\delta_{\mathbf{x}_0}\right) - \Theta(F)}{\epsilon} \tag{66}$$

where $\delta_{\mathbf{x}_0}$ is a probability measure which puts mass 1 at the point $\mathbf{x}_0$ if $(1-\epsilon)F + \epsilon\delta_{\mathbf{x}_0}$ is included into the domain of Θ.

The influence function is a crucial information to calculate asymptotic variance and efficiency of an estimator as

$$\sqrt{n}\left(\Theta(F_N) - \Theta(F)\right) = \sqrt{N} \int_{\mathbb{R}^d} IF\left(\mathbf{y}, \Theta, F\right) dF_N(\mathbf{y}) + \cdots \tag{67}$$

where we used Tylor expansion of the empirical distribution function F_N around true population distribution function F.

The influence function provides us with the knowledge how ϵ contamination on a point $\mathbf{x}_0$ changes the information about the true distribution of the random variable $\mathbf{y}$ which is given by Θ. Thus, it is perceived as a local measure of robustness. To measure global robustness, one can examine a breakdown point ϵ^* of estimator Θ_N at the true population distribution F, given in Definition 3.

Definition 3 (Breakdown point). *The finite-sample breakdown point ϵ^* of an estimator Θ_N at the true population distribution F is defined as*

$$\epsilon^* := \sup\{\epsilon \leq 1 : \sup_{G \in \mathcal{F}_\epsilon} |\Theta_N(G)| < \infty\} \tag{68}$$

Intuitively, it is understood as the maximal contamination which does not cause the estimator to loose valid information about the true distribution F. We may define a finite sample definitions of the breakdown point as

Definition 4. *The breakdown point ϵ_N^* of estimator Θ at the empirical population distribution F_N is defined as*

$$\epsilon_N^*(\Theta, \mathbf{y}_1, \ldots, \mathbf{y}_N) := \max\{n_1 \in \mathbb{Z}, \max_{i_1,\ldots,i_{n_1}} \sup_{\mathbf{z}_1,\ldots,\mathbf{z}_{n_1}} |\Theta(\tilde{F}_N)| < \infty\} \tag{69}$$

where points $\mathbf{y}_{i_1}, \ldots, \mathbf{y}_{n_1}$ were replaced with arbitrary points $\mathbf{z}_1, \ldots, \mathbf{z}_{n_1}$.

Having introduced these formal definitions of what exactly is meant by robust estimators, we overview the most frequently used estimators of a covariance matrix with respect to their robust characteristics according to introduced measures. Let us denote $\boldsymbol{\mu}$, $\mathbf{C}$ as a mean and covariance matrix of $\mathbf{y}$.

6.1.2. M-Estimators

In the study of (Maronna 1976) and (Huber and Ronchetti 2009) on the robust estimation of covariance matrix, the authors define one of the first classes of robust estimators, called M-estimators, which are a generalized version of Maximum Log-liklihood Estimators (MLE) where

$$\Theta_N = arg \max_{\Theta \in \Omega} \prod_{n=1}^{N} f(\mathbf{y}_n) \Leftrightarrow \Theta_N = arg \min_{\Theta \in \Omega} \sum_{n=1}^{N} -\log f(\mathbf{y}_n). \tag{70}$$

The idea behind M-estimators, is to replace the density function in Equation (70), f, with function $\rho : \mathbb{R}_+ \to \mathbb{R}$ which down weights outliers, that is

Definition 5 (M-estimators). *The M-estimator of a parameter Θ is defined as a solution to the problem*

$$\Theta_N = \operatorname{argmin}_{\Theta \in \Omega} \sum_{n=1}^{N} \rho(d_n). \tag{71}$$

for a function $\rho : \mathbb{R}_+ \to \mathbb{R}$ where $d_n^2 = (\mathbf{y}_n - \boldsymbol{\mu})\,\mathbf{C}^{-1}\,(\mathbf{y}_n - \boldsymbol{\mu})^T$ is a Mahalanobias distance of $\mathbf{y}_n$.

Remark 3. *If ρ is a continuous function, denoting its derivative $\rho' = \psi$, the estimator $\hat{\Theta}_N$ satisfies*

$$\begin{aligned} &\sum_{n=1}^{N} \frac{\psi(d_n)}{d_n} \mathbf{C}^{-\frac{1}{2}} (\mathbf{y}_n - \boldsymbol{\mu}) = 0 \\ &\sum_{n=1}^{N} \frac{\psi(d_n)}{d_n} \mathbf{C}^{-\frac{1}{2}} (\mathbf{y}_n - \boldsymbol{\mu})^T (\mathbf{y}_n - \boldsymbol{\mu})\, \mathbf{C}^{-\frac{1}{2}} = \mathbf{0} \end{aligned} \tag{72}$$

which are the robust analogue of the typical normal type equations one would solve in MLE estimations in regression for instance.

Remark 4. *If we additionally assume that* $\mathbf{y}$ *is a random vector from elliptical family with density of the form*

$$f(\mathbf{y};\boldsymbol{\mu},\mathbf{C}) = c^{-1}|\mathbf{C}|^{-\frac{1}{2}}g\left(d^2(\mathbf{y},\Theta)\right). \tag{73}$$

with $g:\mathbb{R}_+\to\mathbb{R}_+$ *being a density generator of random variable* $\mathbf{y}$*, the solution to the problem Equation* (71) *is equivalent to*

$$\begin{aligned}
&\sum_{n=1}^{N}\frac{\psi(d_n)}{d_n}\mathbf{C}^{-\frac{1}{2}}(\mathbf{y}_n-\boldsymbol{\mu})=0\\
&\sum_{n=1}^{N}\frac{\psi(d_n)}{d_n}\mathbf{C}^{-\frac{1}{2}}(\mathbf{y}_n-\boldsymbol{\mu})^T(\mathbf{y}_n-\boldsymbol{\mu})\mathbf{C}^{-\frac{1}{2}}=\mathbb{I}_d
\end{aligned} \tag{74}$$

More generalized notation is used in (Maronna 1976) and (Huber and Ronchetti 2009) who introduce functions $u_1,u_2:\mathbb{R}_+\to\mathbb{R}$ to rewrite Equation (74) as follows in Definition 6.

Definition 6. *The M-estimator* Θ_N *of the parameter* Θ *of a location and scatter of random variable* $\mathbf{y}$ *from elliptical family, is defined as a solution to*

$$\begin{aligned}
&\sum_{n=1}^{N}u_1(d_n)(\mathbf{y}_n-\boldsymbol{\mu})=0\\
&\sum_{n=1}^{N}u_2\left(d_n^2\right)\mathbf{C}^{-\frac{1}{2}}(\mathbf{y}_n-\boldsymbol{\mu})^T(\mathbf{y}_n-\boldsymbol{\mu})\mathbf{C}^{-\frac{1}{2}}=\mathbb{I}_d
\end{aligned} \tag{75}$$

for functions $u_1,u_2:\mathbb{R}_+\to\mathbb{R}$*, given its* N *realisations.*

The authors provide conditions for u_1 and u_2 to ensure existence and uniqueness of Equation (75) and its normal asymptotic distribution with $-\frac{1}{2}$ convergence. (Maronna 1976) proves the breakdown point of Equation (75) to be very sensitive to dimensionality of the data as $\epsilon^*=\frac{1}{d+1}$.

Recall that in this study, we want to compute a variance of every variable rather than a covariance matrix (Algorithm 1) what makes a M-estimator a very suitable tool. What is more, the robustness of M-estimators does not depend on the sample size. It is another advantage of an M-estimator when working with population data as has a very limited number of observation available.

Remark 5. *As an example of function* u_1 *and* u_2*, (Huber 1964) gives the following*

$$u_1(s)=\frac{\psi_H(s,k)}{s},\ u_2(s)=\frac{\psi_H(s,k^2)}{s},\ \rho_H(s)=\begin{cases}\frac{1}{2}s^2 & |s|<k\\ \frac{1}{2}|s|-\frac{1}{2}k^2 & |s|\geq k\end{cases} \tag{76}$$

for $\psi_H(s,k)=\rho'_H(s,k)$ *and the tuning constant* k*.*

Defining estimator with ρ_H is proven to have the minimal maximal asymptotic variance of all affine invariant estimators under the assumption that the sample $\mathbf{y}_1,\ldots,\mathbf{y}_N$ is normally distributed with zero mean and identity covariance matrix.

For the problem of only scatter estimation, (Tyler 1987) introduced a function $u_2(s)=\frac{d}{s}$, which is investigated in details by (Frahm and Jaekel 2010).

Definition 7. *Tyler's estimator of an covariance matrix for unbounded function* $u_2(s)=\frac{d}{s}$ *is obtained by solving*

$$\frac{d}{N}\sum_{n=1}^{N}\frac{(\mathbf{y}_n-\boldsymbol{\mu})^T(\mathbf{y}_n-\boldsymbol{\mu})}{(\mathbf{y}_n-\boldsymbol{\mu})\mathbf{C}^{-1}(\mathbf{y}_n-\boldsymbol{\mu})^T}=\mathbf{C}. \tag{77}$$

Lemma 1. *Under the assumption of generalized elliptical distribution of* $\mathbf{y}$*, the solution Equation (77) exists and is unique up to the scalar parameter.*

Recall that u_2 is not bounded and hence does not satisfy the conditions described in (Maronna 1976) or (Huber and Ronchetti 2009). Therefore the uniqueness can be obtain up to the scaling parameter.

Lemma 2. *if* $\mathbf{y}$ *belongs to generalized elliptical distribution, Tyler's estimator from Definition 7 is strongly consistent with true covariance matrix, if it exists, up to the scaling factor and has normal asymptotic distribution with convergence rate* $-\frac{1}{2}$.

The asymptotic variance of Tyler's M-estimator, which was analysed i.e., by the author of (Tyler 1987), is proven to have the lowest maximum bias among all normally distributed estimators for symmetric elliptical family random variables.

For a point contamination, the maximal breakdown point of the estimator is equal to $\epsilon^* = \frac{1}{d}$ as proved in (Tyler 1987). The later study shows that for any other contamination, the maximal breakdown point is between

$$\frac{1}{d+1} \leq \epsilon^* \leq \frac{1}{d} \tag{78}$$

Furthermore, Tyler's M-estimator is an MLE estimator of angular Gaussian distribution. To show this property we use the following Lemma

Lemma 3. *If* $\mathbf{y}$ *has generalized elliptical distribution then* $\mathbf{y} =_d \boldsymbol{\mu} + R\mathbf{C}^{\frac{1}{2}}\mathbf{u}$ *for* $\mathbf{u}$ *being uniformly distributed random variable on the unit d dimensional sphere and R being a scalar variable.*

Recall that R is a component which is responsible for generating tails of $\mathbf{y}$ distribution.

Remark 6. *If R is absolutely continuous and independent from* $\mathbf{u}$*, the generator of probability density function of centred* $\mathbf{y}$*,* $\tilde{\mathbf{y}}$*, is given by* $f(\tilde{\mathbf{y}}) := \frac{\Gamma(\frac{r}{2})}{2\pi^{\frac{r}{2}}}\tilde{\mathbf{y}}^{-\frac{r-1}{2}} f_R(\sqrt{\tilde{\mathbf{y}}})$ *for* $r = rank(\mathbf{C})$ *and* f_R *being probability density function of R. Then* $\mathbf{y}$ *is symmetrically distributed.*

Remark 7. *If the variable R is allowed to be negative and has a dependence structure with uniformly distributed* $\mathbf{u}$*, the distribution of* $\mathbf{y}$ *is called generalized elliptical distribution. The generalised elliptical family allows to model asymmetric and tail dependent distribution of* $\mathbf{y}$.

Theorem 5 (Distribution-free Tyler estimator)**.** *The estimator introduced by Definition 7 is distribution-free, i.e., it does not depend on values of R.*

Proof. Following Lemma 3 we can notice that

$$\mathbf{z} := \frac{\mathbf{y}-\boldsymbol{\mu}}{||\mathbf{y}-\boldsymbol{\mu}||_F} = \frac{R\mathbf{u}\mathbf{C}^{\frac{1}{2}}}{||R\mathbf{u}\mathbf{C}^{\frac{1}{2}}||_F} \stackrel{d}{=} sign(R)\frac{\mathbf{u}\mathbf{C}^{\frac{1}{2}}}{||\mathbf{u}\mathbf{C}^{\frac{1}{2}}||_F}. \tag{79}$$

and is robust against extreme realisations of R as does not depend on the values of R. $||\cdot||_F$ denotes the Frobenius norm. Rewriting Equation (77) using N realisations of $\mathbf{z}$, $\mathbf{z}_1, \ldots \mathbf{z}_N$, we obtain

$$\mathbf{C} = \frac{d}{N}\sum_{n=1}^{N}\frac{\mathbf{z}_n^T\mathbf{z}_n}{\mathbf{z}_n\mathbf{C}^{-1}\mathbf{z}_n^T} = \frac{d}{N}\sum_{n=1}^{N}\frac{\mathbf{C}^{-\frac{1}{2}}\mathbf{u}_n^T\mathbf{u}_n\mathbf{C}^{-\frac{1}{2}}}{\mathbf{u}_n^T\mathbf{u}_n} \tag{80}$$

□

Tyler's estimator is invariant under any change of distribution of R i.e., it is distribution - free.

Theorem 6. *The estimator introduced by Definition 7 is MLE estimator of Angular Gaussian Distribution.*

Proof. Since the probability density function of $\mathbf{v} = \frac{\mathbf{u}\mathbf{C}^{\frac{1}{2}}}{||\mathbf{u}\mathbf{C}^{\frac{1}{2}}||_F}$ is given by

$$f_v(\mathbf{v}) = \frac{\Gamma\left(\frac{d}{2}\right)}{2\pi^{\frac{d}{2}}} \frac{|\mathbf{C}^{-1}|^{\frac{1}{2}}}{||\mathbf{v}\mathbf{C}^{-\frac{1}{2}}||_F^{\frac{d}{2}}}. \tag{81}$$

Having N realisations of $\mathbf{v}$, $\mathbf{v}_1, \ldots, \mathbf{v}_N$, the logliklihood function is given by

$$\begin{aligned} \log \mathcal{L}(\mathbf{v}_1, \ldots, \mathbf{v}_N; \mathbf{C}) &= \sum_{n=1}^{N} \log f_v(\mathbf{v}_n) = \text{const} + \frac{N}{2} + \log|\mathbf{C}^{-1}| - \frac{d}{2}\sum_{n=1}^{N} \log\left(\mathbf{v}_n \mathbf{C}^{-1}\mathbf{v}_n^T\right) \\ &= \text{const} + \frac{N}{2} + \log|\mathbf{C}^{-1}| - \frac{d}{2}\sum_{n=1}^{N} \log\left(\mathbf{z}_n \mathbf{C}^{-1}\mathbf{z}_n^T\right) \end{aligned} \tag{82}$$

Since $\mathcal{P}^d$ is an open set, the maximizer of $\log \mathcal{L}$ with respect to $\mathbf{C}$ is the stationary point. By setting

$$\begin{aligned} &\frac{\partial \log \mathcal{L}}{\partial \mathbf{C}^{-1}} = \mathbf{0} \Leftrightarrow \\ &\frac{N}{2}(2\mathbf{C} - diag\mathbf{C}) - \frac{d}{2}\sum_{n=1}^{N} \frac{2\mathbf{s}_n^T\mathbf{s}_n - diag(\tilde{\mathbf{y}}_n^T\tilde{\mathbf{y}}_n)}{\tilde{\mathbf{y}}_n\mathbf{C}^{-1}\tilde{\mathbf{y}}_n^T} = \mathbf{0} \Leftrightarrow \\ &N\mathbf{C} - d\sum_{n=1}^{N} \frac{(\mathbf{y}_n - \boldsymbol{\mu})^T(\mathbf{y}_n - \boldsymbol{\mu})}{(\mathbf{y}_n - \boldsymbol{\mu})\mathbf{C}^{-1}(\mathbf{y}_n - \boldsymbol{\mu})^T} = \mathbf{0} \end{aligned} \tag{83}$$

what is precisely equal to Equation (77). □

The solution to the estimation problem of Tyler's estimator is in a form $x = f(x)$ what allows us to use the fix - point iteration scheme with $i+1$ step

$$\mathbf{C}^{(i+1)} = \frac{d}{N}\sum_{n=1}^{N} \frac{(\mathbf{y}_n - \boldsymbol{\mu})^T(\mathbf{y}_n - \boldsymbol{\mu})}{(\mathbf{y}_n - \boldsymbol{\mu})\mathbf{C}^{(i)(-1)}(\mathbf{y}_n - \boldsymbol{\mu})^T}. \tag{84}$$

Lemma 4. *The fix-point algorithm Equation* (84) *converges to $a\mathbf{C}$ for a scalar $a > 0$.*

Proof. Since $f(\mathbf{C}) = \frac{d}{N}\sum_{n=1}^{N} \frac{(\mathbf{y}_n - \boldsymbol{\mu})^T(\mathbf{y}_n - \boldsymbol{\mu})}{(\mathbf{y}_n - \boldsymbol{\mu})\mathbf{C}^{-1}(\mathbf{y}_n - \boldsymbol{\mu})^T}$ being continuous on $\mathcal{P}^d$, the algorithm converges to $\mathbf{C}$ for a scalar $a > 0$. □

Following (Tyler 1987), let us define the following function $M : \mathcal{P}^d \to \mathcal{P}^d$ such that

$$M(\Gamma) = \frac{d}{N}\sum_{n=1}^{N} \frac{\Gamma^{\frac{1}{2}}(\mathbf{y}_n - \boldsymbol{\mu})^T(\mathbf{y}_n - \boldsymbol{\mu})\Gamma^{\frac{1}{2}}}{(\mathbf{y}_n - \boldsymbol{\mu})\Gamma(\mathbf{y}_n - \boldsymbol{\mu})^T} \tag{85}$$

The fixed point iteration step Equation (84) can be rewritten as

$$\mathbf{C}^{(i+1)} = \mathbf{C}^{(i)\frac{1}{2}} M\left(\mathbf{C}^{(i)(-1)}\right)\mathbf{C}^{(i)\frac{1}{2}} \tag{86}$$

Denoting $\Gamma^{(i)} = \mathbf{C}^{(i)(-1)}$ and $\mathbf{M}^{(k)} = M\left(\Gamma^{(i)}\right)$ we get

$$\Gamma^{(i+1)} = \Gamma^{(i)\frac{1}{2}}\mathbf{M}^{(i)(-1)}\Gamma^{(i)\frac{1}{2}} \tag{87}$$

In order to deal with the lack of uniqueness of the solution to Equation (84), (Tyler 1987) restricts the search space to the positive definite symmetric matrices with trace equal to 1 by

$$\Gamma^{(i+1)} = \frac{\Gamma^{(i)\frac{1}{2}}\mathbf{M}^{(i)(-1)}\Gamma^{(i)\frac{1}{2}}}{tr\left(\Gamma^{(i)\frac{1}{2}}\mathbf{M}^{(i)(-1)}\Gamma^{(i)\frac{1}{2}}\right)} = \frac{\Gamma^{(i)\frac{1}{2}}\mathbf{M}^{(i)(-1)}\Gamma^{(i)\frac{1}{2}}}{tr\left(\Gamma^{(i)}\mathbf{M}^{(i)(-1)}\right)}. \tag{88}$$

That way, it is ensured that $tr(\Gamma^{(i+1)}) = 1$. In his study, Tyler proves that the convergence of the sequence $\Gamma^{(i+1)}$ to a non singular matrix Γ implies $M(\Gamma) = \mathbb{I}_d$

Theorem 7. *(Tyler 1987) If the following conditions hold:*

1. *the sample* $\mathbf{y}_1, \ldots, \mathbf{y}_N$ *does not contains values equal to* $\boldsymbol{\mu}$
2. *the empirical distribution measure* F_N *of the sample satisfies* $F_N(S) < \frac{1}{d}$*, for* S *being a any proper subspace of* $\mathbb{R}^d$
3. *for some the mth smallest eigenvalue of* $\Gamma^{(i)}$*, it is holds that* $\lambda_{m,d} > \frac{d}{rank(S)} F_N(S)$ *where* S *is any proper subspace of* $\mathbb{R}^d$

then $\Gamma^{(i)} \to \Gamma$ *and* $M(\Gamma) = \mathbb{I}_d$.

Remark 8. *Generally, to deal with lack of uniqueness of Equation* (84)*, a common practice is to impose additional constraints such as* $|\mathbf{C}| = 1$ *as in (Frahm and Jaekel 2010) or* $tr\mathbf{C} = 1$ *as in (Tyler 1987) or (Sun et al. 2016).*

6.1.3. S-Estimators

As the robustness of the class of M-estimators is highly influenced by dimensionality of the data, we introduce an extension to the problem Equation (71) and define class of S-estimator. The class was firstly introduced by (Rousseeuw and Yohai 1984) and extended to multivariate setting by (Davies 1987)

Definition 8 (S-estimator). *S-estimator of a parameter* Θ *is defined as a solution to*

$$\begin{aligned} &\Theta_N = \min_{\Theta \in \Omega} |\mathbf{C}| \text{ subject to} \\ &\int \rho\left(d(\mathbf{y}, \Theta)\right) dF_N(\mathbf{y}) \geq b_0 \end{aligned} \tag{89}$$

where the constant b_0 *is a mean of* $\rho(d_y)$*, where* d_y *is a Mahalanobias distance of the random vector* $\mathbf{y}$ *under an assumption of the distribution of* $\mathbf{y}$*, that is*

$$b_0 = \mathbb{E}\left[\rho\left(d_y\right)\right] = \mathbb{E}\left[\rho\left(||\mathbf{y} - \mu||_F\right)\right] = \frac{\pi^{\frac{d}{2}}}{\Gamma\left(\frac{d}{2}\right)} \int_0^{\infty} \rho(r) f(r) r^{d-1} dr. \tag{90}$$

Function ρ *is defined as in Definition 5.*

Remark 9. *If* ρ *is continuous then the problem Equation* (89) *is an equality.*

In the study of (Davies 1987), the author investigates the properties of S-estimators under the assumption of elliptically distributed $\mathbf{y}$. (Davies 1987) gives the general assumptions on function $\rho : \mathbb{R}_+ \to [0, 1]$, e.g., being continuous on its domain and zero c such that $0 < c < \infty$. The author proves that under these assumptions and if $nb_0 \geq d + 1$, Equation (89) has at least one solution for non singular estimate $\Theta = (\mu, \mathbf{C})$.

The work of (Davies 1987) proves consistency of the estimator Θ_N and its uniqueness under these assumptions. When additionally ρ has a continuous third derivative, the solution to Equation (89), is asymptotically normal with $-\frac{1}{2}$ convergence.

Let us denote $\epsilon = 1 - b_0$. Following (Davies 1987), if $N(1-2\epsilon) \geq N+1$, and the sample is in general position, that is no more that d points of the sample lies on $(d-1)$-dimensional hyperplane, then the finite-sample breakdown point is equal to

$$\epsilon_N^* = \frac{[N\epsilon]+1}{N} \Rightarrow \lim_{n\to\infty} \epsilon_n^* = \epsilon = \epsilon^*. \tag{91}$$

In the paper (Lopuhaa 1989), there is introduced an alternative definition of S-estimators, considering function $\rho : \mathbb{R}_+ \to [0,\infty)$ and investigates the relation between S-estimators and M-estimators. He imposes stronger assumptions on the function ρ than are required to make his definition of S-estimators equivalent to Davis's definition (Davies 1987) by transforming $\rho \to 1 - \frac{\rho}{\sup \rho}$. Under the assumption of elliptical distribution of $\mathbf{y}$, the author shows that any solution to the problem Equation (89) satisfies Equation (71). He rewrites the problem Equation (89) as the similar to Equation (74) using Lagrangian

$$\log \mathcal{L}_N(\Theta,\lambda) = \log|\mathbf{C}| - \lambda\left[\frac{1}{N}\sum_{n=1}^{N}\rho(d_n) - b_0\right] \tag{92}$$

to obtain the equivalent set of equations

$$(\Theta_N,\lambda) = \underset{\Theta\in\Omega,\lambda\in\mathbb{R}}{\operatorname{argmin}} \log \mathcal{L}_N(\Theta,\lambda) \Rightarrow \begin{cases} \frac{1}{N}\sum_{n=1}^{N} u(d_n)(\mathbf{y}_n - \boldsymbol{\mu}) = 0 \\ \frac{d}{N}\sum_{n=1}^{N} \frac{u(d_n)}{v(d_n)} (\mathbf{y}_n - \boldsymbol{\mu})^T (\mathbf{y}_n - \boldsymbol{\mu}) = \mathbf{C}, \end{cases} \tag{93}$$

for $u(s) = \frac{\psi(s)}{s}$ and $v(s) = \psi(s)s - \rho(s) + b_0$. The term $-\rho(s) + b_0$ substitutes Lagrangian multiplier λ. Hence, every solution to Equation (89) is a solution to Equation (93) what is M-estimator problem defined by Equation (75).

The author of (Lopuhaa 1989) argues that S-estimators achieve the same asymptotic variance as corresponding M-estimators but as dimensionality of data increases, they have higher breakdown point than M-estimators.

Remark 10. *The example of functions which satisfies the conditions of uniqueness and existence of Equation* (89) *are Tuckey's biweight functions, that is*

$$\rho_B(s) = \begin{cases} \frac{s^2}{2} - \frac{s^4}{2k^2} + \frac{s^6}{6k^4} & |s| \leq k \\ \frac{k^2}{6} & |s| \geq k \end{cases} \Rightarrow \psi_B(s) = s\left(1 - \left(\frac{s}{k}\right)^2\right)^2 \mathbf{1}_{[-k,k]}(s) \tag{94}$$

The breakdown point of the S-estimator for $\rho = 1 - \frac{\rho_B}{\sup \rho_B}$ *is equal to*

$$\epsilon^* = \frac{[N(1-b_0)]+1}{N} = \frac{\left[\frac{N}{\sup \rho_B}\mathbb{E}\{\rho_B(\mathbf{y}-\boldsymbol{\mu})\}\right]+1}{N} \tag{95}$$

7. Data

The examined data consists of male and female mortality and demographic data obtained from Human Mortality Database (http://www.mortality.org) for European countries. The Table 1 summarizes the availability of the data for all the countries included into the study.

We use four different sets of mortality data, raw data: Birth counts and Death counts, and life tables: Life Expectancy at Birth and Death Rates. We conduct separate analysis for female and male populations.

The time series vary in terms of the number of available observations. The longest time series is provided by Swedish and French mortality data, starting from 1751 and 1816, respectively. The shortest time series are given for Greece and Slovenia, 1983–2014 and 1981–2013, respectively.

With regards to Birth counts and Life expectancy at Birth, the information per country in time point is one dimensional, i.e., annual counts of live births by sex in year t (Birth counts) or the expected life span of a person born in year t (Life Expectancy at Birth). Hence, a single observation in these cases consists of the number of entries equal to the number of countries included into the study, that is 31 listed in Table 1, per gender.

Table 1. The availability of the demographic data per country (Human Mortality Database).

Country	Life Expectancy ($E0$)	No. Births	Death Rate (m_x)	No. Deaths
Austria	1947–2014	1871–2014	1947–2014	1947–2014
Belarus	1959–2014	1959–2014	1959–2014	1959–2014
Belgium	1841–2015	1840–2015	1841–2015	1841–2015
Czech Republic	1950–2010	1947–2014	1950–2014	1950–2014
Denmark	1835–2014	1835–2014	1835–2014	1835–2014
Estonia	1959–2013	1959–2013	1959–2013	1959–2013
Finland	1878–2012	1865–2012	1878–2012	1878–2012
France	1816–2014	1806–2014	1816–2014	1816–2014
East Germany	1956–2013	1946–2013	1956–2013	1956–2013
West Germany	1956–2013	1946–2013	1956–2013	1956–2013
Greece	1981–2013	1981–2013	1981–2013	1981–2013
Estonia	1959–2013	1959–2013	1959–2013	1959–2013
Hungary	1950–2014	1950–2014	1950–2014	1950–2014
Iceland	1838–2013	1838–2013	1838–2013	1838–2013
Ireland	1950–2014	1950–2014	1950–2014	1950–2014
Italy	1872–2012	1862–2012	1872–2012	1872–2012
Latvia	1959–2013	1959–2013	1959–2013	1959–2013
Lithuania	1959–2013	1959–2013	1959–2013	1959–2013
Luxembourg	1960–2014	1950–2014	1960–2014	1960–2014
Netherlands	1850–2012	1850–2012	1850–2012	1850–2012
Norway	1846–2014	1846–2014	1846–2014	1846–2014
Poland	1958–2014	1958–2014	1958–2014	1958–2014
Portugal	1940–2012	1886–2012	1940–2012	1940–2012
Russia	1959–2014	1959–2014	1959–2014	1959–2014
Slovakia	1950–2014	1950–2014	1950–2014	1950–2014
Slovenia	1983–2014	1983–2014	1983–2014	1983–2014
Spain	1908–2014	1908–2014	1908–2014	1908–2014
Sweden	1751–2014	1747–2014	1751–2014	1751–2014
Switzerland	1876–2014	1871–2014	1876–2014	1876–2014
United Kingdom	1922–2013	1922–2013	1922–2013	1922–2013
Ukraine	1959–2013	1946–2013	1959–2013	1959–2013

The age specific information is provided for Death counts and Death Rates. A single observation per country in time t describes a number of deaths of people with ages from 0 to 110+ (Death counts) or number of deaths for ages from 0 to 110+ scaled to the size of that population, per unit of time (Death Rates). The availability of time series is different among age groups. Usually, the shortest time series are collected for age groups above 100 years.

Since the Lee-Carter model with the cohort effect has been already reported to be prone to over-fitting when fitted to short time series (the currently available mortality data is classified as a short time series), we decide to work with a data aggregated in the format "5 × 1", i.e., by 5-year age group per calendar year. The ages are grouped into following stratifications: 0, 1–4, 10–14, 15–19, 20–24, 25–29, 30–34, 35–39, 40–44, 45–49, 5–9, 50–54, 55–59, 60–64, 65–69, 70–74, 75–79, 80–84, 85–89, 90–94, 95–99, 100–104, 105–110, 110+ as additing additional latent processes increases the number of parameters to estimate.

A single observation in Deaths or Death Rates consist of the number of entries equal to the number of countries included into the study (i.e., 31) times the number of age groups, that is 24. It accounts for the information in time t available for all 31 countries among all 24 age groups.

7.1. Preprocessing of Data

Human Mortality Database (HMD) team applies several preprocessing procedures that aim to "clean" Death counts and population sizes before using them in order to calculate and distribute death rates and life tables. The subsequent steps are discussed in the technical report (Wilmoth et al. 2007). The adjustments are applied in order to distribute people of unknown age across age groups and splitting data into age categories, i.e., from age stratification "5 × 1" to "1 × 1" and from "1 × 1" to Lexis triangles. The common practice is to use a regression model for splitting deaths counts in format "1 × 1" to Lexis triangles and apply cubic splines to split "5 × 1" to "1 × 1". Additionally to the adjustments applied to Deaths counts, the age specific population size is estimated using four methods: linear interpolation, intercensal survival, extinct cohorts and survivor ratios.

The life tables are calculated using Lexis triangles and population sizes. Before death rates are converted into the probabilities of death, the rates at older ages (80 and above) are smoothed using logistic regression. The "abridged" life tables are calculated based on the Lexis triangles tables rather than the raw data. It ensures the both sets of tables to contain identical values of life expectancy and other quantities.

Recall that the smoothing applied to the mortality data can influence the feature extraction and the diminish the effect of robust versus non-robust versions of feature extraction methodology which we study in this paper. The topic is further discussed in Section 8.

Additionally to the briefly discussed procedures which have been already applied to the data in HMD, we needed to adjust the data to provide reliable information about missing values. We notice the ambiguity in labelling unavailable data which is either denoted by "NA" value or "0". Death Rates, Birth counts and Life Expectancy at Birth are unlikely to produce values equal to "0". Hence we replace all "0" which appeared in these data sets by "NA". The zeros which appear in Deaths counts in older age groups are more difficult to handle as there is no certainty whether there was no person in particular age group who died or the record has missing values. Due to this fact we decided to limit our analysis to age groups up to 90 and again replace any "0" by "NA".

7.2. Missing Data

The following subsection is a summary of different types of missingness across countries, age groups and sexes which occurs in the demographic data set analysed in our study. The findings of the subsection are the following: among the Birth related data where a total observation is of vector-type (one dimensional information per country), the incompleteness of data is due to a general unavailability of the information per country. However, for Death related data where a total observation is of matrix-type (a age specific vector of information per country), we notice a patter of single missing values in time point which fits definition of MAR. In the subsequent section with the empirical analysis of the data set under the derived framework of Probabilistic Principal Component Analysis, we assumed MAR type of missingness. Extending this assumption requires calculating the integral from Equation (34) and incorporating it to PPCA framework.

7.2.1. Observed Patterns of Missingness

Missing data appear when no value is available for a component of the observation vector. The Probabilistic Principal Component Analysis with missing data discussed in Section 5.3 handles missing data by filling them with projection using principal components that are calculated from available information. Thus, the more missing data is present for a given variable, the less impact this variable has on the specification of the projection over the assumptions. The results for variables with missing data are more influenced by our assumption of the distributions from Section 5, as will be discussed in detail below.

In order to handle missing values we need to understand and study how their pattern. In the following part we demonstrate the three patterns of missingness which are present in the analysed data sets:

Type 1: no information about a variable in a few observations for a given country;
Type 2: no information about a variable in all observations for a given country;
Type 3: general unavailability of information about all variables for a country except for a limited set of observations.

The analysis is conducted separately for four data sets and sexes. We show the results for four cases where we segment the data among four proportions of missing entries per total observation with maximal percentage of missing entries equal to: 0%, 25%, 50% and 75%. For instance, a single observation of Birth counts is 31 dimensional. When we analyse the data set with respect to the case 50%, we exclude all observation, when the number of missing entries per observation is greater than $0.5 \times 31 \approx 15$.

In the case of no missing data, that is 0% for Death counts and Death Rates in Females, the number of rows without missing entries is too small for any significant analysis. Due to this fact we drop the minimal number of columns which have the highest number of missing entries in order to collect significant sample for our analysis.

The results of the analysis are similar among Birth counts and Life Expectancy at Birth and Death counts and Death Rates. Hence we discuss the patterns of missingness in Number of Births and Number of Deaths.

7.2.2. Births

The left plot of Figure 1 shows the percentage of missing entries per observation vector of total births over all countries considered versus calendar years for Births counts disaggregated for Females and Males. The sample starts in 1751 (Swedish data) and spans to 2014. Until 1946, the sample has a percentage of missing entries above 50% (the middle vertical red line on the plot). The sample of case 25% starts in 1950. We observe the same missing values pattern between female and male population (the corresponding lines for populations overlap and only the black line, corresponding to male population, is visible).

Figure 2 indicates the availability of data per country (y axis) versus the calendar year (x axis). The black colour denotes points in time when the data is not available for a given country. The Swedish data is not labelled by any black entry except in 2014 as it is the longest time series. Recall that the missing data pattern which is characteristics for this data set is a limited availability of data for a given country. From the empirical analysis of the data we learn that the missing entries do not appear randomly. However, it does not violate the assumed behaviour of missingness and we can still proceed with the methodology of feature extraction described in the previous parts of the paper.

The red vertical lines correspond to the starting points of the subsamples when the maximum number of missing entries per row (an observation in time) is equal to (from the left side on corresponding plots) 75%, 50% and 25%. The subsamples for the cases 25% and 0% provide with principal components which are determined by almost equal sizes of information from every country included into the analysis for the examined period of time. However, the calculation of the components for the subsample in the case 75% is dominated by the time series of countries which are not available before 1950. Therefore, the calculated features are more prone to be impacted by the distribution assumptions and convey less information about dynamics present in the examined period of time that the components obtained from longer time series.

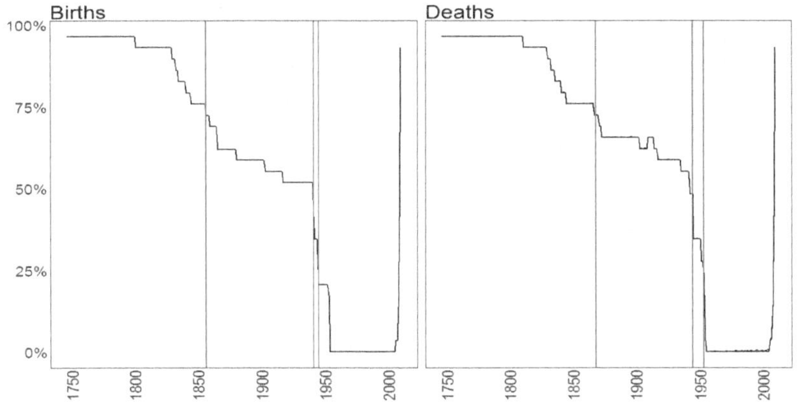

Figure 1. The percentage of missing entries (y axis) per observation vector over time (x axis) for the Births counts (left plot) and Deaths counts (right plot) for female (blue line) and male (blacke line) population. Red vertical lines correspond to the starting points in time of samples when maximum of missing entries is equal to (from the left side on corresponding plots) 75%, 50% and 25%.

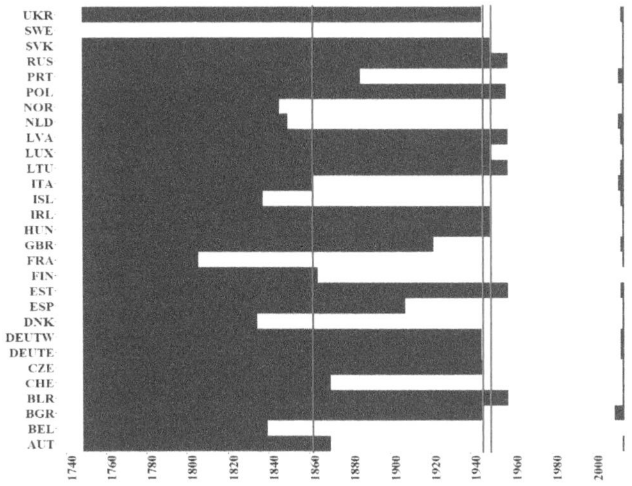

Figure 2. The indicator of a missing value (black colour) per country (y axis) over time (x axis) for the Births counts for female population. Red vertical lines correspond to the starting points in time when samples with maximum of missing entries is equal to (from the left side on corresponding plots) 75%, 50% and 25%.

7.2.3. Deaths

The single observation of Death counts is a 504 dimensional vector which reflect the numbers of death per country and age group in time. The proportion of non missing entries per calendar year, again disaggregated by gender for Death counts is shown on the right plot in Figure 1. The percentage of missing entries decreases slower than for Births counts (the slope of the curve is flattener) which indicates the longer distance between the cases 50% and 25%. We notice the discrepancies in the patterns of missing values between female and male population. Interestingly, the female population data has no observations without missing values.

It is also informative to demonstrate the pattern of missing values per age group, as displayed in Figures 3 and 4 below. Red vertical lines correspond to the starting points in calendar time for the total proportions of missing data corresponding to the cases 50% and 25%. We observe a new pattern of missing values: particular variables have a few missing observations within the subsample. The pattern occurs mainly after 1950 in age groups between 1 and 25 (darker shade of blue for single observations) or in age group 95–100. The other interesting analysis can be done when we display the patterns of missigness which are present by age and per country, which is shown in Figures 5 and 6, again disaggregated by gender. The pattern is present only for the subset of countries. For instance, data related to the Irish population has higher percentage of missing values among only four age groups. Still, the dominant pattern of missingness is the availability of the information for a country which is limited to some period of time.

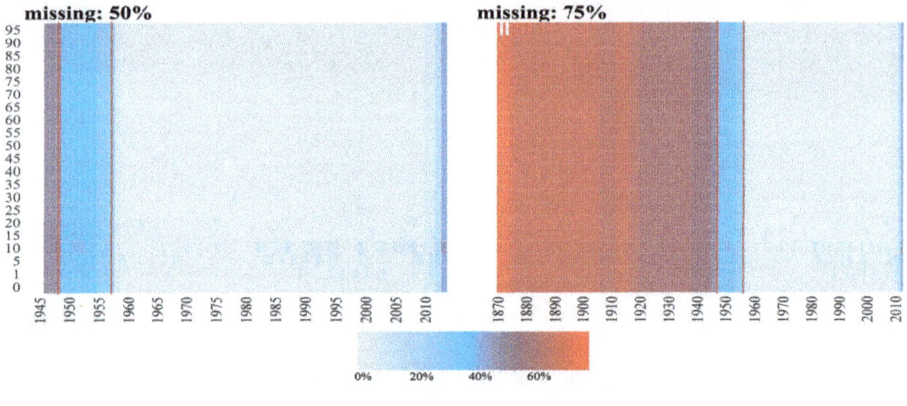

Figure 3. Percentages of missing values (denoted by diffrent colours) per observation for Number of Deaths for Females per age groups (y axis) over time (x axis). The titles of the subplots indicate the case of missing values (50%, 75%). The percentage for a given country and given age group is computed dividing number of missing values by number of countries. Red vertical lines correspond to the starting points in time when the cases 50% and 25% start (from the left to right side on corresponding plots).

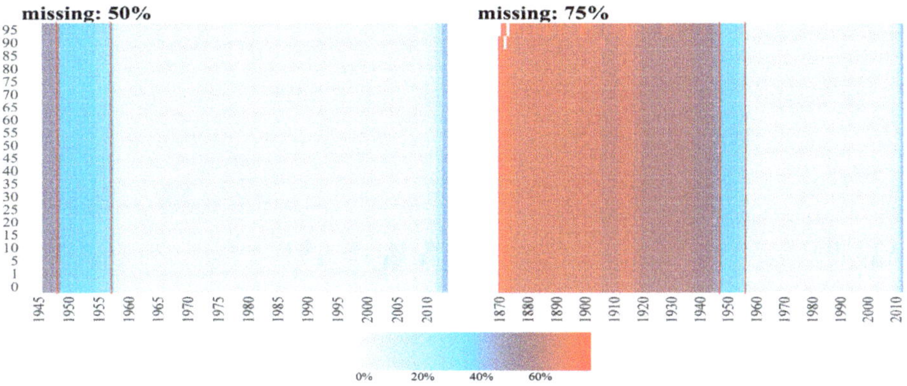

Figure 4. Percentages of missing values (denoted by diffrent colours) per observation for Number of Deaths for Males per age groups (y axis) over time (x axis). The titles of the subplots indicate the case of missing values (50%, 75%). The percentage for a given country and given age group is computed dividing number of missing values by number of countries. Red vertical lines correspond to the starting points in time when the cases 50% and 25% starts (from the left to right side on corresponding plots).

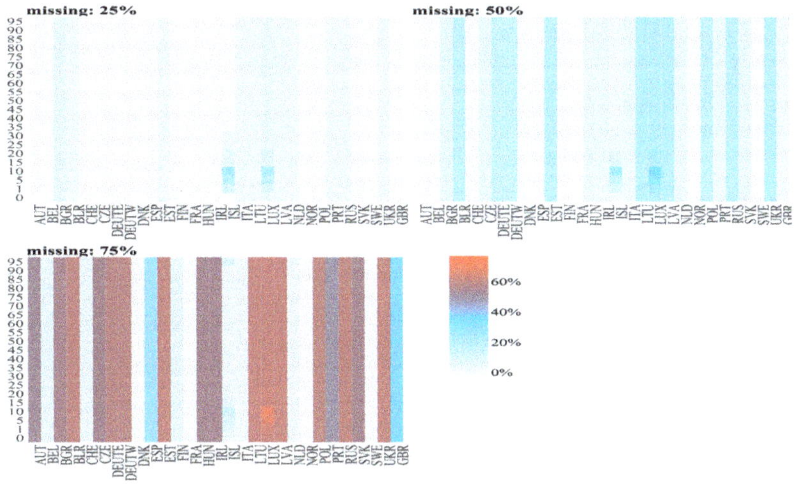

Figure 5. Percentages of missing values (denoted by diffrent colours) for Number of Deaths for Females per country (x axis) and age group (y axis). The titles of the subplots indicate the case of missing values (25%, 50%, 75%). The percentage of missing values for a given country and an age group is calculated dividing number of missing values by length of subsample which is different for different cases.

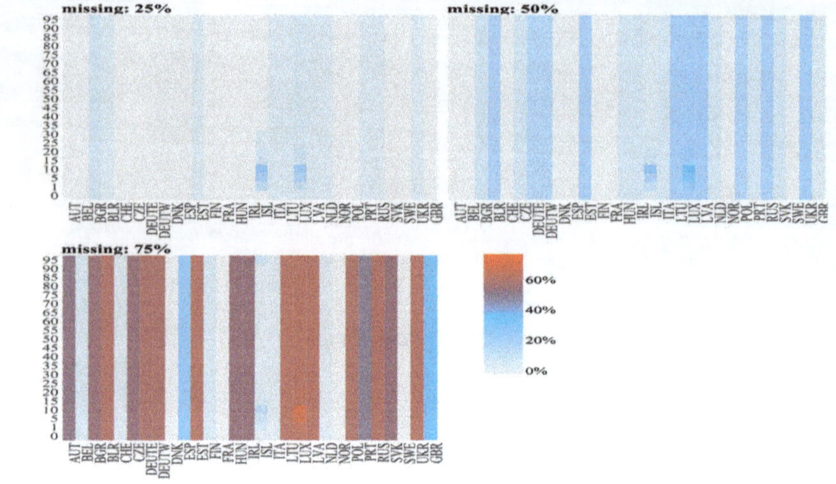

Figure 6. Percentages of missing values (denoted by diffrent colours) for Number of Deaths for Males per country (x axis) and age group (y axis). The titles of the subplots indicate the case of missing values (25%, 50%, 75%). The percentage of missing values for a given country and an age group is calculated dividing number of missing values by length of subsample which is different for different cases.

8. Feature Extraction from European Demographic Data via Probabilistic Principal Component Analysis

The following section provides results for the feature extraction using the methodology introduced in Section 5 and applied to different types of European demographic data sets. The attention is drawn to the effect of simple and straightforward robustification overviewed in the previous sections which application we demonstrate on overviewed data sets. The main observation from this study is the difference in the consistency of the features over time and proportion of missigness for two frameworks, robust and non-robust. The features calculated using the means of robust estimators are more consistent over time and over different proportions of missigness that their non robust alternatives. It is especially visible for the features extracted from data that has not been previously preprocessed, e.g., Birth counts. The effect of robustification is smaller if a data set has been smoothed as Life Expectancy at Birth.

8.1. The Assessment of the Methodology

We conduct a comparison between robust and non-robust Probabilistic Principal Component Analysis (PPCA) in a stochastic setting. We undertake this exercise in order to incorporate the most meaningful eigenvectors as exogenous factors to the model in Equation (8). Each of the datasets discussed in the section is treated separately, that is, we compute the eigenvectors for Births, Life Expectancy at Birth, Deaths and Death Rates. Recall, an observation in time t, $\mathbf{y}_t$, conveys the information about a given data set in calendar year t from the 31 countries listed in Table 1. Hence, an observation of Births or Life Expectancy is 31 dimensional. Since Deaths and Death Rates carry the information which is age group specific, a single observation in these data sets is equal to the number of countries times the number of age groups.

The following section summarizes the results of PCA according to

- Population: Females and Males;
- Subsamples referring to maximum allowed proportion of missing values per an observation: 0% (no missing), 25%, 50% and 75% as discussed in Section 7.2;

- Type of the standardisation procedure: robust and non-robust, which are used for the estimators of location and covariance in the PPCA framework.

We use M-estimators of the covariance and mean as a robust alternative to the sample estimators. As discussed in Section 6.1.2, the class of M-estimator has a very good performance in small dimensions as its robustness is a function of the dimensionality and not the sample size. Since the data we use is not a long time series and we standardize every variable marginally (Algorithm 1), this simple estimator should provide us with reliable outcomes. In particular, we consider the Huber type M-estimators as discussed in Remark 5 which are characterized by normal asymptotic distribution with convergence rate of $\frac{1}{2}$ and several characteristics ensuring both uniqueness and optimality of the estimation Additionally, it is the estimator of covariance which has the minimal asymptotic variance among all estimators for Gaussian data. Thus, the choice is consistent with our assumption of normally distributed data for the treatment of missingness in the PPCA framework which we outlined in Section 5.

Among the objects which we analyse are eigenvectors, eigenvalues, scores and Mahalanobias distances which use estimated covariance matrix $\hat{\mathbf{C}} = \mathbf{W}\mathbf{W}^T + \sigma^2\mathbb{I}_d$ calculated by iteratively evaluated σ^2 and the projection matrix $\mathbf{W}$. The Mahalanobias distance is measured around vector $\mathbf{0}$ (the data has been centred), and is therefore given by

$$d_n^2 := d^2\left(\mathbf{y}_n, \hat{\mathbf{C}}\right) = \mathbf{y}_n \hat{\mathbf{C}}^{-1} \mathbf{y}_n^T. \tag{96}$$

The results show how distant from the assumed long term mean is a single observation.

The EM algorithm described in Section 5 provides the eigenvectors corresponding to the k largest eigenvalues. Due to the specifics of the data (small number of observations), it would be difficult to incorporate many factors into the model from Equation (8) and achieve reliable estimation results. This is primarily a result of the curse of dimensionality in the parameter space that would lead in this case to diffusivity in the resulting likelihood utilised in the estimation. The latent states and static parameters will become difficult to filter and estimate. Thus, we limit our analysis to $k = 3$ main eigenvectors which explain most of the variability as shows the standard PCA with non missing data conducted separately for each country showed.

8.2. Births

The results of PPCA for Births counts among Females and Males are similar. It is the outcome which follows general intuition as there is no external factor which influences differently the births of woman and man in European countries. Also, recall that the Birth counts are the least pre-processed data set in out analysis.

Figure 7 shows the Mahalanobias distances (x axis) of Number of Births over the time (y axis) for female (a) and male (b) population. Each sub-panel consists of two plots, which present results for data being standardized by robust (lower plots) and non-robust (upper plots) estimators of the mean and covariance matrix. Different colours of lines depict distances for subsamples where maximum allowed proportion of missigness per an observation is 0%, 25%, 50% and 75%. Recall, that the subsamples starts in different times and therefore the corresponding results are the outcome of the estimation on different data with different impacts of distribution assumptions.

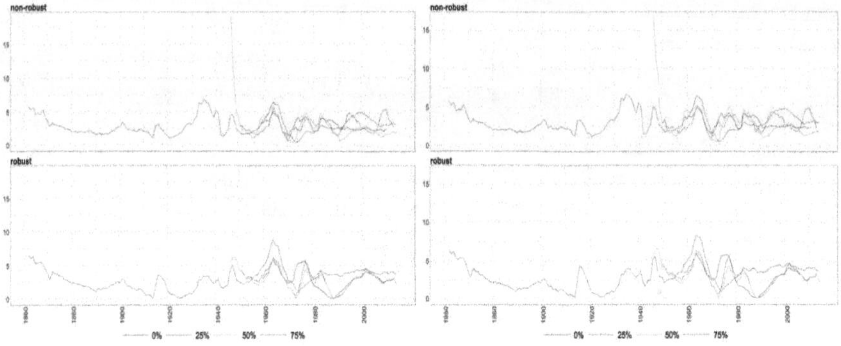

(**a**) (**b**)

Figure 7. The Mahalanobias distances obtained using Probabilistic Principal Component Analysis (PPCA) for Females (**a**) and Males (**b**) Births over time (x axis). Different colours of lines correspond to the cases of different percentages of maximal missing values in a signle observation (light blue (75%), dark brown (50%), dark blue (25%), light brown (0%)). Every subfigure is divided into two subplots corresponding to robust estimation of standard divinations (upper plot) and sample one (bottom plot).

As expected, the effect of robust standardisation is substantial since the framework produces features by down-weights outliers in data. The distances which correspond to the robust standardisation, are more aligned historically, that is, are more 'robust' when the missingness increases. It indicates that robust standardisation of data captures more efficiently the characteristics of the population distribution. Recall the earliest non-robust Mahalanobias distance of 50% case which is very distant from the statistic in the same calendar year but for the 75% missingness case. For the robust case, the corresponding distances are more aligned what demonstrates the effect of robustness.

Since the subsample of the 75% missingness case is substantially longer, we expect the PPCA results to be different as the sample captures more regimes present in demographic data. Also, the sample has higher number of missing values which are estimated using the projection based on assumption of normal distribution. It also impacts the outcomes of PPCA.

The eigenvalues of estimated covariance matrices are shown in Figure 8. Different colours of lines highlight eigenvalues which correspond to different cases of missingness. Upper panels show the results for non-robust framework whereas bottom plots for the robust one. The magnitude of eigenvalues as well as the spreads between them over different levels of accepted missingness are higher for robust case.

The 75% case of missingness results in smaller discrepancies between eigenvalues for robust and non-robust frameworks. The corresponding eigenvectors exhibit similar behaviour what is shown in Figure 9. The discrepancies between the robust and non-robust eigenvectors are more significant for the cases with smaller proportions of missing values per observation. This outcome can be justified by the fact that the case of 75% is more affected by the priori assumptions of the normal distributions. The discrepancies between two methods of standardisation got smaller as the projection of missing values starts to dominate the estimation of the principal components. The robust and non-robust estimators similarly capture the information about the normal distribution.

The blue dotted vertical lines on the plots of eigenvectors disaggregate the outcomes into developed and developing countries listed in Table 1. Regardless of the case of missingness (except 75% case) and type of the standardisation, we notice resembling features for countries from each of the groups.

We would expect the alignment of the robust scores as it has been observed for the corresponding Mahalanobias distances. However, the described PPCA methodology does not re-estimate the mean. The data is centred one during the initialisation. In the presence of missing values, their projection changes the mean and the data is centred only at the start of the procedure. This, the mean is only static when there is no missing data. This simplification of the framework results in different levels of the scores in Figure 10.

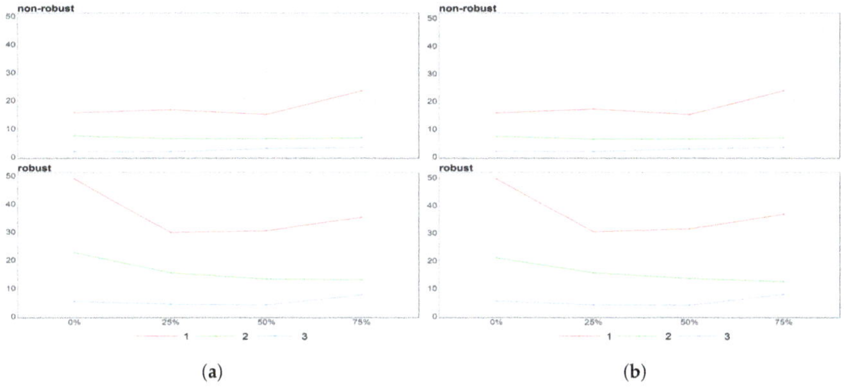

Figure 8. The eigenvalues obtained using PPCA for Females (**a**) and Males (**b**) population of Number of Birthsfor different percentages of maximal missing entries in rows (x axis). Colours of lines corresponds to different eigenvalues, first (light brown), second (dark blue) and third (dark brown) highest. Every subfigure is divided into two subplots corresponding to robust estimation of standard divinations (upper plot) and sample one (bottom plot).

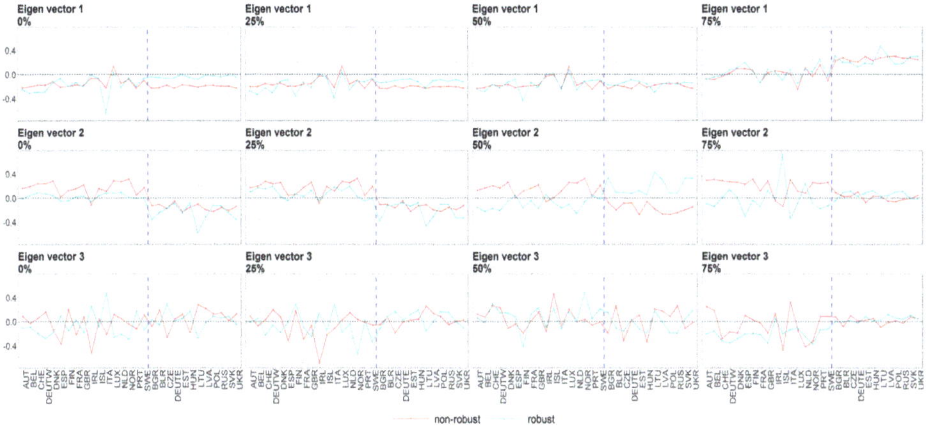

Figure 9. The eigenvectors (y axis) over the joint distribution of countries (x axis) obtained using PPCA for Females in Births. Every row of subfigure corresponds to a different eigenvector. Every column corresponds to different case of missing values (0%, 25%, 50% and 75%). The blue line corresponds to robust standardisation whereas red line to non-robust standardisation of data.

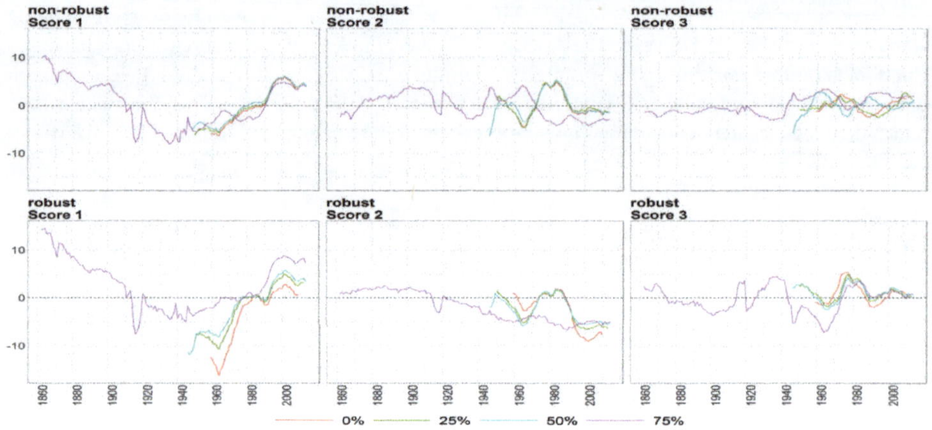

Figure 10. The scores (y axis) over time (x axis) obtained using PPCA for Females in Births. Colours of lines correspond to the scores calculated on subsample different cases of missing values (0%, 25%, 50% and 75%, refer to legend). The plots placed in the first row correspond to the results using non- robust standardization of entry data, where the second row correspond to robust standardisation. The plots scores, first, second and thirds are ordered by columns.

8.3. Life Expectancy at Birth

As mentioned in Section 7.1, Birth counts are the only data set in our analysis, which has been not modified or preprocessed before being available in HMD. The stages of several adjustments which are applied to the Death counts and population sizes result in a smaller number of outliers in Life Expectancy at Birth. The outcomes of PPCA for the data which is standardized using robust and non-robust estimators of mean and covariance matrix do not vary so significantly as in Birth counts over different proportions of missigness.

The robust Mahalanobias distances in Figure 11 are slightly more distant than their non-robust equivalents. However, the distances for different cases of missing values are similarly aligned in both cases in contrast to Birth counts. We may observe the same pattern among the scores of three principal components in Figures 15 and 16.

Figures 12, 13 and 14 show eigenvalues and eigenvectors for Females and Males respectively. Only the results for the 75% case of missingness exhibit more variation among the standardisation procedures. Since the subsample corresponding to 75% case is significantly longer, the discrepancies can be again rationalized by the two reasons: effect of the priori assumption on distributions in Section 5 and higher number of captured regimes in the data. Moreover, anakysing the outcomes from the aggregation among the European countries, we notice that the second eigenvector has opposite signs for the countries of the two countries groups. Recall that its values are more volatile for the male population of developing countries (except for the case of 75% of missing values).

The obtained scores for Life Expectancy at Birth are shown in Figures 15 and 16. The levels of scores are very close to zero. It is an expected outcome as we differenced the data since it exhibits polynomial trend. The distribution of differences is expected to have zero mean. Hence, the scores are aligned for all the cases of missingness and distributed around zero what is negligibly affected by the simplification of the discussed framework. However, the two methodologies of the standardisation result in different magnitudes of scores. Since the corresponding eigenvectors are very similar for two standardisations, the magnitude is a reliable indicator whether an observation is outlying.

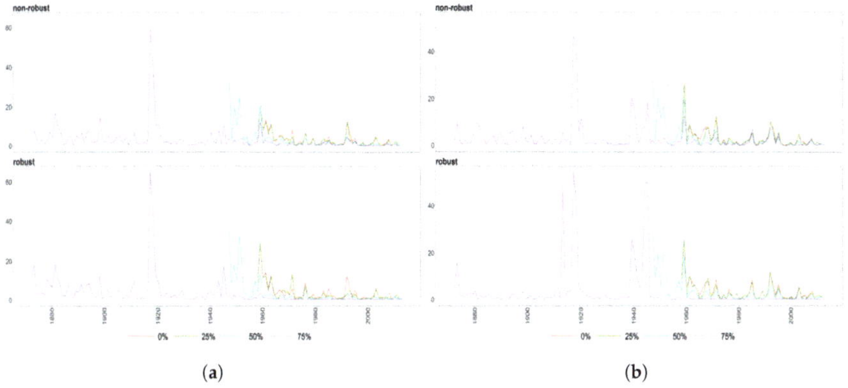

Figure 11. The Mahalanobias distances obtained using PPCA for Females (**a**) and Males (**b**) of Life Expectancy at Birth over time (x axis). Different colours of lines correspond to the cases of different percentages of maximal missing entries in rows (light blue (75%), dark brown (50%), dark blue (25%), light brown (0%)). Every subfigure is divided into two subplots corresponding to the robust estimation of standard divinations (upper plot) and sample one (bottom plot).

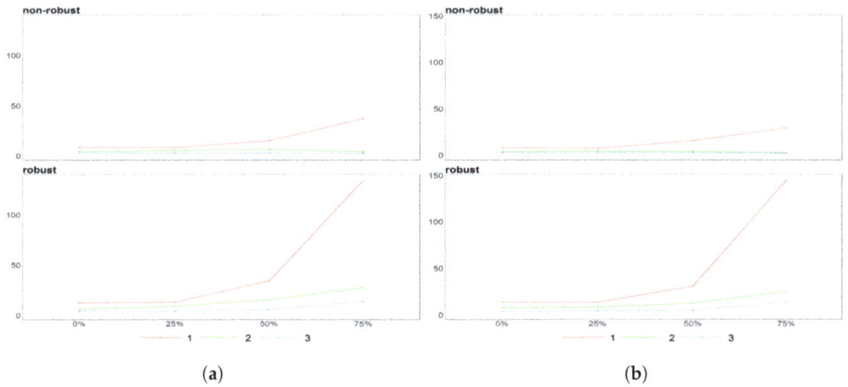

Figure 12. The eigenvalues obtained using PPCA for Females (**a**) and Males (**b**) of Life Expectancy at Birth data for different percentages of maximal missing entries in rows (x axis). Colours of lines corresponds to different eigenvalues, first (light brown), second (dark blue) and third (dark brown) highest. Every subfigure is divided into two subplots corresponding to robust estimation of standard divinations (upper plot) and sample one (bottom plot).

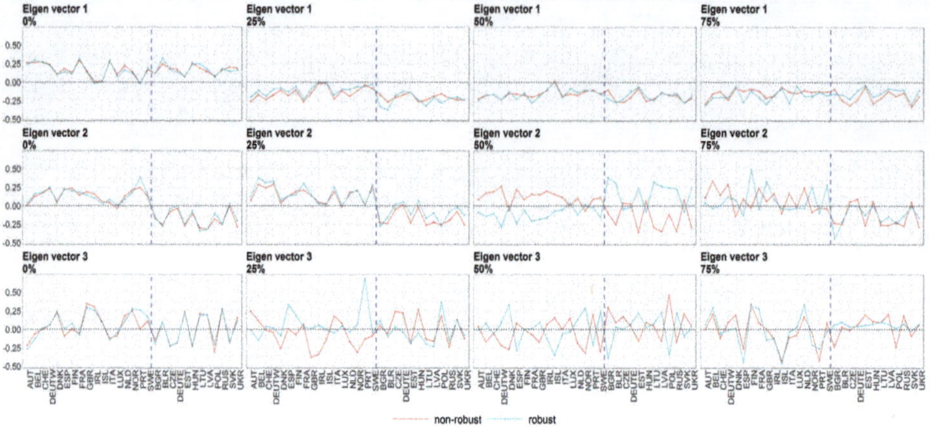

Figure 13. The eigenvectors (y axis) over the joint distribution of countries (x axis) obtained using PPCA for female population of Life Expectancy at Birth. Every row of subfigure corresponds to different eigenvector. Every column corresponds to different level of maximum missing values per observation (0%, 25%, 50% and 75%). The blue line corresponds to robust standardisation whereas red line to non-robust standardisation of data.

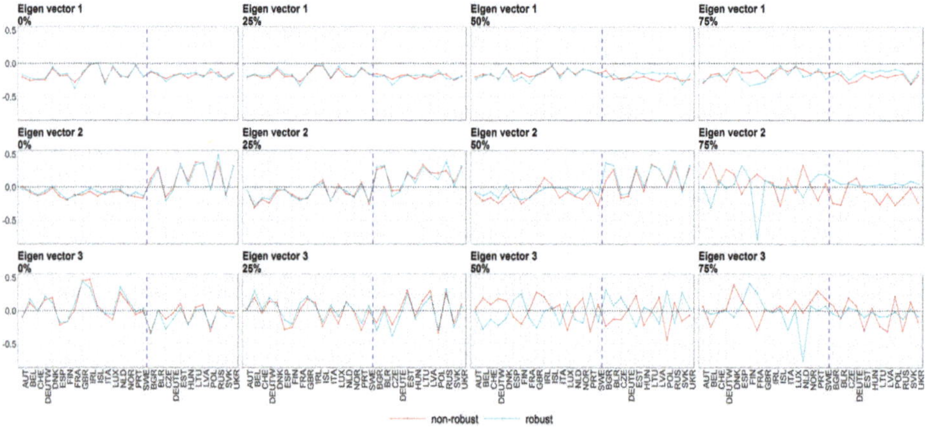

Figure 14. The eigenvectors (y axis) over the joint distribution of countries (x axis) obtained using PPCA for male population of Life Expectancy at Birth. Every row of subfigure corresponds to different eigenvector. Every column corresponds to different level of maximum missing values per observation (0%, 25%, 50% and 75%). The blue line corresponds to robust standardisation whereas red line to non-robust standardisation of data.

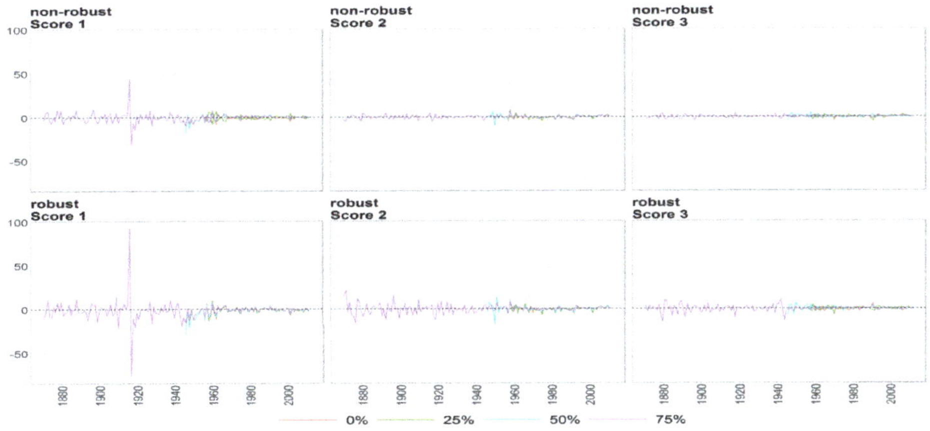

Figure 15. The scores (y axis) over time (x axis) obtained using PPCA for female population of Life Expectancy at Birth. Colours of lines correspond to the scores calculated on subsample where are different levels of maximum missing values per observation (0%, 25%, 50% and 75%, refer to legend). The plots placed in the first row correspond to the results using non- robust standardization of entry data, where the second row correspond to robust standardisation. The plots of scores are ordered by columns.

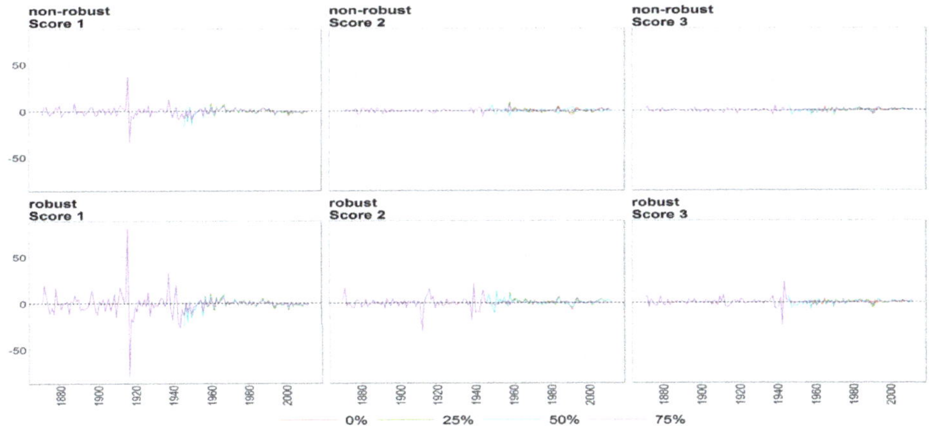

Figure 16. The scores (y axis) over the time (x axis) obtained using PPCA for Males of Life Expectancy at Birth. Colours of lines correspond to the scores calculated on subsample where are different levels of maximum missing values per observation (0%, 25%, 50% and 75%, refer to legend). The plots placed in the first row correspond to the results using non- robust standardization of entry data, where the second row correspond to robust standardisation. The plots of scores are ordered by columns.

8.4. Deaths

The Mahalanobias distances for the Deaths counts exhibit resembling behaviour for Females regardless of the standardisation procedure. The discrepancies between the statistics are more substantial for the male population what is highlighted in Figure 17.

The eigenvalues of the non-robust estimator of the covariance matrix does not vary between the cases of missingness up to 50%. The plots are shown in Figure 18. For the case 75% the first eigenvalue starts to dominate more significantly than for other missigness cases, especially for Females. On the other hand, the robust eigenvalues are more volatile. Especially the results for Females provide unexpected outcomes for the case 50% in comparison to the case 25% even though the subsamples for these cases differ only by a few calendar years in mid 1940. With regards to the Males, we observe that the dominance of first eigenvalue increases with the number of missing values.

The corresponding eigenvectors are shown in Figures 19 and 20 for Females and Males respectively. The colours of the heatmaps correspond to the magnitude of components of eigenvector which are country (x axis) and age group (y axis) specific. The non-robust estimation results in the eigenvectors with smaller magnitude and smoother within the age groups and countries. Recall, that the distribution of colours for the robust case has bigger spreads between values (so called "bumps") what is highlighted by more intense colours of blue and red. The exception is made for the case of 75%.

The vertical black dotted lines on the heatmaps divides the countries listed on x axis as developed (left side) and developing (right side). Again, this order of results stresses the differences between the eigenvectors within these two groups of countries. The first eigenvector for developing countries has the break point around age group of 40 for all cases of missingness for the male population and all cases except 50% for the female population. The eigenvector for developed countries has a break point for age group in 80 for female population and 75 for male population with additional break in 35 for 0% and 25% cases.

The case of 75 is analysed separately. The first eigenvectors do not differ within two types of standardisation but exhibit the structure which is country group specific. The developed countries are characterized by the uniformed values around zero for all age groups. The vectors of developing countries are more volatile with breaks around 20–30 for Males and even more volatile for Females. The second eigenvector differs within both types of standardisation and among two groups of countries. It is almost constant around zero for Males in developing countries and more volatile for Males in developed countries with breaks in age groups between 50 and 60. Second eigenvector for Females resembles third eigenvector of Males .

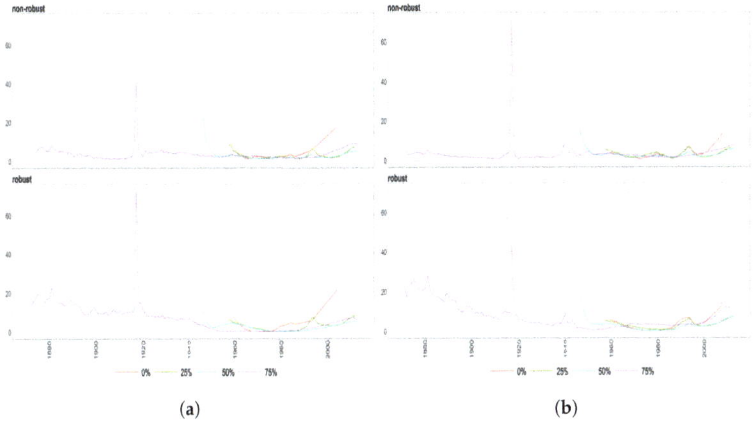

Figure 17. The Mahalanobias distances obtained using PPCA for Females (**a**) and Males (**b**) of Number of Death over time (x axis). Different colours of lines correspond to the cases of different percentages of maximal missing entries in rows (light blue (75%), dark brown (50%), dark blue (25%), light brown (0%)). Every subfigure is divided into two subplots corresponding to robust estimation of standard divinations (upper plot) and sample one (bottom plot).

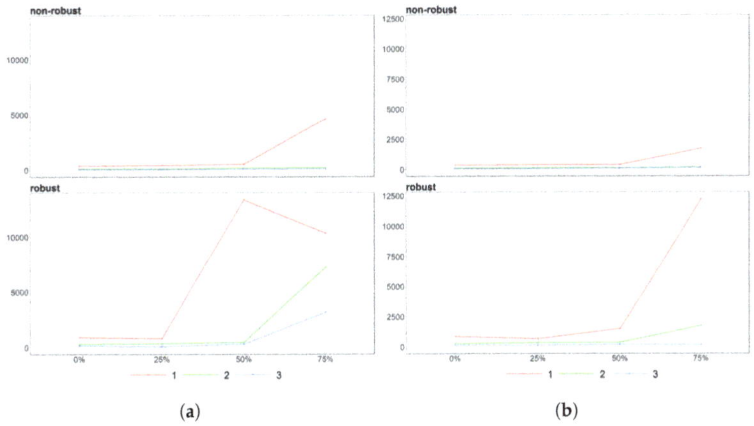

Figure 18. The eigenvalues of Deaths counts obtained using PPCA for Females (**a**) and Males (**b**) over diferent cases of missing entries (x axis). Colours of lines corresponds to different eigenvalues, first (light brown), second (dark blue) and third (dark brown) highest. Every subfigure is divided into two subplots corresponding to robust estimation of standard deviations (upper plot) and sample one (bottom plot).

The scores are presented in Figures 21 and 22. The second and third scores of Males are smoother in contrary to results for Females. The exception is made for the case 75% which results vary both among sexes and standardization procedures.

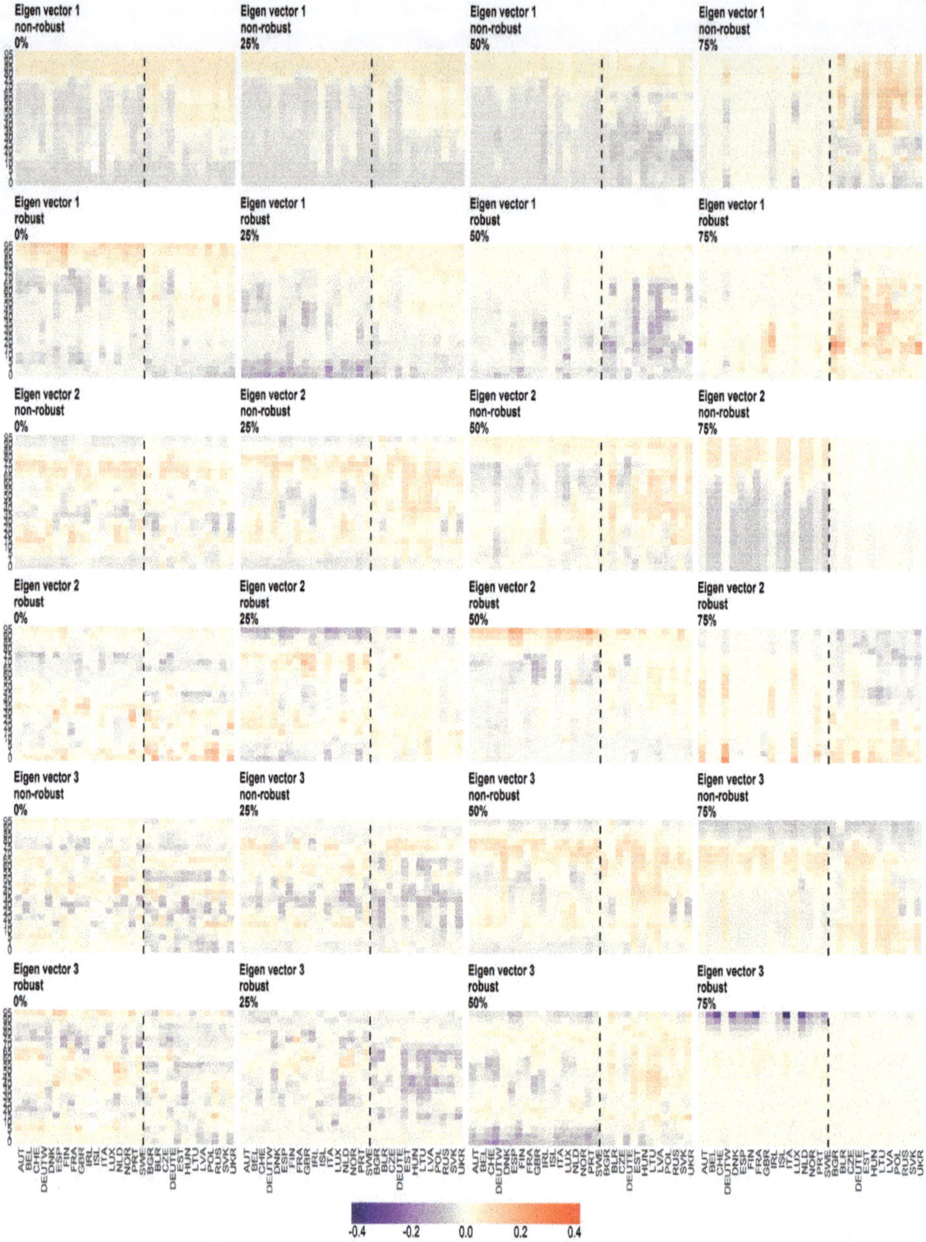

Figure 19. The eigenvectors of Death counts (y axis) over age groups (y axis) and countries (x axis) obtained using PPCA for Females. Every row of subfigure corresponds to different eigenvector. Every column corresponds to different level of maximum missing values per observation (0%, 25%, 50% and 75%). The blue line corresponds to robust standardisation whereas red line to non-robust standardisation of data.

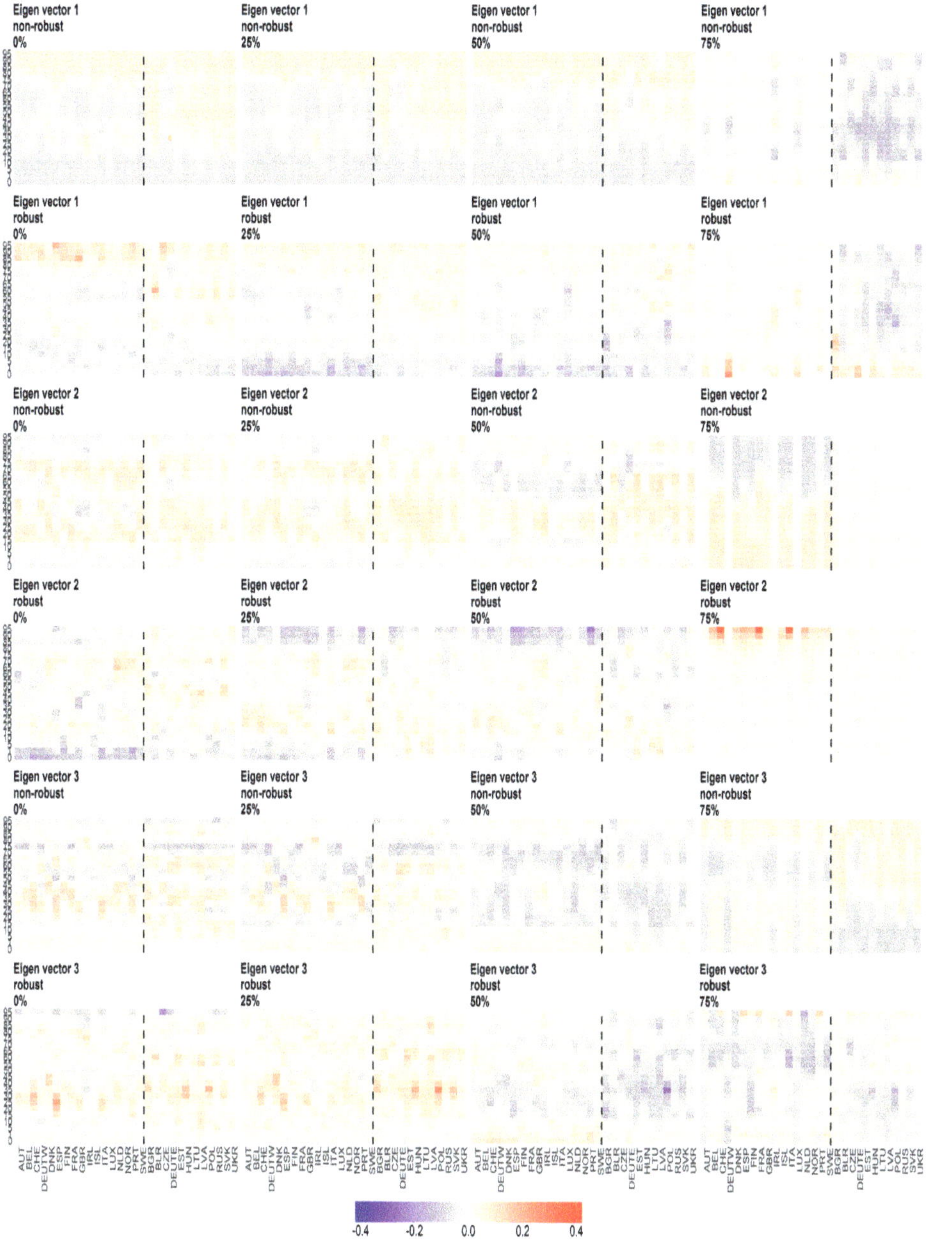

Figure 20. The eigenvectors of Death counts (y axis) over age groups (y axis) and countries (x axis) obtained using PPCA for Males . Every row of subfigure corresponds to different eigenvector. Every column corresponds to different level of maximum missing values per observation (0%, 25%, 50% and 75%). The blue line corresponds to robust standardisation whereas red line to non-robust standardisation of data.

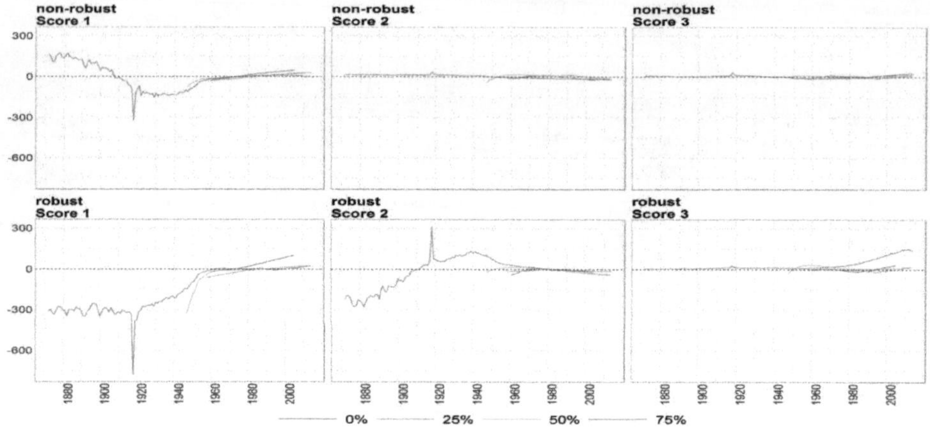

Figure 21. The scores (y axis) over time (x axis) obtained using PPCA for female population of Number of Deaths. Colours of lines correspond to the scores calculated on subsample where are different levels of maximum missing values per observation (0%, 25%, 50% and 75%, refer to legend). The plots placed in the first row correspond to the results using non- robust standardization of entry data, where the second row correspond to robust standardisation. The plots of scores are ordered by columns.

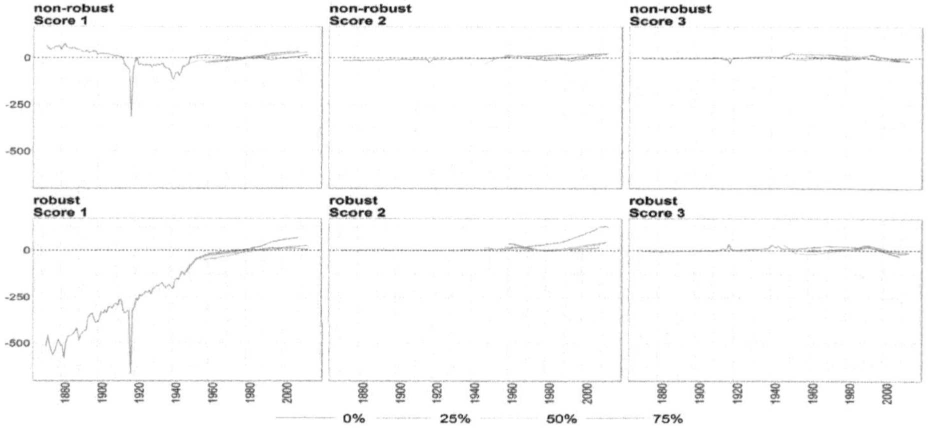

Figure 22. The scores (y axis) over time (x axis) obtained using PPCA for male population of Number of Deaths. Colours of lines correspond to the scores calculated on subsample where are different levels of maximum missing values per observation (0%, 25%, 50% and 75%, refer to legend). The plots placed in the first row correspond to the results using non- robust standardization of entry data, where the second row correspond to robust standardisation. The plots of scores are ordered by columns.

8.5. Death Rates

The analysis for Death Rates provides with similar conclusions as for Death counts. The corresponding Figures are 23, 24, 25 and 26 respectively. The only discrepancies are exhibited by the eigenvalues for Males for the 75% case as they are more aligned and higher in terms of magnitude from other cases than the corresponding eigenvalues in the Deaths counts analysis.

As shown in Figures 27 and 28 the robustification does not influenced greatly the estimation of eigenvectors. As the Deaths Rates are preprocessed and smoothed before being distributed by HMD, we again conclude that the preprocessing decreased number of outlying data points. In this particular case, the robust standardisation is similarly informative about the the true distribution as the non robust one.

Also, recall the similarity of results among different cases of missingness, especially for first eigenvector. The second and third ones are smoother for high levels of missigness. The colour map is affected by the scaling parameter $(1, -1)$ which may cause red to become blue, but except this fact, we see resembling outcomes.

The three most meaningful eigenvectors differ among two groups of analysed countries: developed and developing. The corresponding results are divided by the vertical black dotted lines. The first eigenvectors of developed countries is very smooth among age groups. For developing countries we observe U shape structure with peak in 45–60 age groups for Males and similarly for Females in the cases with small proportion of missigness. When we allow more missing values, the eigenvectors for Females in developed countries are closer to zero and flat among age groups whereas for developing countries are more distant and volatile.

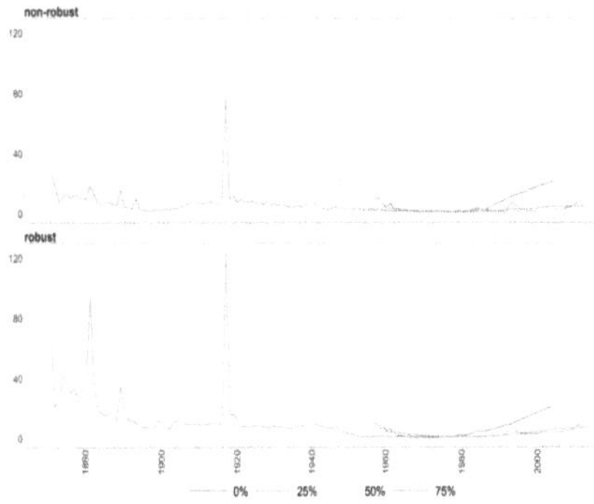

(**a**)

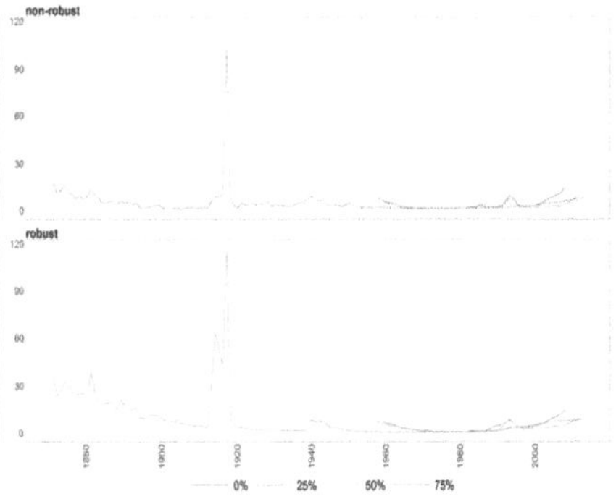

(**b**)

Figure 23. The Mahalanobias distances obtained using PPCA for female (**a**) and male (**b**) population of Death Rates over time (x axis). Different colours of lines correspond to the cases of different percentages of maximal missing entries in rows (light blue (75%), dark brown (50%), dark blue (25%), light brown (0%)). Every subfigure is divided into two subplots corresponding to robust estimation of standard divinations (upper plot) and sample one (bottom plot).

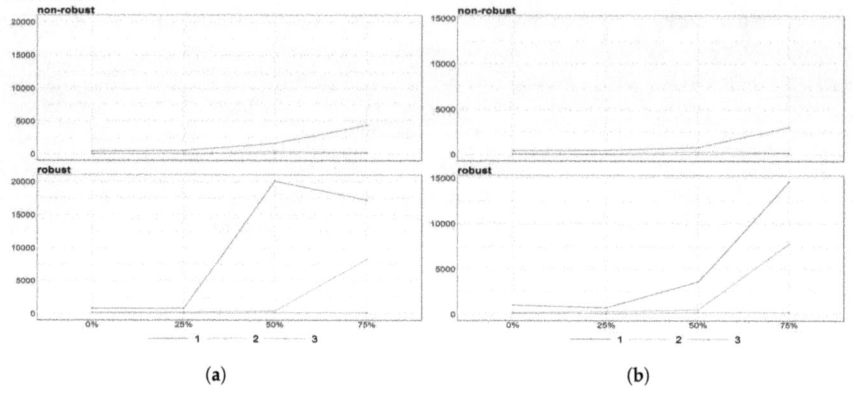

Figure 24. The eigenvalues obtained using PPCA for female (**a**) and male (**b**) population of Death Rates for different percentages of maximal missing entries in rows (x axis). Colours of lines corresponds to different eigenvalues, first (light brown), second (dark blue) and third (dark brown) highest. Every subfigure is divided into two subplots corresponding to robust estimation of standard divinations (upper plot) and sample one (bottom plot).

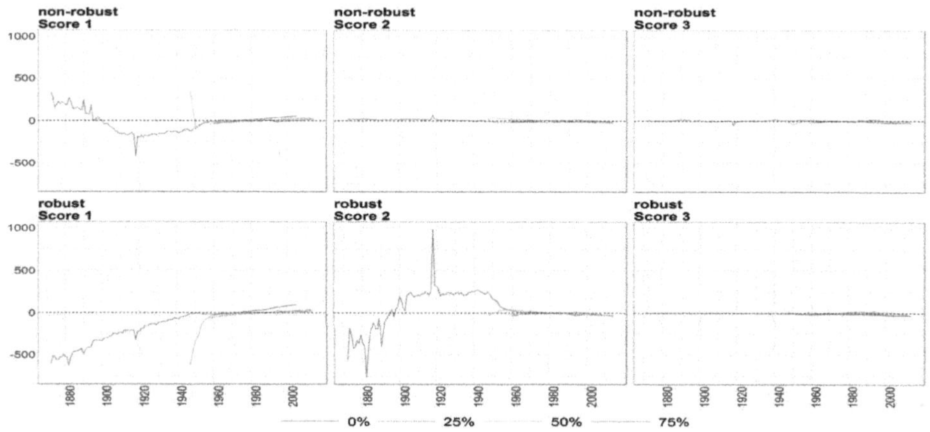

Figure 25. The scores (y axis) over time (x axis) obtained using PPCA for female population of Death Rates. Colours of lines correspond to the scores calculated on subsample where are different levels of maximum missing values per observation (0%, 25%, 50% and 75%, refer to legend). The plots placed in the first row correspond to the results using non- robust standardization of entry data, where the second row correspond to robust standardisation. The plots of scores are ordered by columns.

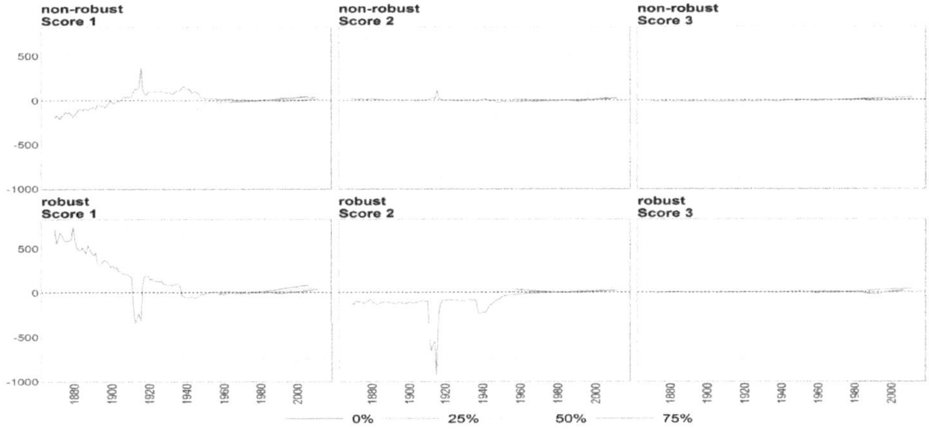

Figure 26. The scores (y axis) over time (x axis) obtained using PPCA for male population of Death Rates. Colours of lines correspond to the scores calculated on subsample where are different levels of maximum missing values per observation (0%, 25%, 50% and 75%, refer to legend). The plots placed in the first row correspond to the results using non- robust standardization of entry data, where the second row correspond to robust standardisation. The plots of scores are ordered by columns.

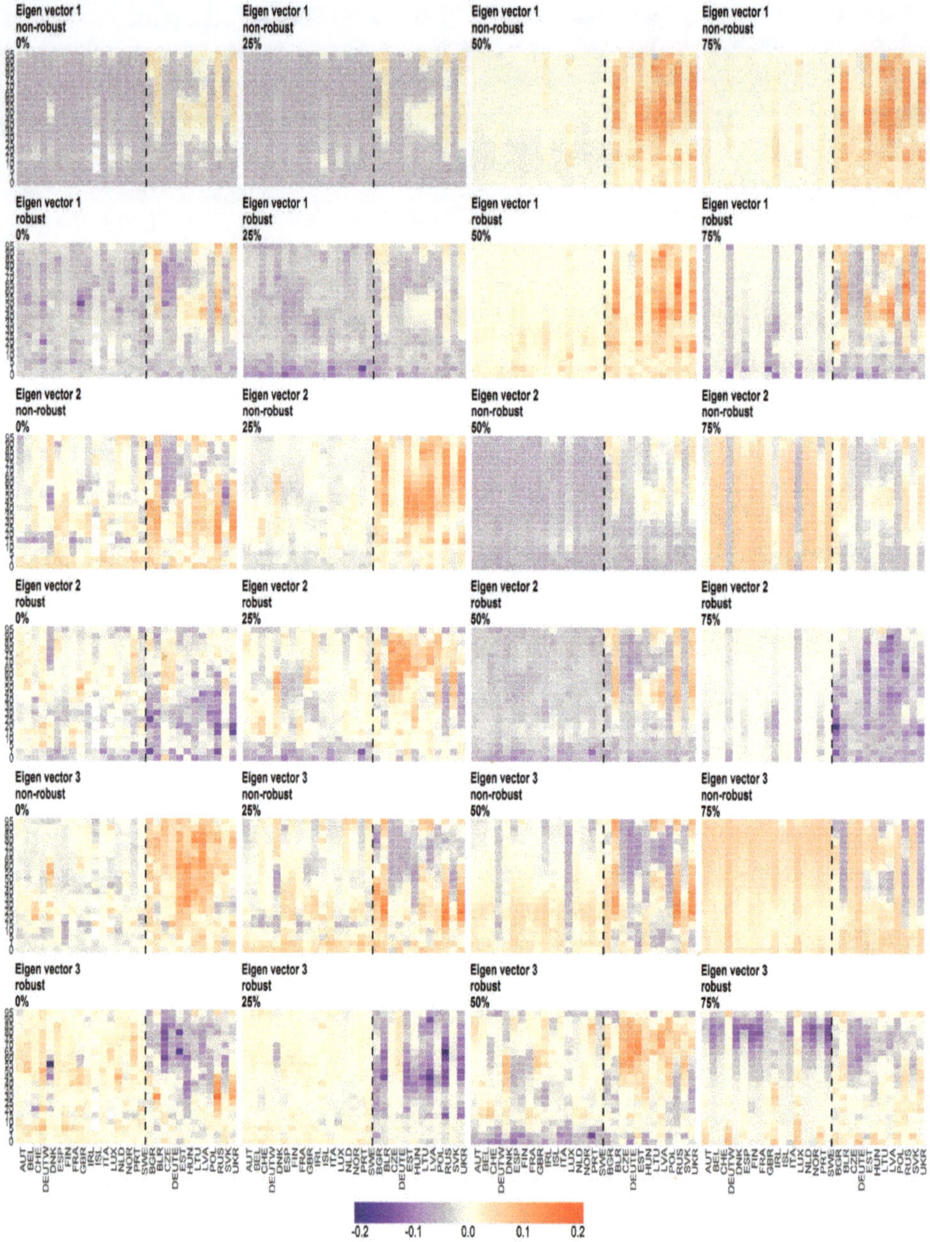

Figure 27. The eigenvectors (y axis) over the joint distribution of countries (x axis) obtained using PPCA for female population of Death Rates. Every row of subfigure corresponds to different eigenvector. Every column corresponds to different level of maximum missing values per observation (0%, 25%, 50% and 75%). The blue line corresponds to robust standardisation whereas red line to non-robust standardisation of data.

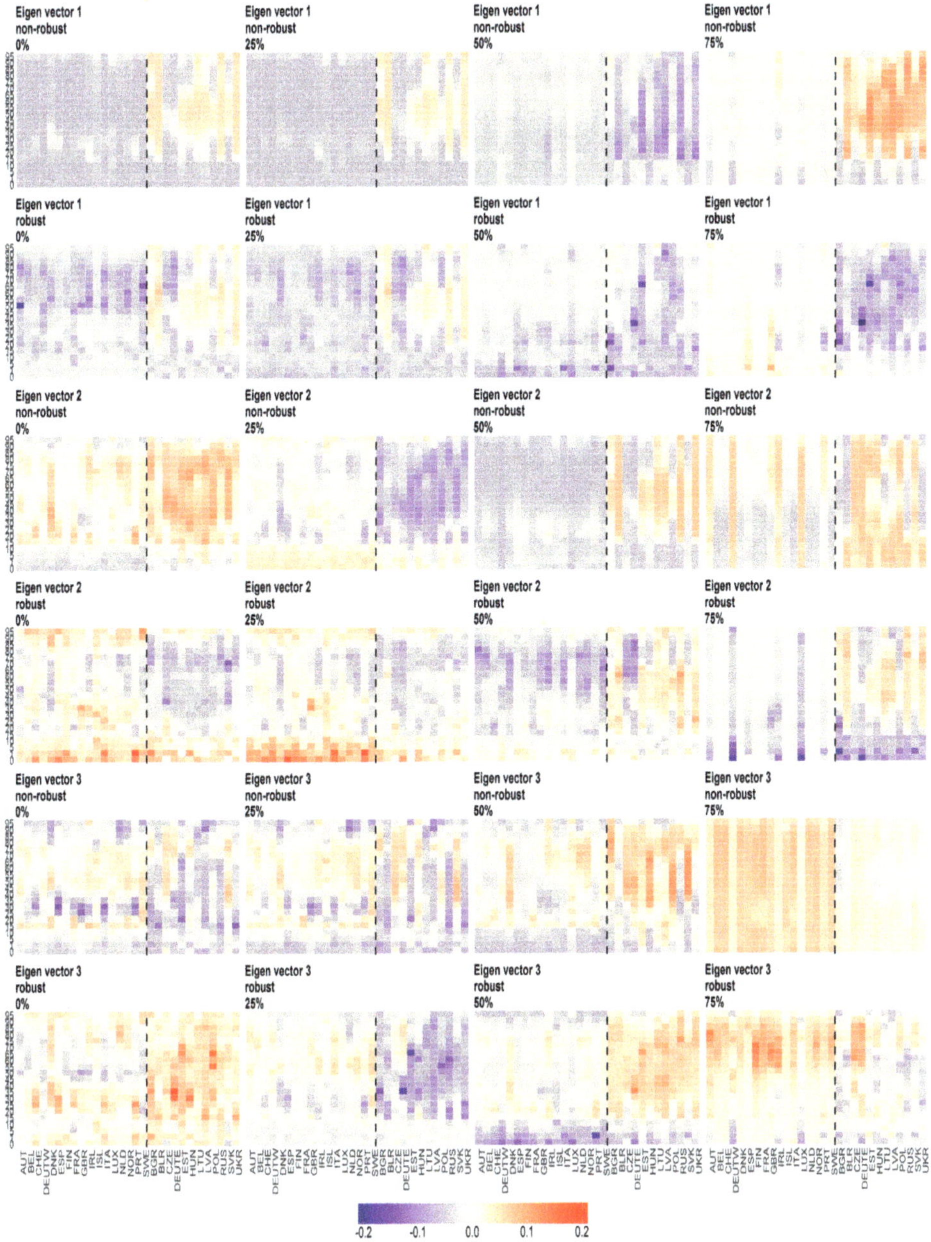

Figure 28. The eigenvectors (y axis) over the joint distribution of countries (x axis) obtained using PPCA for male population of Death Rates. Every row of subfigure corresponds to different eigenvector. Every column corresponds to different level of maximum missing values per observation (0%, 25%, 50% and 75%). The blue line corresponds to robust standardisation whereas red line to non-robust standardisation of data.

9. Stochastic Mortality Models for UK utilizing Factor Extraction from European Demographic Data

In this section we demonstrate the results of incorporating features extracted from European demographic data in the stochastic mortality model for British female mortality data over a study period of 1922 to 2014 with 10 years ahead forecasting validation.

The key findings are that the utilisation of demographic features improves the in-sample and out-of-sample predictive posterior mean Bayesian point estimation and forecasts for the log death rates. Additionally, the employed robustification methodology reduces the variances of the error terms in both observation and state equations and produces a better out-of-sample fit than its non-robust alternative. It indicates that the features extracted in the robust manner are more consistent over time and capture better the information about the true distribution of the demographic data.

The model which has the smallest mean square error of estimation and prediction adds the age-specific components to the latent process. It is later referred as DFM-PC-B. However, the other examined models, which also improve the predictability of the log death rates, are useful in terms of the interpretation as they reveal the individual country specific impacts of each of the European countries data on British female log death rates.

9.1. Description of the Models

Before presenting the real data example we note that all the Bayesian models developed and Markov chain samplers constructed were first tested on synthetic case studies in which the true parameters and state variables are known. The performance was found to be very good and this provides confidence in the accuracy and performance behaviour of the methods and models developed. The synthetic study results are provided in technical appendix and are not discussed in this paper. The use of synthetic data enables us to validate the estimation by Forward-Backward Kalman Filter with Gibbs Sampler. The models that we considered in our simulations and empirical studies are labelled by

LCC: Lee-Carter model with the stochastic cohort effect given by Equations (2) and (3);

DFM-PC: Demographic factor model which incorporates ϱ_t into LCC given by Equation (8). Please refer to Appendix B for illustration how the models from this class are created;

- **DFM-PC-B:** The mean of first principal component of Birth counts as a static parameter, age specific element of ϱ_t;
- **DFM-PC-D-r:** The first principal component of Death counts (which is age and country specific) as an exogenous factor, one element of ϱ_t corresponds to a country specific subvector of the component, robust standardisation;
- **DFM-PC-D-s:** The first principal component of Death counts (which is age and country specific) as an exogenous factor, one element of ϱ_t corresponds to a country specific subvector of the component, non-robust standardisation;
- **DFM-PC-Mx-r:** The first principal component of Death Rates (which is age and country specific) as an exogenous factor, one element of ϱ_t corresponds to a country specific subvector of the component, robust standardisation;
- **DFM-PC-Mx-s:** The first principal component of Death Rates (which is age and country specific) as an exogenous factor, one element of ϱ_t corresponds to a country specific subvector of the component, non-robust standardisation;

The models of the class DFM-PC address **Case 1** from Section 3, where factors are incorporated into the observation Equation (2). The factors are obtained by performing PPCA jointly on the set of data for all countries listed in Table 1 excluding the following specific countries: United Kingdom (as it is our response variable), Greece and Slovakia (due to short time series).

DFM-PC-B incorporates the mean of the first principal component of the Birth counts which is a country specific vector. The matrix $\tilde{\mathbf{F}}$ is a 21×21 diagonal matrix with the mean on the diagonal.

Hence, ϱ_t which correspond to the model DFM-PC-B, is a 21 dimensional, age specific state process and attempts to capture an age-specific dynamic in addition to the cohort-period effects.

The models DFM-PC-D-r, DFM-PC-D-s and DFM-PC-Mx-r and DFM-PC-Mx-s incorporate the first component of Death counts and Death Rates, respectively. Recall that the components for these data sets can be presented as age specific and country specific matrices as shown in Section 8. Due to the high dimensionality of the problem, we want the one element of ϱ_t to correspond to the subvector of the first component which is specific only for one country. Such a subvector has 21 dimensions which correspond to the age groups. Hence, ϱ_t is a 28 dimensional country specific state process. The country specific subvectors of the first components are placed in the columns of the 21×28 matrix $\tilde{\mathbf{F}}$. The last letter of the name of the models DFM-PC-D and DFM-PC-Mx denotes the type of the standardisation which is applied to the data before performing PPCA: robust (by M-estimator) or non-robust (sample estimator).

In the following part we analyse the population mortality from United Kingdom based on the models listed above and Bayesian methodology studied in this paper. We then examine the models in terms of the forecasting properties of death rates.

9.2. Setup

For the Bayesian estimation of models, we assume the priors given in the Appendix A.3 and A.4 to be

$$\begin{aligned} &\kappa_0 \sim \mathcal{N}(0,10^2), \quad ,\gamma_0 \sim \mathcal{N}(0,10^2), \quad \alpha_x \sim \mathcal{N}(0,10^2), \quad \beta_x \sim \mathcal{N}(0,10^2), \\ &\sigma_\epsilon^2 \sim \mathrm{IG}(2.01,0.01), \quad \theta \sim \mathcal{N}(0,10^2), \eta \sim \mathcal{N}(0,10^2), \quad \lambda \sim \mathcal{N}_{[-1,1]}(0,10^2), \\ &\sigma_\kappa^2 \sim \mathrm{IG}(2.01,0.01), \quad \sigma_\gamma^2 \sim \mathrm{IG}(2.01,0.01), \quad \varrho_0^i \sim \mathcal{N}(0,10^2,) \\ &[\boldsymbol{\Omega}]_{i,j} \sim \mathcal{N}(0,10^2), \quad \Psi_j \sim \mathcal{N}(0,10^2), \quad \sigma_\varrho^2 \sim \mathrm{IG}(2.01,0.01). \end{aligned}$$

The number of iterations of the Markov chain is 50,000 for LCC model and 200,000 for other models with 90% burn-in. The chain is initialised at $\boldsymbol{\alpha} = \bar{\mathbf{y}}_{1:T}$, $\beta_x = \frac{1}{21}$, $\sigma_\epsilon^2 = 0.0005$, $\theta = -0.005$, $\eta = -0.02$, $\sigma_\kappa^2 = 0.01$, $\sigma_\gamma^2 = 0.0005$, $\sigma_\varrho^2 = 1.0$, $[\boldsymbol{\Omega}]_{i,i} = \frac{1}{m}$ for m being either number of countries or number of age groups (depending on the model). The convergence of the sampler has been tested on synthetic data studies. The synthetic data study revealed that the estimation of the drift parameters corresponding to the factor state process model ϱ_t converges very slowly for shorter time series such as those found in mortality data. Thus, we decided to set these parameters to zero and do not sample them in this study.

9.3. Estimation of Static Parameters

Estimated values of the static parameters (except $\boldsymbol{\alpha}$, $\boldsymbol{\beta}$ and $\boldsymbol{\Omega}$) for the British female mortality data (1922–2003) are shown in Table 2. The rest of the estimated static parameters is displayed in Figures 29, 30 and 31. The results are shown under different models listed in the first columns of the table or indicated by the colour of lines on the plots.

The static parameters of the factor process under DFM-PC-B model are age specific. In addition to the cohort and period effect, they provide supplementary information related to the corresponding age groups. Figure 29 shows the estimated diagonal elements of the transition matrix $\boldsymbol{\Omega}$ under the model. The parameters with values close to unity indicate that the factor state process corresponding to these parameters have a slowly decreasing dynamic. The elements of the state processes which correspond to the values of parameters closer to zero, are characterized by higher decrease. The parameters which are negative and close to zero indicate that the corresponding latent state processes fluctuate around zero.

With regards to DFM-PC-B model which incorporates age specific latent processes (supplementary to cohort effect), the elements of $\boldsymbol{\Omega}$ which are positive and close to zero, describe the decreasing dynamic of the corresponding age specific processes. These latent processes are shown to have more significant impact on death rate modelling when the sample starts, however, this impact decreases over time and the cohort effect becomes sufficient to model log death rates in these age groups. For instance, recall the age groups between 70–80 in Figure 29. Such process can be interpreted as a period effects which are specific for particular age groups. The elements of $\boldsymbol{\Omega}$ which are close to unity describe the latent process which have consistent impact or its lack over the time. If they have an effect on log death rates (i.e., their domain is not close to zero), they covey age-specific information which is supplementary to cohort and period effect and consistently demanded by the model over the time.

With regards to $\boldsymbol{\Omega}$ estimated under models DFM-PC-D-r, DFM-PC-D-s and DFM-PC-Mx-r and DFM-PC-Mx-s, it refers to the country specific features. Here the parameters are related to the influences of the specific countries on British female log death rates. The plots with the estimates and their confidence intervals are displayed in Figure 31. For instance, estimates of $\boldsymbol{\Omega}$ under all models agrees on lack of effects of Austrian or Bulgarian demographic data on the log death rates over whole sample span. On the other hand, the estimate of the parameter corresponding to Belarusian eigenvector is close to unity under all models and therefore highlights the informative effect of the feature on British log mortality rates which is consistent over the times.

It is worth to point out that the values of estimated variances of the observation and state equations error terms are higher for DFM-PC-D-s and DFM-PC-Mx-s where the data has been non-robustly standardized. These models are examined to have a greater mean square error of in-sample and out-of-sample fit than their robust alternatives as shown in Table 4. Hence, the robustification procedure employed in this study improved the overall goodness of fit of the considered models. The features which have been extracted from European demographic data by means of robust estimators of mean and covariance are shown to provide the information which is consistent over the times and conveys the better knowledge about the true distribution of the demographic data sets.

Table 2. Bayesian posterior mean estimators with 95% posterior credible intervals for the estimation of the static parameters $\left(\lambda,\ \theta,\ \eta, \sigma^2_\epsilon,\ \sigma^2_\gamma,\ \sigma^2_\kappa, \sigma^2_\varrho\right)$ of $\log m_{x,t}$.

Model	λ	θ	η	σ^2_ϵ	σ^2_γ	σ^2_κ	σ^2_ϱ
LCC	0.998 (0.994; 1)	−0.154 (−0.331; 0.026)	−0.024 (−0.034; −0.014)	6.4×10^{-3} $(6\times10^{-3}; 6.9\times10^{-3})$	2×10^{-3} $(1.4\times10^{-3}; 2.8\times10^{-3})$	0.663 (0.449; 0.96)	
DFM-PC-B	0.991 (0.968; 1)	−0.332 (−0.53; −0.137)	−0.005 (−0.01; 0.002)	8×10^{-4} $(6\times10^{-4}; 9\times10^{-4})$	5×10^{-4} $(4\times10^{-4}; 7\times10^{-4})$	0.753 (0.537; 1.055)	0.049 (0.042; 0.057)
DFM-PC-D-r	0.949 (0.913; 0.992)	−0.246 (−0.415; −0.101)	0.011 (−0.002; 0.021)	1×10^{-3} $(9\times10^{-4}; 1.1\times10^{-3})$	5×10^{-4} $(4\times10^{-4}; 8\times10^{-4})$	0.39 (0.227; 0.739)	0.092 (0.074; 0.113)
DFM-PC-D-s	0.998 (0.993; 1)	−0.093 (−0.221; 0.029)	−0.019 (−0.025; −0.013)	1.3×10^{-4} $(1.1\times10^{-4}; 1.4\times10^{-4})$	8×10^{-4} $(5\times10^{-4}; 1.1\times10^{-3})$	0.324 (0.152; 0.616)	0.144 (0.114; 0.178)
DFM-PC-Mx-r	0.985 (0.959; 0.999)	−0.042 (−0.115; 0)	−0.013 (−0.02; −0.007)	8×10^{-4} $(7\times10^{-4}; 1\times10^{-3})$	6×10^{-4} $(4\times10^{-4}; 8\times10^{-4})$	0.044 (0.002; 0.116)	0.08 (0.066; 0.094)
DFM-PC-Mx-s	0.999 (0.995; 1)	−0.024 (−0.111; 0.044)	−0.02 (−0.03; −0.01)	1.2×10^{-4} $(8\times10^{-4}; 2.1\times10^{-4})$	1.7×10^{-3} $(1.2\times10^{-3}; 2.3\times10^{-3})$	0.036 (0.001; 0.137)	0.834 (0.594; 0.994)

We did not choose to calculate the MLE estimates of the parameter's in our models as it has been documented that even for the standard period-cohort type Lee-Carter stochastic mortality models, the classical MLE estimation frameworks can produce convergence and estimation challenges due to gradient based and method of scoring recursive optimization methods getting stuck in local optima of the marginal likelihood surface. We refer the interested reader to the paper Fung et al. (2017) where we discuss such issues in more depth. Therefore, instead of resolving the known problems that may arise with classical MLE estimations of such models, which may be further compounded in the extended models we developed in the frequentist setting, we have chosen to stick with the Bayesian modelling paradigm and to report an analogue result to the MLE that may be obtained from Bayesian inference, in the case of uninformative priors. That is we have relative uninformative priors and so we can report the Maximum a-postiori (MAP) posterior mode estimator for the parameters as the Bayesian analogue of the MLE, defined as

$$\boldsymbol{\psi}^{MAP} = \underset{\boldsymbol{\psi}}{\text{argmax}}\, \pi(\varrho_{0:T}, \boldsymbol{\psi}|\mathbf{y}_{1:T}) \tag{97}$$

for $\pi\left(\varrho_{0:T}, \boldsymbol{\psi}|\mathbf{y}_{1:T}\right)$ being a joint posterior density of the states $\varrho_{0:T}$ and the vector of static parameters $\boldsymbol{\psi}$ given the observation $\mathbf{y}_{1:T}$ as introduced in Appendix A.

The MAP estimates and MLE should be similar in the case of uninformative priors, with the advantage that the MAP estimation is obtained via an MCMC sampler output, which is less prone to the types of estimation challenges experienced in gradient descent methods working directly with the Instead, as we used fairly uninformative priors, note that the MAP estimate of the posterior is a case of uninformative priors will correspond to MLE estimates. Please refer to Table 3 for the analogous of point estimates to the outcomes of Table 2.

Table 3. The MAP estimates of the static parameters $\left(\lambda,\ \theta,\ \eta, \sigma^2_\epsilon,\ \sigma^2_\gamma,\ \sigma^2_\kappa, \sigma^2_\varrho\right)$ of $\log m_{x,t}$.

Model	λ	θ	η	σ^2_ϵ	σ^2_γ	σ^2_κ	σ^2_ϱ
LCC	0.999	−0.155	−0.024	0.0064	0.0019	0.6172	–
DFM-PC-B	0.998	−0.331	−0.005	8.00×10^{-4}	5.00×10^{-4}	0.7279	0.0487
DFM-PC-D-r	0.948	−0.253	0.012	0.001	5.00×10^{-4}	0.3234	0.0895
DFM-PC-D-s	0.999	−0.095	−0.02	0.0013	7.00×10^{-4}	0.3005	0.1416
DFM-PC-Mx-r	0.995	−0.023	−0.012	7.00×10^{-4}	6.00×10^{-4}	0.029	0.0818
DFM-PC-Mx-s	1	−0.023	−0.021	9.00×10^{-4}	0.0016	0.0088	0.8583

9.4. Filtering of Latent Variables

The Bayesian posterior mean estimates of the latent stochastic mortality factors in the models for κ_t in the top panel and for γ^0_t in the bottom panel of Figure 32. The colours of lines denote the filtered processes under different models. As expected, adding new state variables related to the factors significantly changes the dynamics of the period and cohort effect state processes. The blue line correspond to the cohort=period only LCC model. The increase of κ_t and decrease of γ^0_t at the end of the sample is greater for this model in contrast to the the other examined models.

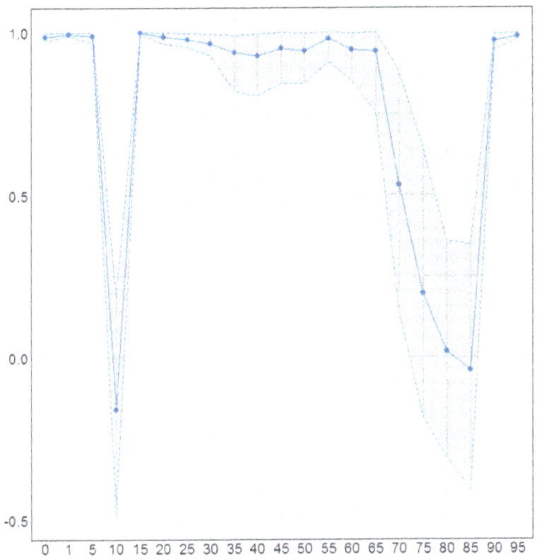

Figure 29. Bayesian posterior mean estimators with 95% posterior credible intervals for the estimation of the age-specific diagonal elements of the transition matrix $\boldsymbol{\Omega}$ (x axis) under DFM-PC-B.

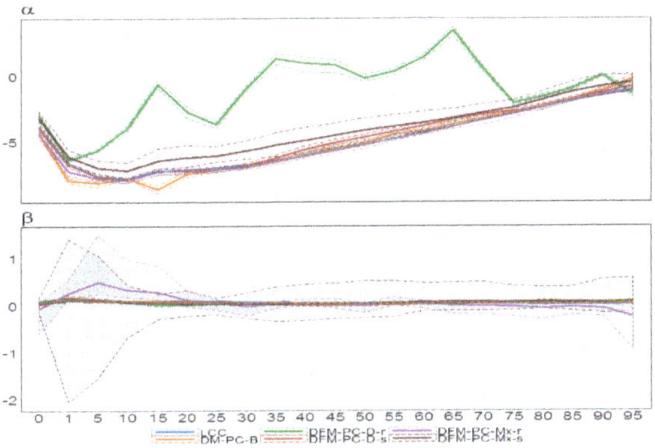

Figure 30. Bayesian posterior estimators with 95% posterior credible intervals for the estimation of $\boldsymbol{\alpha}$ and $\boldsymbol{\beta}$ under different models (colours of lines) for British female mortality data (1922–2002).

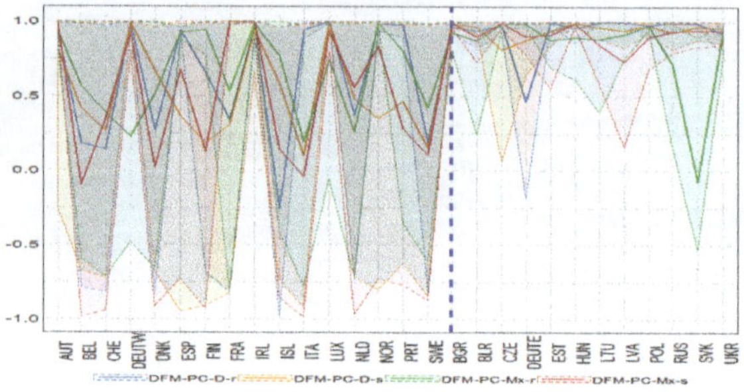

Figure 31. Bayesian posterior mean estimators with 95% posterior credible intervals for the estimation of the diagonal elements of the transition matrix $\boldsymbol{\Omega}$ (x axis) under DFM-PC-D-r, DFM-PC-D-s, DFM-PC-Mx-r and DFM-PC-Mx-s models (colours of lines). The dashed blue line divides the set of countries into developed (on the left side) and developing (on the right hand side) European countries, respectively.

The dynamic of the cohort effect latent process vector γ_t over time, which is age group specific, is shown in Figure 34. The panels correspond to the Bayesian posterior mean estimates of the process under different models. The age group specific features, which has been utilised in DFM-PC-B model, clearly provide LCC model with supplementary information to the cohort effect state processes. The corresponding ϱ_t reduces the variability of the cohort effect process with comparison to the cohort effect estimated under LCC model (the colours of the surface on DFM-PC-B panel are plain and variance of the error term is smaller). The state processes corresponding to the factors under DFM-PC-B model are shown in Figure 33. Recall that in the contrast to the cohort and period effects processes, the latent process vector ϱ_t under the model DFM-PC-B has age group specific stochastic components (κ_t is calendar year specific and γ_t is '0' age group and calendar year specific). As κ_t latent process estimated under DFM-PC-B is not distant from the corresponding estimated under LCC model for majority of the sample, we can conclude that the additional state processes given by this model provide supplementary, age-specific information to the cohort effect process γ_t^0.

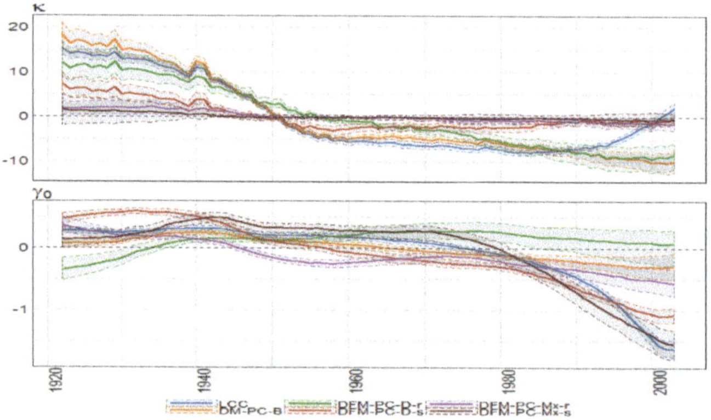

Figure 32. The Bayesian posterior mean estimates with 95% posterior credible intervals for κ_t (upper panel) and cohort effect state process γ_t^0 (lower panel) under different models (colours of lines) for British female log death rates during 1922–2002.

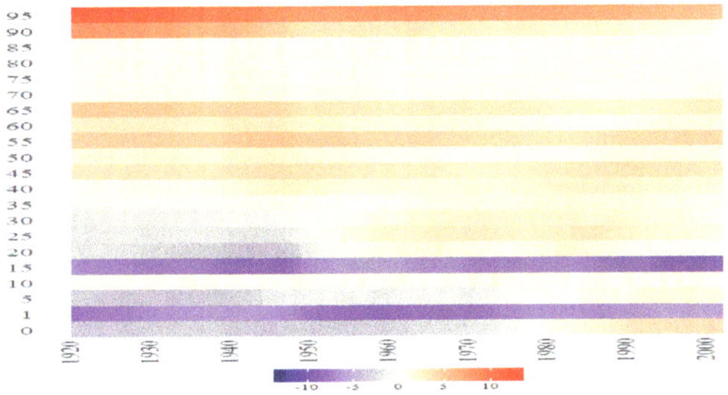

Figure 33. The Bayesian posterior mean estimates for ϱ_t across age groups (y axis) over time (x axis) under DFM-PC-B model for British female log death rates during 1922–2002.

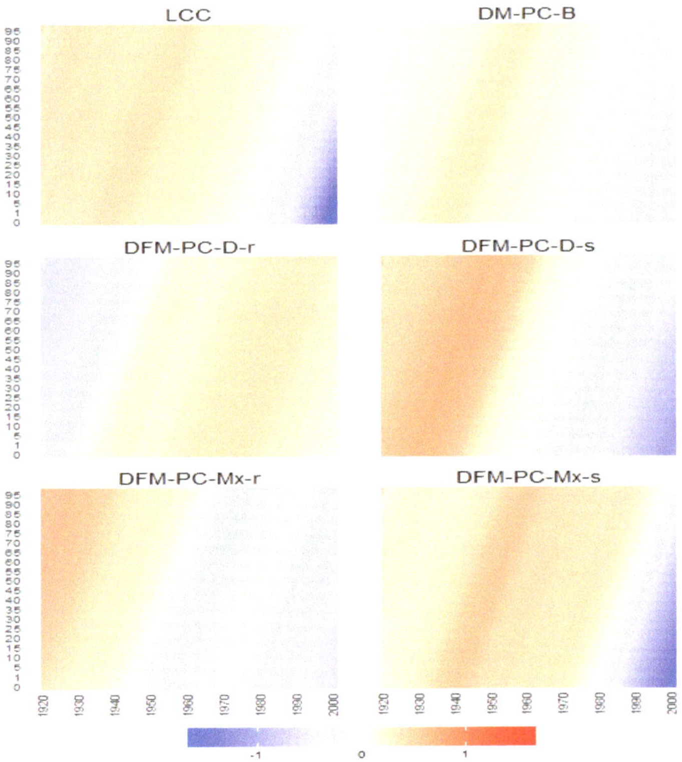

Figure 34. The Bayesian posterior mean estimates for the cohort effect latent processes vector γ_t across age groups (y axis) over time (x axis) under different models for British female log death rates during 1922–2002.

The models DFM-PC-D-r, DFM-PC-D-s, DFM-PC-Mx-r and DFM-PC-Mx-s are characterized by the processes which correspond to the country specific vectors with elements related to age groups.

The models attempt to address the question whether the structure of demographic data from European countries can be an efficient explanatory variable for British mortality. Figures 32 and 34 show that dynamics of period and cohort effect state processes are sensitive to different sets of features extracted from demographic data as well as a standardisation methodology. Figures 33 and 35 provide insight into how these variables change the information extracted from the models. The information highlight the impact of the first components of the considered countries on British mortality rates. As the components are orthonormal, $\varrho_t^{country}$ indicates the magnitude of this effect. To be consistent with the country set specific notation from Section 8, the blue vertical line divides the results into two categories: results for the developed countries (below the blue line) and developing countries (above the blue line). The processes which moves closely to zero give information that the data of country they correspond to has small influence on the mortality rates from United Kingdom. The developed models when incorporating the demographic features from the European countries, indicate the significance of the factor loading from a given country on the mortality of UK. Hence, we can specify the countries which has a positive effect on the mortality of United Kingdom (factor state processes are negative), neutral (factor state processes are fluctuate around zero) or negative (factor state processes are positive and enlarge log death rates).

For a given model it is not true that all factors which correspond to the age specific vectors of features from European countries, have an influence in the causal fashion on the UK morality data in the same way. As such, what we are showing in the plots Figure 31 (or Figure 29 for DFM-PC-B models) that some countries have very wide posterior credible intervals (the flat posterior) for $\boldsymbol{\Omega}$ which is in an alignment with the findings in Figure 36 (Figure 33 for DFM-PC-B model) where we see that indeed for those countries the ϱ_t upon a model indicate insignificant effect on UK log mortality rate. Let us consider the example of DFM-PC-Mx-s (the red colours of lines on both of the plots) for Belgium (BEL) and Austria (AUT). We see in Figure 36, that the effect of Austrian factor to the British mortality data, expressed by the dynamic of ϱ_{AUT}, is non-zero over the time. On the other has, the element of ϱ_t corresponding to Belgium, labelled by ϱ_{BEL} does not load significantly in any way on the UK mortality experience. As a consequence we see that the posterior for this country on $\boldsymbol{\Omega}$ is also very flat when the credit intervals of Ω_{AUT} on Austria are significantly narrower. This simply means that the factor loading of Belgium does not influence the UK mortality experience.

Hence, to conclude this discussion, we note that when we look at the results in Figure 36, they show the effect of each individual countries influence on the UK mortality experience. In fact, what we learn is that some countries have a mean of 0 with large uncertainty, these countries maybe interpreted as not having an influence on the mortality experience of the UK.

The four models are more consistent about the set of countries which does not have any effect on the log death rates of United Kingdom Females. The models corresponding to the non-robust standardisation indicate bigger impact of western Europe countries whereas their robust alternatives indicate the significance of the patterns from Easter and Central Europe countries as Lithua, Poland or Russia.

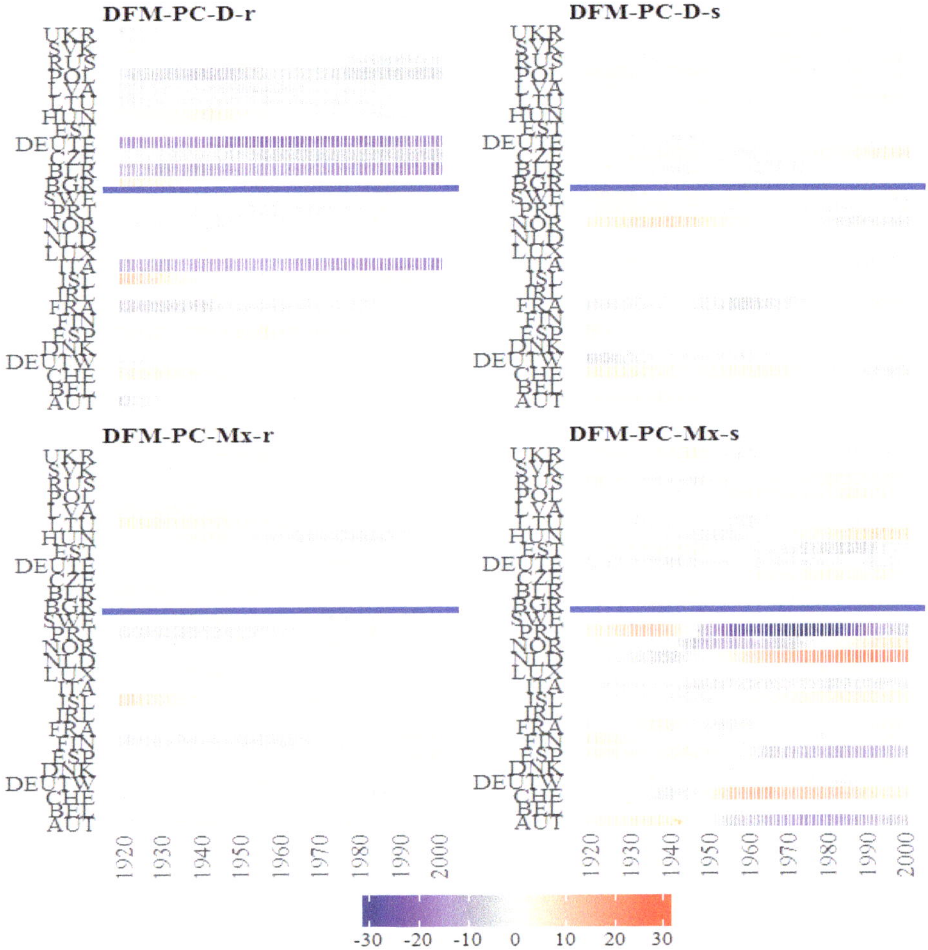

Figure 35. The Bayesian posterior mean estimates for ϱ_t across countries (y axis) over time (x axis) under the models from the classes DFM-PC-D and DFM-PC-Mx for British female log death rates during 1922–2002. The vertical blue line divides sets into developed (on the left side) and developing (on the right sie) European countries.

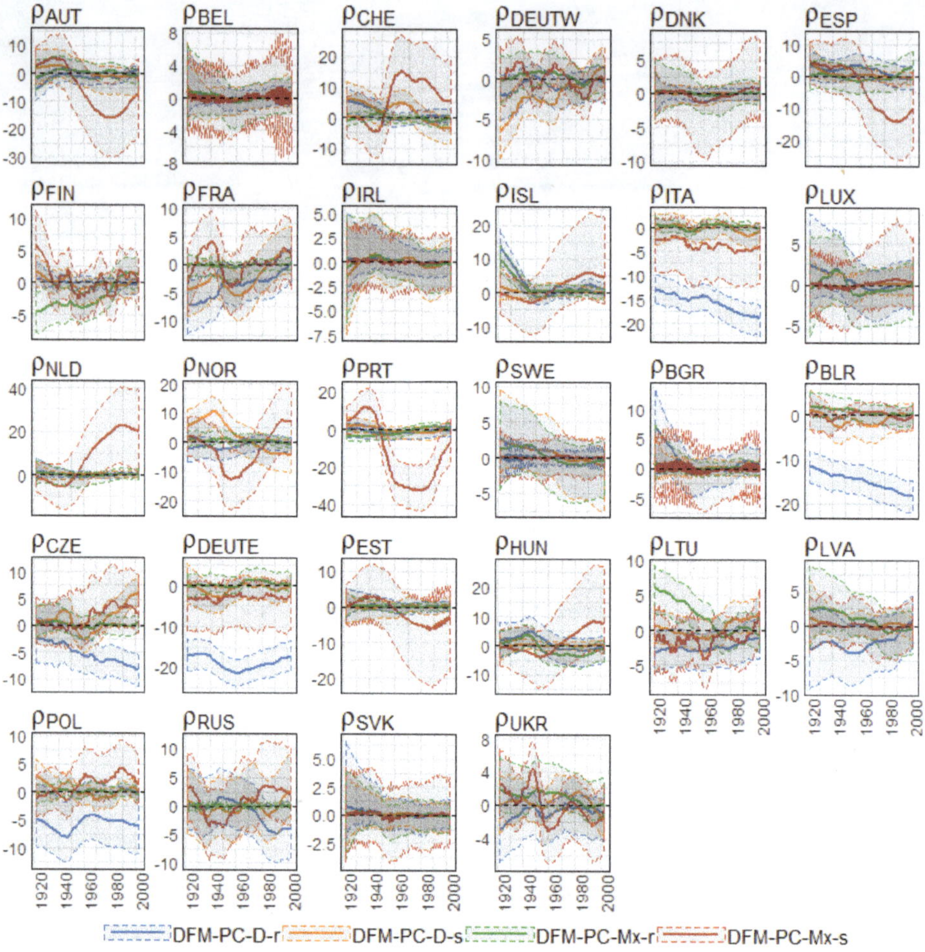

Figure 36. The Bayesian posterior mean estimates with 95% posterior credible intervals for ϱ_t across countries (different panels) overtime (x axis) under the models from the classes DFM-PC-D and DFM-PC-Mx (colours of lines) for British female log death rates during 1922–2002.

9.5. In-Sample and Out-of-Sample Performance

In this section, we investigate the in-sample and out-of-sample performance of the mortality models summarized in the introduction to this section. The model selection is based on two in-sample performance measures, MSE (Mean Square Error) and DIC (Deviance Information Criterion), whereas the forecasting performance examined based on MSEP (Mean Square Error of Prediction) using two forecasting distributions of log death rates, the one obtained by Gibbs sampler and the one provided by Kalman Filter.

9.5.1. Model Selection

The device information criterion is a popular measure in Bayesian setting which trades off model fit against its complexity (the effective of parameters) as introduced in (Spiegelhalter et al. 2002). Among the various versions of DIC we decided to use so-called conditional DIC which treats the latent states as parameters when calculating the conditional loglikelihood, for details please refer to (Celeux et al. 2006). The conditional loglikelihood if given by

$$\log \mathcal{L}_{\mathbf{y}_t|\boldsymbol{\varphi}_t,\boldsymbol{\psi}}\left(\boldsymbol{\psi},\boldsymbol{\varphi}_{1:N};\mathbf{y}_{1:N}\right) = -\frac{1}{2}\sum_{x=x_1}^{x_p}\sum_{t=1}^{N}\left(\log 2\pi\sigma_\epsilon^2 + \frac{\left(y_{x,t} - \alpha_x - [\tilde{\boldsymbol{B}}]_{x,\cdot}\boldsymbol{\varphi}_t\right)^2}{\sigma_\epsilon^2}\right) \tag{98}$$

By denoting $\boldsymbol{\psi} = (\boldsymbol{\varphi}_t, \boldsymbol{\psi})$ we define the deviance of the model as follows

$$D(\boldsymbol{\psi}) := -2\log \mathcal{L}_{\mathbf{y}_t|\boldsymbol{\psi}}\left(\boldsymbol{\psi};\mathbf{y}_{1:N}\right). \tag{99}$$

The function h as it is independent of the model specifications, is usually considered to be equal to 1. Hence, the effective number of parameters is defined as

$$p_D := \bar{D}(\boldsymbol{\psi}) - D(\bar{\boldsymbol{\psi}}) \tag{100}$$

where $\bar{D}(\boldsymbol{\psi})$ is a mean of deviance over different samples of the vector $\boldsymbol{\psi}$ and $D(\bar{\boldsymbol{\psi}})$ is a deviance of the posteriori mean of the vector of parameters
$bm\psi$. The DIC then is defined as

$$DIC := \bar{D}(\boldsymbol{\psi}) + p_D = 2\bar{D}(\boldsymbol{\psi}) - D(\bar{\boldsymbol{\psi}}) \tag{101}$$

which can be calculated using the MCMC samples.

In addition to DIC, we calculate the mean square errors (MSE) for considered models, defined as the mean of the difference between the observed data, $\mathbf{y}_t$, and the mean of the in-sample one-step ahead model forecast given by Kalman Filter, $\mathbf{f}_t = \mathbb{E}[\mathbf{y}_t|\boldsymbol{\psi}, \mathbf{y}_{1:(t-1)}]$ given in Equation (A3b). Therefore, we define $\mathbf{e}_t := \mathbf{y}_t - \mathbf{f}_t$ and

$$\text{MSE}(\bar{\boldsymbol{\psi}}) := \mathbb{E}\left[\mathbf{e}_t\mathbf{e}_t^T\right] \tag{102}$$

where for the point estimator of the vector of static parameters $\boldsymbol{\psi}$ we use the vector of posterior means.

9.5.2. Forcasting Distribution

The Bayesian state-space framework allows us to obtain the forecasting distributions using MCMC samples given by

$$\pi\left(\mathbf{y}_{T+m}|\mathbf{y}_{1:T}\right) = \int \pi\left(\mathbf{y}_{T+m}|\boldsymbol{\varphi}_{T+m},\boldsymbol{\psi}\right)\pi\left(\boldsymbol{\varphi}_{T+m}|\boldsymbol{\varphi}_{T+m-1},\boldsymbol{\psi}\right)...\pi\left(\boldsymbol{\varphi}_T,\boldsymbol{\psi}|\mathbf{y}_{1:T}\right)d\boldsymbol{\psi}d\boldsymbol{\varphi}_{T:T+m} \tag{103}$$

where $\boldsymbol{\psi}$ is the static parameter vector and $\boldsymbol{\varphi}_t$ is a state process vector. Following [104 lcstatespace], by sampling recursively, we obtain the following forecasting distributions, when (i) denotes a sample

$$\begin{aligned}\boldsymbol{\varphi}_{T+k}^{(i)} &\sim \mathcal{N}\left(\tilde{\boldsymbol{\Lambda}}^{(i)}\boldsymbol{\varphi}_{T+k-1}^{(i)} + \tilde{\boldsymbol{\Theta}}^{(i)}, \tilde{\boldsymbol{\Upsilon}}^{(i)}\right)\\ \mathbf{y}_{T+k}^{(i)} &\sim \mathcal{N}\left(\boldsymbol{\alpha}^{(i)} + \tilde{\mathbf{B}}_t^{(i)}\boldsymbol{\varphi}_{T+k-1}^{(i)} + \tilde{\boldsymbol{\Theta}}^{(i)}, \sigma_\epsilon^{2(i)}\mathbb{I}_d\right).\end{aligned} \tag{104}$$

Alternatively, we can use the forecasting distribution given by the Kalman Filter, that is

$$\begin{aligned}\boldsymbol{\varphi}_{T+k} &\sim \mathcal{N}\left(\tilde{\boldsymbol{\Lambda}}\boldsymbol{\varphi}_{T+k-1} + \tilde{\boldsymbol{\Theta}}, \tilde{\boldsymbol{\Upsilon}}\right)\\ \mathbf{y}_{T+k} &\sim \mathcal{N}\left(\boldsymbol{\alpha} + \tilde{\mathbf{B}}_t\boldsymbol{\varphi}_{T+k-1} + \tilde{\boldsymbol{\Theta}}, \sigma_\epsilon^2\mathbb{I}_d\right).\end{aligned} \tag{105}$$

for the static parameters which has been estimated by averages within sampled realisation provided by the Gibbs sampler. Let us define mean square error of prediction function as follow

$$\text{MSEP}(\boldsymbol{\psi}) := \mathbb{E}\left[\left(\mathbf{y}_{T+k} - \mathbb{E}\left[\mathbf{y}_{T+k}|\mathbf{y}_{1:T}, \boldsymbol{\psi}\right]\right)\left(\mathbf{y}_{T+k} - \mathbb{E}\left[\mathbf{y}_{T+k}|\mathbf{y}_{1:T}, \boldsymbol{\psi}\right]\right)^{T}\right]. \tag{106}$$

Therefore the mean square error of prediction using MCMC distribution is calculated as a mean of MSEP($\boldsymbol{\psi}$) over different samples of the vector $\boldsymbol{\psi}$ and denoted by MSEP_{MCMC}. The mean square error of prediction using the distribution provided by Kalman Filter is calculated the posterior mean of the vector of parameters $\boldsymbol{\psi}$.

9.5.3. Comparison of the Models

We choose for out-of-sample study last 10 years of the available sample for British Female death rates. The calibration period is 1922–2002. The Table 4 summarizes the calculated mean squared errors of the estimated observations using Kalman Filter (MSE), deviance information criterion (DIC) and mean square errors of predictions using the MCMC distribution (MSEP_{MCMC}) and the Kalman Filter distribution (MSEP_{Kalman}). The results confirm that adding the features, which has been extracted from demographic data, as an additional explanatory variable to the LCC model improves both in-sample fit out-of-sample fit and therefore the predictability of log death rates. The plots with age group specific prediction results can be found in Figure 37.

Table 4. Mean square error of the fit of the models to the data (MSE), deviance information criterion (DIC) and mean square errors of predictions using forecasting distributions given by MCMC samples (MSEP_{MCMC}) and Kalman Filter (MSEP_{Kalman}).

Model	MSE	DIC	MSEP_{MCMC}	MSEP_{Kalman}
LCC	0.0097	−3627	0.1778	0.1774
DFM-PC-B	0.0072	−6500	0.0057	0.0062
DFM-PC-D-r	0.0182	−6380	0.0177	0.0251
DFM-PC-D-s	0.0065	−5996	0.0185	0.0156
DFM-PC-Mx-r	0.0081	−8225	0.0111	0.0129
DFM-PC-Mx-s	0.0174	−3951	0.0692	0.0285

For the in-sample performance, the MSE and DIC agree to the group of two best performing models, DFM-PC-B and DFM-PC-Mx-r, however are conflicted with regards to the group of two worse performing models. Due to assessing the performance of the model considering its complexity, DIC more successfully captures the models which result in poorest out-of-sample performance, LCC and DFM-PC-Ms respectively. Especially it is worth to notice significant over-fitting of the LCC model which is further investigated in Section 10. Recall, that using MSE as model selection criterion would not be sufficient to choose the model with good performance. In terms of MSE, the in-sample performance of LCC model is comparable to DFM-PC-B model, while DIC labels the model as one with the worse explanatory power.

10. Additional Remarks on Modelling and Forecasting Results

While conducting the study we encountered two issues which are worth separate discussion, the influence of the stratification on the class of Lee-Carter models and the intuition behind the vector $\boldsymbol{\alpha}$ in the model Equation (8) when we incorporate the demographic features.

10.1. The Affect of the Stratification and Identification Constraints on Estimation of Stochastic Lee-Carter Type Models

We draw the readers attention at this point to the substantially lower predictive accuracy of the Lee-Carter cohort (LCC) model in comparison to the models which employ demographic factors, as shown in Table 4. This is especially important since such LCC models, without factors have been previously documented to have better out-of-sample performance for UK data when no age stratification is applied.

We explain the steps we have taken to explore this feature that the reviewer has pointed out. Firstly, we clarify this is not a problem with the sampler or the prior specification, rather it is related to the particular suitability of different model structures under particular assumptions in the model. We explore this, specifically with respect to age group stratification and its influence on the model fit and performance.

Please note that the stratification was adopted, where we looked at 20 sets of age groups in 5 year buckets to reduce the dimensionality of the model, of course this can influence the model fit and the assumptions made regarding model simplification and cohort interpretation. Therefore, we decided to include additional studies to investigate these effects more carefully and in the process we believe we may also address the question raised by the reviewer on this point. Our attention has been drawn to two points: rapid increase of κ_t in 2000 and the substantially lower predictive accuracy of Lee-Carter cohort (LCC) model in comparison to the models which employ demographic factors as shown in Table 3. Since the LCC model has been documented to has better out-of-sample explanatory power for the UK data when there is no stratification, we decided to undertake an additional investigation. In particular, in this new class of studies, we explore in more detail the effect of age stratification and the appropriate choice of adjustment of model assumptions and identification constraints to be performed in order to compare models in a meaningful manner. The details are described below and in the manuscript in Section 10. The notation of the models which we decided to analyse are the following

LC: Lee-Carter model

$$\log m_{x,t} = \alpha_x + \beta_x \kappa_t,$$

with the constraints

$$\sum_x \beta_x = 1, \sum_t \kappa_t = 0,$$

LCC: Simplified Lee-Carter cohort model

$$\log m_{x,t} = \alpha_x + \beta_x \kappa_t + \gamma_{t-x},$$

with the constraints

$$\sum_x \beta_x = 1, \sum_t \kappa_t = 0, \sum_{c=t_1-x_p}^{t_N-x_1} \gamma_c = 0.$$

LCCF: Lee-Carter full cohort model

$$\log m_{x,t} = \alpha_x + \beta_x \kappa_t + \beta_x^{\gamma} \gamma_{t-x},$$

with the constraints

$$\sum_x \beta_x = 1, \sum_x \beta_x^{\gamma} = 1, \sum_t \kappa_t = 0, \sum_{c=t_1-x_p}^{t_N-x_1} \gamma_c = 0.$$

In this study we consider two age group stratifications, the 1×1 study which has 100 age groups per year and the more parsimonious class of models given by the 5×1 age group stratification with 21 age groups. Since the number of ages groups differs among stratified and non-stratified mortality data, that is, we have 21 age groups for the data in "5×1" format, we expect that the parameters and latent variables, which are estimated using above constraints, may differ in magnitude. Therefore, in order to ensure comparability of the results when we examine the stratification effect on the family of Lee-Carter models, one must therefore to standardize the magnitude of parameters and variables of models in order to compare between the stratified and non-stratified case. We demonstrate in the new studies that such a problem may be resolved via a simple scaling adjustment to the identification constraints in order to resolve this issue. Hence, we introduce the scaling parameter $a > 0$. The models with imposed adjustment are denoted by lower index *adj* as follows

LC$_{adj}$: Lee-Carter model

$$\log m_{x,t} = \alpha_x + \beta_x \kappa_t,$$

with the constraints

$$\sum_x \beta_x = \frac{1}{a}, \sum_t \kappa_t = 0,$$

LCC$_{adj}$: Simplified Lee-Carter cohort model

$$\log m_{x,t} = \alpha_x + \beta_x \kappa_t + \gamma_{t-x},$$

with the constraints

$$\sum_x \beta_x = \frac{1}{a}, \sum_t \kappa_t = 0, \sum_{c=t_1-x_p}^{t_N-x_1} \gamma_c = 0.$$

LCCF$_{adj}$: Lee-Carter full cohort model

$$\log m_{x,t} = \alpha_x + \beta_x \kappa_t + \beta_x^{\gamma} \gamma_{t-x},$$

with the constraints

$$\sum_x \beta_x = \frac{1}{a}, \sum_x \beta_x^{\gamma} = \frac{1}{a}, \sum_t \kappa_t = 0, \sum_{c=t_1-x_p}^{t_N-x_1} \gamma_c = 0.$$

Lastly, in order to distinguish between the results of the models for stratified and non-stratified data, we denote the models for stratified data with the lower index "5×1" and for non-stratified data with "1×1", for instance, the results for the Lee-Carter model LC for stratified data are denoted by $LC_{5\times1}$ and the results for the same model for a data without any stratification are denoted by $LC_{1\times1}$.

10.1.1. The Estimates of the Static Parameters and Filtered Latent Variables

The list of models, which have been examined and are discussed in this subsection, is given in the first column of Table 5. In addition to LC, LCC and LCCF models, we include into the comparison also the models with adjusted constraints for the mortality data in format "5×1" with the adjustment parameter $a = \frac{\#\text{ age groups 1x1}}{\#\text{ age groups 5x1}} = \frac{100}{21} \approx 4.762$ being a proportion between the number of age groups in in the 1×1 stratification and the 5×5 stratification of the age groups in the mortality data.

The Bayesian posterior estimators of the static parameters α_x and β across age groups are shown in Figure 38 when the Bayesian posterior mean estimates of period effect κ_t and cohort effect state process γ_t^0 are shown in Figure 39.

The first straightforward remark on the investigation is to note that there is an inconsequential influence of both the stratification and the adjustment to the identification constraint for stratification, when investigating the estimation of the level vector of the model, as denoted by parameter vector α.

Also, the basic Lee-Carter models is not affected by the stratification as both its in-sample and out-of-sample quality of fit is comparable among data with format "5×1" and "1×1". However, the estimates of β for $LC_{5\times1}$ are greater in the magnitude in comparison to $LC_{1\times1}$ model which appears to be an offset by a smaller slope of the filtered κ_t. Importantly, we note that when the adjustment to the number of age groups is imposed, the β and κ_t for $LC_{5\times1,adj}$ are in line to those of $LC_{1\times1}$ and the model still keeps comparable explanatory power. This observation gives us the intuition that the stratification influences mainly the cohort effect. This is something that we intuitively can understand due to the interplay between age stratification and cohort effect.

Table 5. Mean square error of the fit of the models to the data (MSE) and mean square errors of predictions using forecasting distributions given by MCMC samples ($MSEP_{MCMC}$) and Kalman Filter ($MSEP_{Kalman}$). The models highlated by bold font exhibit significant levels of over-fitting.

Model	MSE	$MSEP_{MCMC}$	$MSEP_{Kalman}$
$LC_{1\times1}$	0.0128	0.0577	0.0568
$LC_{5\times1}$	0.0113	0.0457	0.0457
$LC_{5\times1,adj}$	0.0116	0.0512	0.0516
$LCC_{1\times1}$	0.0079	0.0249	0.0243
$LCC_{5\times1}$	**0.0097**	**0.1778**	**0.1774**
$LCC_{5\times1,adj}$	0.0099	0.1664	0.1625
$LCCF_{1\times1}$	**0.2588**	**0.4735**	**0.6150**
$LCCF_{5\times1}$	0.0107	0.0458	0.0464
$LCCF_{5\times1,adj}$	0.0131	0.0481	0.0508

The results in Table 5 shows that the out-of-sample quality of the fit for the $LCC_{5\times1}$ model is significantly lower than the corresponding result for $LCC_{1\times1}$. As the adjustment, that is $LCC_{5\times1,adj}$ model, produces similar outcomes, the discrepancy in the out-of-sample quality of fit between LCC model applied to "5×1" and "1×1" data is not caused by the smaller number of age groups and therefore different magnitude of estimates of β and κ_t (recall Figures 38 and 39). Since the discrepancy of the in-sample explanatory power is smaller between the models, we observe that the LCC model tends to over-fit when applied to stratified data.

We begin discussion of these results by noting the following finding. There appears to be an interplay present between the model parsimony and the bias and variance in the results for both in-sample fits and out-of-sample forecasts, as reflected by the Mean Squared Error (MSE) results, which is more largely affected by the model structure rather than stratification effects.

For instance, we see that the more parsimonious model choices, corresponding to say the three LC sub-family of models always had a larger MSE than the less parsimonious class of simplified LCC model. That is the in-sample MSE improved by around an order of magnitude when we incorporated extra structure corresponding to the cohort feature. This was not influenced by the age stratification reformed. We conjecture that although the LC models will have potentially lower variance, due to less model parameters to be estimated, the in-sample MSE is still worse generally due to increased bias that may arise from not capturing sufficiently the stochastic structure of the data.

Furthermore, we also see a pronounced effect of stratification on the out-of-sample forecast performance of the simplified class of LCC models in which no adjustment was made for the stratification effect. This indicates that the adjustment we propose to use when undertaking age-group stratification can substantially reduce the bias in the resulting model estimates when we compare between the simplified $LCC_{5\times1}$ model and the adjusted form.

Thirdly, we observe that the most flexible class of LCC model, the non-simplified LCCF class of models was significantly affected by removing the age stratification of 5×1 compared to the 1×1 case. To understand this, we have significantly increased the dimension of the model parameters to be estimated in the $LCCF_{1\times1}$ compared to the $LCCF_{5\times1}$. This we believe produces a poor in sample and out-of-sample MSE and MSEP due to the resulting over-fitting and increased variance in the model estimates, compared to the simplified LCC model equivalents. However, importantly the stratification effect is significant here, the dimension reduction in model parameters in the $LCCF_{5\times1}$ compared to the $LCCF_{1\times1}$ reduces the variance in the estimates of the mortality in sample and out-of-sample as well as providing additional degrees of freedom to also reduce the bias that arises from the constrained version of the $LCC_{5\times1}$ model, resulting in the optimal MSE and MSEP performance.

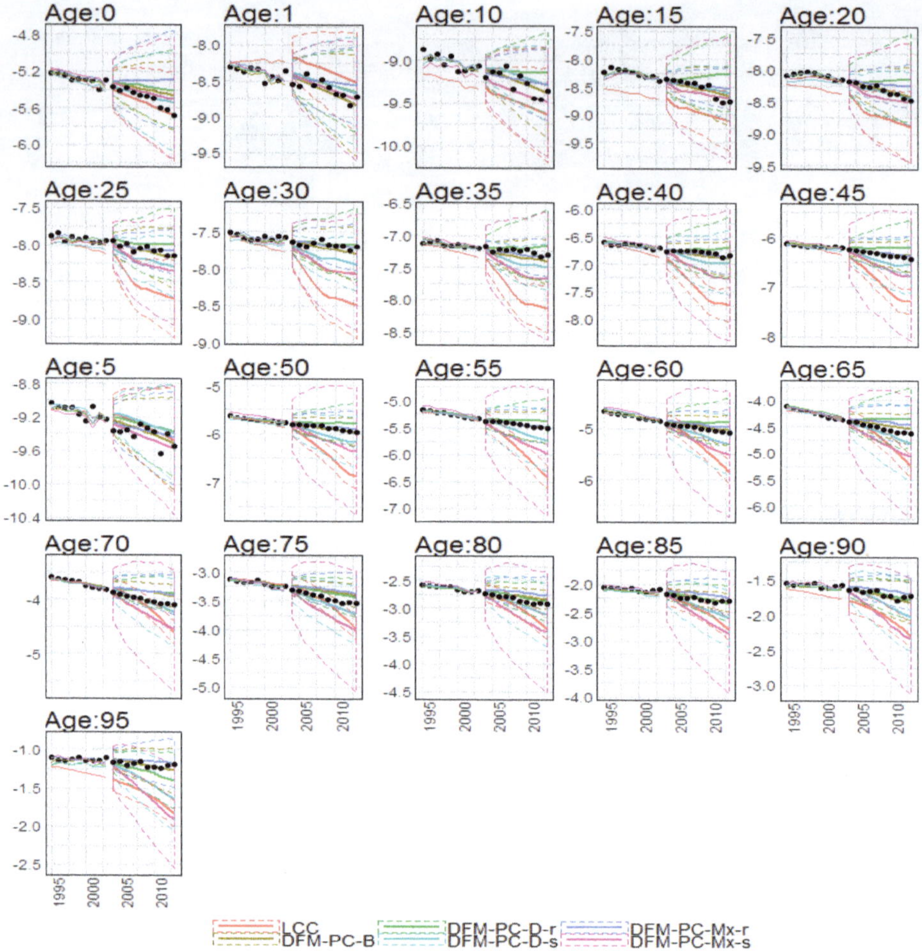

Figure 37. 10-year out-of-sample forecasted log death (y axis) rates of different age groups (different subplots) under different models (colours of lines) with corresponding prediction intervals. Calibration period: 1922–2002

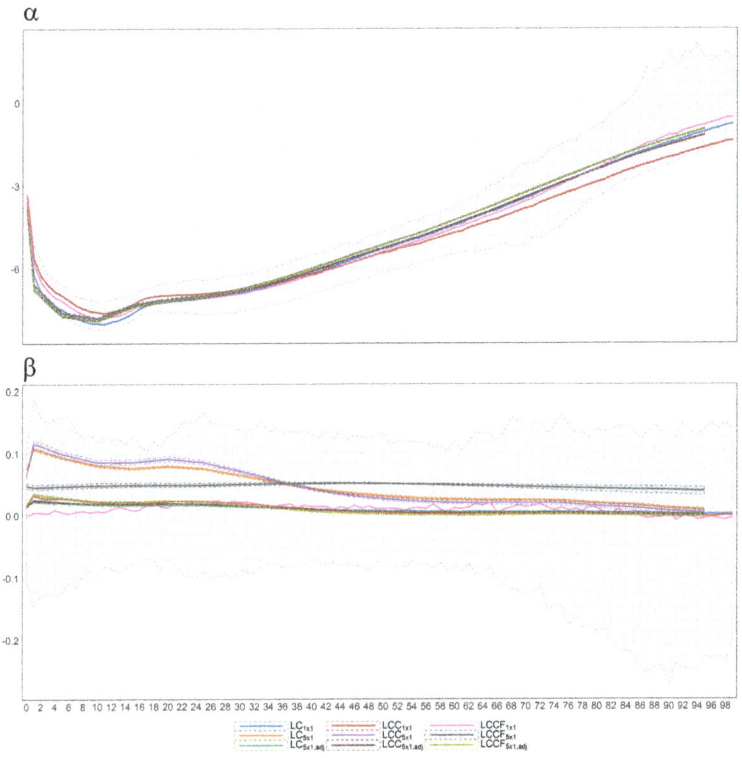

Figure 38. Bayesian posterior estimators with 95% posterior credible intervals for the estimation of $\boldsymbol{\alpha}$ and $\boldsymbol{\beta}$ under different models (colours of lines) for British female mortality data (1922–2002).

10.2. The Estimates of the Intercept for the Factor Model DFM-PC-D-r

The following study addresses the interpretation of the estimates of $\boldsymbol{\alpha}$ under the the new class of stochastic mortality factor model in comparison to the standard Lee-Carter models without the matrix with demographic factors. Please refer to Section 10.2. The argument we proposed to interpret $\boldsymbol{\alpha}$ is adjusted to the fact that we have the exogenous factors incorporated into our model compared to standard Lee-Carter model. As such, we argue that the the interpretation of the intercept should now incorporate both $\boldsymbol{\alpha}$, the classical intercept, and the term $\tilde{\mathbf{F}}_t\varrho_t$ corresponding to the intercept which arises from the exogenous factors. In the time series context this is considered as a stochastic intercept. Hence the interpretation of $\boldsymbol{\alpha}$ typically adopted in the classical stochastic Lee-Carter type period-cohort models, does not hold under the new model, since we have now incorporated the additional structure corresponding to the regression term from the demographic factors. The expression $\tilde{\mathbf{F}}_t\varrho_t$ which is added to the observation equation provides with time-varying supplementary information to the static level given by $\boldsymbol{\alpha}$. To validate this claim we have undertaken the additional studies which demonstrate when we combine the $\boldsymbol{\alpha}$ with this component of the model, the posterior mean of this quantity behaves in analogues fashion to what you would expect on the posterior mean of $\boldsymbol{\alpha}$ in the standard, non-factor class of Lee-Carter models. This is interesting as it shows the factor influence and additional interpretation to the level contributed by the long-term demographic exogenous factors. The plot in Figure 40 shows the Bayesian posterior mean estimates with 95% creditable intervals of $\boldsymbol{\alpha} + \tilde{\mathbf{F}}_t\varrho_t^T$ averaged over time, whereas Figure 41 illustrates the posteriori mean over time. The level of the expression on either of plots is below zero and behaves in a fashion we would have expected from α in standard Lee-Carter models. It confirms our interpretation as well as answers the question asked by the reviewer.

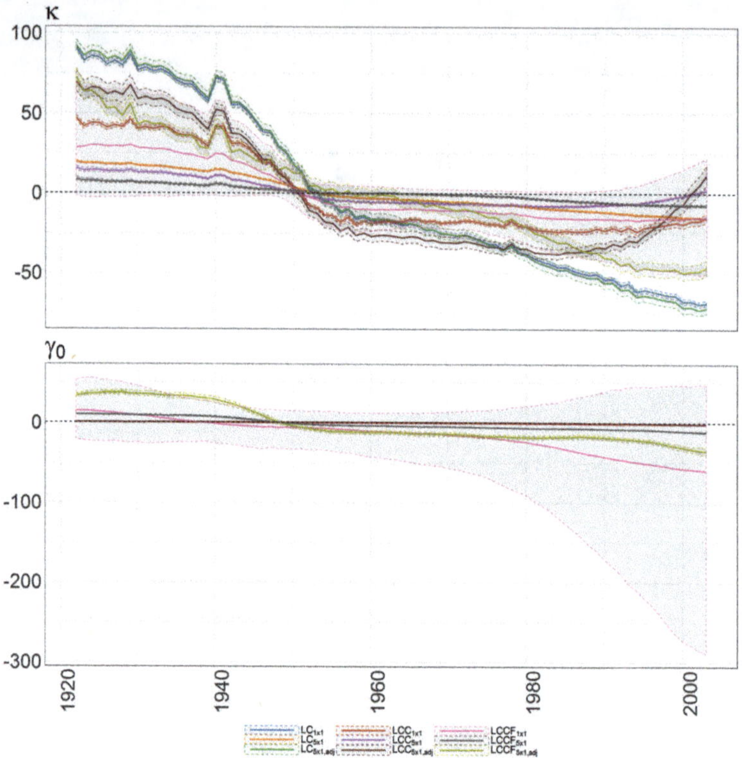

Figure 39. The Bayesian posterior mean estimates with 95% posterior credible intervals for κ_t (**upper panel**) and cohort effect state process γ_t^0 (**lower panel**) under different models (colours of lines) for British female log death rates during 1922–2002.

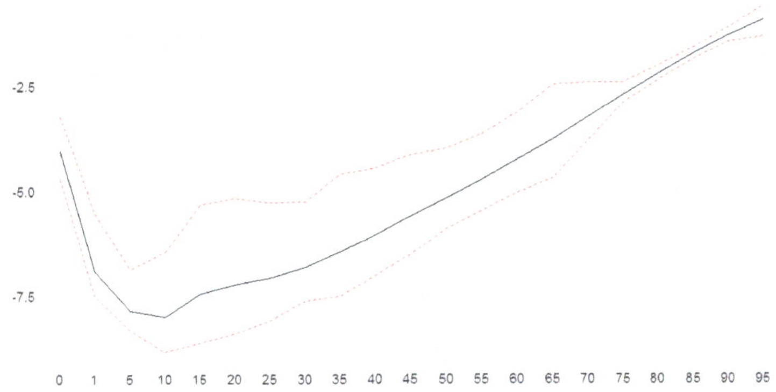

Figure 40. The Bayesian posterior mean estimates with 95% posterior credible intervals average over time for $\boldsymbol{\alpha} + \tilde{\mathbf{F}}_t \varrho_t$ for DFM-PC-D-r.

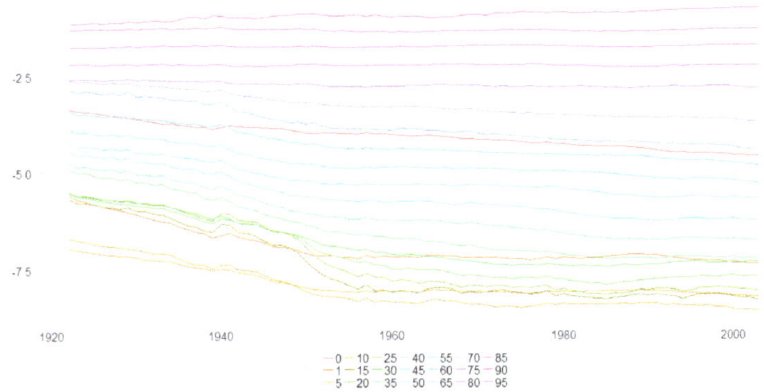

Figure 41. The Bayesian posterior mean estimates of $\boldsymbol{\alpha} + \tilde{\mathbf{F}}_t \varrho_t^T$ over time for DFM-PC-D-r. Colours of lines are related to the age groups (the elements of the vector $\boldsymbol{\alpha}$).

11. Conclusions

We developed and presented a comprehensive study which focuses on the analysis and the incorporation of demographic data into state-space framework for stochastic mortality modelling. We have extended the well-known Lee-Carter model with stochastic cohort effect by introducing new state processes which correspond to the age-specific dynamic of European female log death rates.

We showed by means of Probabilistic Principal Component Analysis the ideas of extracting the meaningful features from demographic data of European countries and applying them as explanatory variables to the mortality estimation and forecasting. In the presence of short time series and different types of missingness, the suggested methodology aims to be as parsimonious as possible. By analysing of the extracted features, we found more evidences about region specific mortality structures. Also, the features exhibit significant sensitivity to the methodology of estimation of moments. As overviewed in Section 8, the robust alternatives to the sample estimators provide with more consistent results regardless to the number of missing entries, especially if the data has been not preprocessed or smoothed.

The results of applying studied models to the British female log mortality data showed that incorporating the features extracted from European demographic data provide valuable information about the mortality forces which affect British population. Also, the models with dynamic factors exhibit better in-sample and out-of-sample fit than the Lee-Carter model with the cohort effect.

As an additional outcome of the study, we analyse the effect of the stratification of the data on the family of Lee-Carter Model. In Section 10 we argue that the stratification influences mainly the cohort effect process and requires more flexibility of modelling than provided by simplified Lee-Carter cohort model. The investigation showed that the standard Lee-Carter model has similar performance for stratified and none-stratified data, whereas simplified Lee-Carter cohort model is prone to significant overfitting when fitted to stratified data. Also, the investigation shows that stratification helps to resolve the issues of overfitting related to Lee-Carter full cohort due to smaller dimensionality of the observation vector.

There are a few ways in which the paper can be further extended. First of all, with appropriate data it would be straightforward to conduct similar analysis for extended data set, as for gender and region specific disaggregation of mortality and demographic data with the inclusion of various population related factors such as cause-of-death Murray and Lopez (1997); (Girosi and King 2008) or more recently (Gaille and Sherris 2015), midlife conditions as in Gavrilov and Gavrilova (2015) or migration. Secondly, considering different distribution priori assumptions and introducing the methodology to handle more advanced patterns of missigness would benefit in better explanatory power and even more consistent interpretability. We can also improve the framework of feature extraction to account for fat tail distributions by means of different robustification methodologies or extensions to Principal Component analysis such as Independent Component Analysis and their functional alternatives as in Shang and Hyndman (2016).

Acknowledgments: Dorota Toczydlowska and Gareth W. Peters would like to acknowledge the generous support of the Institute of Statistical Mathematics in Tokyo, Japan for providing the opportunity to visit, present and get feedback on aspects of this work. Pavel Shevchenko acknowledges support from the Australian Research Council's Discovery Projects funding scheme (project number: DP160103489).

Author Contributions: Dorota Toczydlowska was the main author of the manuscript and the methodological development and implementations. The co-authors Gareth W. Peters , Man Chung Fung and Pavel V. Shevchenko contributed to aspects of the methodological developments, the derivations, implementations and data analysis.

Conflicts of Interest: The authors declare no conflict of interest.

Appendix A. Bayesian Modelling and Sampling of Demographic Factor Model Extension to the Period-Cohort Stochastic Mortality State-Space Models

In this appendix section we explain the Bayesian models developed for the estimation of the demographic factor model extension to the period-cohort stochastic mortality state-space models that are applied in this paper. These are based on the frameworks detailed and developed in Fung et al. (2016) and Fung et al. (2017).

Appendix A.1. Bayesian Model Development and Inference for Stochastic Mortality Models

The observation and state equations Equations (5a) and (5b) imply that the cohort model that we have formulated here belongs to the linear-Gaussian class of state-space models. As a result one can perform efficient maximum-likelihood or Bayesian estimation on fitting the model to data as discussed in detail in Fung et al. (2016). In this paper we focus on Bayesian inference so that the forecasting distribution can take into account parameter uncertainty.

To achieve these inference goals we must first develop the Bayesian models. In this section we detail the Bayesian estimation of the cohort model Equations (5a) and (5b) and its extensions incorporating population information to state-space formulation Equations (8a) and (8b). We firstly note that the models belong to the linear and Gaussian class of state-space models. As a result one can apply an efficient MCMC estimation algorithm based on Gibbs sampling with conjugate priors combined with forward-backward filtering as described in Fung et al. (2016). We describe procedures using the notation of general cohort model Equations (5a) and (5b) and indicate the differences to considered extensions.

We borrow the notation from the LC cohort model Equations (5a) and (5b) and indicate similarities and differences between Equations (5a) and (5b) and Equations (8a) and (8b) while developing the estimation algorithm. In the general setting, our target density is

$$\pi\left(\boldsymbol{\varphi}_{0:T},\boldsymbol{\psi}|\boldsymbol{y}_{1:T}\right) \tag{A1}$$

where $\boldsymbol{\varphi}_{0:T}$ is a vector of latent variables and $\boldsymbol{\psi}$ is a vector of static parameters. In the case of the cohort LC model $\boldsymbol{\varphi}_{0:T} := (\kappa_{0:T},\gamma_{0:T}^{x_1},\ldots,\gamma_{0:T}^{x_p})$ is the $p+1$ dimensional (for each t) latent state vector and $\boldsymbol{\psi} := (\alpha_{x_3:x_p},\beta_{x_2:x_p},\theta,\eta,\lambda,\sigma_\varepsilon^2,\sigma_\kappa^2,\sigma_\gamma^2)$ is the $2p-1$ dimensional static parameter vector. For extended models, we add vectors of global factors latent variable ϱ_t and its static model parameters. Recall that our proposed identification constraint is given by Equation (6); therefore only $\alpha_{x_3:x_p}$ and $\beta_{x_2:x_p}$ are required to be estimated. We perform block sampling for the latent state via the so-called forward-filtering-backward-sampling (FFBS) algorithm (Carter and Kohn 1994) and the posterior samples of the static parameters are obtained via conjugate priors. The sampling procedure is described in Algorithm 2, where N is the number of MCMC iterations performed.

Algorithm 2 MCMC sampling for $\pi(\boldsymbol{\varphi}_{0:T},\boldsymbol{\psi}|\boldsymbol{y}_{1:T})$

1: Initialise: $\boldsymbol{\psi} = \boldsymbol{\psi}^{(0)}$.
2: **for** $i = 1,\ldots,N$ **do**
3: Sample $\boldsymbol{\varphi}_{0:T}^{(i)}$ from $\pi(\boldsymbol{\varphi}_{0:T}|\boldsymbol{\psi}^{(i-1)},\boldsymbol{y}_{1:T})$ via FFBS (Appendix A.2).
4: **for** $h = 1,\ldots,2p-1$ **do**
5: Sample $\psi_h^{(i)}$ from $\pi(\psi_h|\boldsymbol{\varphi}_{0:T}^{(i)},\boldsymbol{\psi}_{-h}^{(i)},\boldsymbol{y}_{1:T})$, (Appendix A.3)
6: where $\boldsymbol{\psi}_{-h}^{(i)} = (\psi_1^{(i)},\ldots,\psi_{h-1}^{(i)},\psi_{h+1}^{(i-1)},\ldots,\psi_{2p-2}^{(i-1)})$.
7: **end for**
8: **end for**

Appendix A.2. Forward-Backward Filtering for Latent State Dynamics

The FFBS procedure requires to carry out multivariate Kalman filtering forward in time and then sample backwardly using the obtained filtering distributions. For the cohort model Equations (2) and (3) (or Equations (5a) and (5b)), the conditional distributions involved in the multivariate Kalman filtering recursions are given by

$$\begin{aligned}
\boldsymbol{\varphi}_{t-1}|\boldsymbol{y}_{1:t-1} &\sim \mathcal{N}(\boldsymbol{m}_{t-1},C_{t-1}), && \text{(A2a)}\\
\boldsymbol{\varphi}_{t}|\boldsymbol{y}_{1:t-1} &\sim \mathcal{N}(\boldsymbol{a}_{t},R_{t}), && \text{(A2b)}\\
\boldsymbol{y}_{t}|\boldsymbol{y}_{1:t-1} &\sim \mathcal{N}(\boldsymbol{f}_{t},Q_{t}), && \text{(A2c)}\\
\boldsymbol{\varphi}_{t}|\boldsymbol{y}_{1:t} &\sim \mathcal{N}(\boldsymbol{m}_{t},C_{t}) && \text{(A2d)}
\end{aligned}$$

where

$$\begin{aligned}
&\boldsymbol{a}_t = \boldsymbol{\Lambda}\boldsymbol{m}_{t-1} + \boldsymbol{\Theta}, \quad R_t = \boldsymbol{\Lambda}C_{t-1}\boldsymbol{\Lambda}^\top + \Upsilon, && \text{(A3a)}\\
&\boldsymbol{f}_t = \boldsymbol{\alpha} + \mathbf{B}\boldsymbol{a}_t, \quad Q_t = \mathbf{B}R_t\mathbf{B}^\top + \sigma_\varepsilon^2\mathbb{I}_p, && \text{(A3b)}\\
&\boldsymbol{m}_t = \boldsymbol{a}_t + R_t\mathbf{B}^\top Q_t^{-1}(\boldsymbol{y}_t - \boldsymbol{f}_t), \quad C_t = R_t - R_t\mathbf{B}^\top Q_t^{-1}\mathbf{B}R_t. && \text{(A3c)}
\end{aligned}$$

for $t = 1, \ldots, T$. Since

$$\pi(\boldsymbol{\varphi}_{0:T}|\boldsymbol{\psi}, \boldsymbol{y}_{1:T}) = \prod_{t=0}^{T} \pi(\boldsymbol{\varphi}_t|\boldsymbol{\varphi}_{t+1:T}, \boldsymbol{\psi}, \boldsymbol{y}_{1:T}) = \prod_{t=0}^{T} \pi(\boldsymbol{\varphi}_t|\boldsymbol{\varphi}_{t+1}, \boldsymbol{\psi}, \boldsymbol{y}_{1:t}), \tag{A4}$$

We see that for a block sampling of the latent state, one can first draw $\boldsymbol{\varphi}_T$ from $N(\boldsymbol{m}_T, C_T)$ and then, for $t = T-1, \ldots, 1, 0$ (that is backward in time), draws a sample of $\boldsymbol{\varphi}_t|_{\boldsymbol{\varphi}_{t+1}, \boldsymbol{\psi}, \boldsymbol{y}_{1:T}}$ recursively given a sample of $\boldsymbol{\varphi}_{t+1}$. It turns out that $\boldsymbol{\varphi}_t|_{\boldsymbol{\varphi}_{t+1}, \boldsymbol{\psi}, \boldsymbol{y}_{1:T}} \sim \mathcal{N}(\boldsymbol{h}_t, H_t)$ where

$$\boldsymbol{h}_t = \boldsymbol{m}_t + C_t \boldsymbol{\Lambda}^\top R_{t+1}^{-1}(\boldsymbol{\varphi}_{t+1} - \boldsymbol{a}_{t+1}), \tag{A5a}$$

$$H_t = C_t - C_t \boldsymbol{\Lambda}^\top R_{t+1}^{-1} \boldsymbol{\Lambda} C_t, \tag{A5b}$$

based on Kalman smoothing (Carter and Kohn 1994). **For the extended models, we simply need to replace the vectors and matrices of the LC cohort model with objects stressed by tildes from Section 3.**

Appendix A.3. Posteriors for Static Parameters in the Cohort Model

To sample the posterior distribution of the static parameters, we assume the following independent conjugate priors:

$$\alpha_x \sim \mathcal{N}(\tilde{\mu}_\alpha, \tilde{\sigma}_\alpha^2), \quad \beta_x \sim \mathcal{N}(\tilde{\mu}_\beta, \tilde{\sigma}_\beta^2), \quad \theta \sim \mathcal{N}(\tilde{\mu}_\theta, \tilde{\sigma}_\theta^2), \quad \eta \sim \mathcal{N}(\tilde{\mu}_\eta, \tilde{\sigma}_\eta^2) \tag{A6a}$$

$$\lambda \sim \mathcal{N}_{[-1,1]}(\tilde{\mu}_\lambda, \tilde{\sigma}_\lambda^2), \quad \sigma_\varepsilon^2 \sim \mathrm{IG}(\tilde{a}_\varepsilon, \tilde{b}_\varepsilon), \quad \sigma_\kappa^2 \sim \mathrm{IG}(\tilde{a}_\kappa, \tilde{b}_\kappa), \quad \sigma_\gamma^2 \sim \mathrm{IG}(\tilde{a}_\gamma, \tilde{b}_\gamma) \tag{A6b}$$

where $\mathrm{N}_{[-1,1]}$ denotes a truncated Gaussian with support $[-1,1]$ and $\mathrm{IG}(\tilde{a}, \tilde{b})$ denotes an inverse-gamma distribution with mean $\tilde{b}/(\tilde{a}-1)$ and variance $\tilde{b}^2/((\tilde{a}-1)^2(\tilde{a}-2))$ for $\tilde{a} > 2$. The posteriors of the static parameters are then obtained as follows:[1]

$$\alpha_x|\boldsymbol{y}, \boldsymbol{\varphi}, \boldsymbol{\psi}_{-\alpha_x} \sim \mathcal{N}\left(\frac{\tilde{\sigma}_\alpha^2 \sum_{t=1}^T (y_{x,t} - \beta_x \kappa_t - \gamma_t^x) + \tilde{\mu}_\alpha \sigma_\varepsilon^2}{\tilde{\sigma}_\alpha^2 T + \sigma_\varepsilon^2}, \frac{\tilde{\sigma}_\alpha^2 \sigma_\varepsilon^2}{\tilde{\sigma}_\alpha^2 T + \sigma_\varepsilon^2}\right), \tag{A7}$$

$$\beta_x|\boldsymbol{y}, \boldsymbol{\varphi}, \boldsymbol{\psi}_{-\beta_x} \sim \mathcal{N}\left(\frac{\tilde{\sigma}_\beta^2 \sum_{t=1}^T (y_{x,t} - (\alpha_x + \gamma_t^x))\kappa_t + \tilde{\mu}_\beta \sigma_\varepsilon^2}{\tilde{\sigma}_\beta^2 \sum_{t=1}^T \kappa_t^2 + \sigma_\varepsilon^2}, \frac{\tilde{\sigma}_\beta^2 \sigma_\varepsilon^2}{\tilde{\sigma}_\beta^2 \sum_{t=1}^T \kappa_t^2 + \sigma_\varepsilon^2}\right), \tag{A8}$$

$$\theta|\boldsymbol{y}, \boldsymbol{\varphi}, \boldsymbol{\psi}_{-\theta} \sim \mathcal{N}\left(\frac{\tilde{\sigma}_\theta^2 \sum_{t=1}^T (\kappa_t - \kappa_{t-1}) + \tilde{\mu}_\theta \sigma_\kappa^2}{\tilde{\sigma}_\theta^2 T + \sigma_\kappa^2}, \frac{\tilde{\sigma}_\theta^2 \sigma_\kappa^2}{\tilde{\sigma}_\theta^2 T + \sigma_\kappa^2}\right), \tag{A9}$$

$$\eta|\boldsymbol{y}, \boldsymbol{\varphi}, \boldsymbol{\psi}_{-\theta} \sim \mathcal{N}\left(\frac{\tilde{\sigma}_\eta^2 \sum_{t=1}^T (\gamma_t - \lambda \gamma_{t-1}) + \tilde{\mu}_\eta \sigma_\gamma^2}{\tilde{\sigma}_\eta^2 T + \sigma_\gamma^2}, \frac{\tilde{\sigma}_\eta^2 \sigma_\gamma^2}{\tilde{\sigma}_\eta^2 T + \sigma_\gamma^2}\right), \tag{A10}$$

$$\lambda|\boldsymbol{y}, \boldsymbol{\varphi}, \boldsymbol{\psi}_{-\lambda} \sim \mathcal{N}_{[-1,1]}\left(\frac{\tilde{\sigma}_\lambda^2 \sum_{t=1}^T ((\gamma_t^{x_1} - \eta)\gamma_{t-1}^{x_1}) + \tilde{\mu}_\lambda \sigma_\gamma^2}{\tilde{\sigma}_\lambda^2 \sum_{t=1}^T (\gamma_{t-1}^{x_1})^2 + \sigma_\gamma^2}, \frac{\tilde{\sigma}_\lambda^2 \sigma_\gamma^2}{\tilde{\sigma}_\lambda^2 \sum_{t=1}^T (\gamma_{t-1}^{x_1})^2 + \sigma_\gamma^2}\right), \tag{A11}$$

$$\sigma_\varepsilon^2|\boldsymbol{y}, \boldsymbol{\varphi}, \boldsymbol{\psi}_{-\sigma_\varepsilon^2} \sim \mathrm{IG}\left(\tilde{a}_\varepsilon + \frac{pT}{2}, \tilde{b}_\varepsilon + \frac{1}{2}\sum_{x=x_1}^{x_p}\sum_{t=1}^{T}(y_{x,t} - (\alpha_x + \beta_x \kappa_t + \gamma_t^x))^2\right), \tag{A12}$$

$$\sigma_\kappa^2|\boldsymbol{y}, \boldsymbol{\varphi}, \boldsymbol{\psi}_{-\sigma_\kappa^2} \sim \mathrm{IG}\left(\tilde{a}_\kappa + \frac{T}{2}, \tilde{b}_\kappa + \frac{1}{2}\sum_{t=1}^{T}(\kappa_t - (\kappa_{t-1} + \theta))^2\right), \tag{A13}$$

$$\sigma_\gamma^2|\boldsymbol{y}, \boldsymbol{\varphi}, \boldsymbol{\psi}_{-\sigma_\gamma^2} \sim \mathrm{IG}\left(\tilde{a}_\gamma + \frac{T}{2}, \tilde{b}_\gamma + \frac{1}{2}\sum_{t=1}^{T}(\gamma_t^{x_1} - \lambda \gamma_{t-1}^{x_1})^2\right). \tag{A14}$$

---

1 For simplicity, we denote $\boldsymbol{y} = \boldsymbol{y}_{1:T}, \boldsymbol{\varphi} = \boldsymbol{\varphi}_{0:T}$ and $\boldsymbol{\psi}_{-h} = (\psi_1, \ldots, \psi_{h-1}, \psi_{h+1}, \ldots, \psi_{2p-2})$.

Appendix A.4. Posteriors for Static Parameters in the Extended Models

In order to develope sampling algorithm for models incorporating European countries population information, we add the conjugate priori assumptions to Equation (A6) related to static parameters of Equation (7)

$$[\boldsymbol{\Omega}]_{i,j} \sim \mathcal{N}(\tilde{\mu}_{\Omega}, \tilde{\sigma}^2_{\Omega}), \quad \Psi_j \sim \mathcal{N}(\tilde{\mu}_{\Psi}, \tilde{\sigma}^2_{\Psi}), \quad \sigma^2_{\varrho} \sim \mathrm{IG}(\tilde{a}_{\varrho}, \tilde{b}_{\varrho}) \tag{A15}$$

The posteriors of static parameters from Equation (7) are essential for Gibbs backward sampling regardless of the considered case for the extended model. We refer by small letters i, j to ages x_i, $x_j \in \{x_1, \dots, x_p\}$, for $i, j \in \{1, \dots, p\}$, and letters $m, l \in \{1, \dots, k\}$ to the components of the matrix $\mathbf{F}_t$. An element labelled as im corresponds to $[\mathbf{F}_t]_{i,m}$ or a latent variable ϱ_t^{im}. Then

$$\Psi_{im}|\boldsymbol{y}, \tilde{\boldsymbol{\varphi}}, \boldsymbol{\psi}_{-\Psi_{im}} \sim \mathrm{N}\left(\frac{\tilde{\sigma}^2_{\Psi}\sum_{t=1}^{T}(\varrho_t^{im} - \boldsymbol{\varrho}_{t-1}^{T}[\boldsymbol{\Omega}]_{im,\cdot}) + \tilde{\mu}_{\psi}\sigma^2_{\varrho}}{\tilde{\sigma}^2_{\Psi}T + \sigma^2_{\varrho}}, \frac{\tilde{\sigma}^2_{\Psi}\sigma^2_{\varrho}}{\tilde{\sigma}^2_{\Psi}T + \sigma^2_{\varrho}}\right),$$

$$[\boldsymbol{\Omega}]_{im,jl}|\boldsymbol{y}, \tilde{\boldsymbol{\varphi}}, \boldsymbol{\psi}_{-[\boldsymbol{\Omega}]_{im,jl}} \sim$$
$$\mathcal{N}\left(\frac{\tilde{\sigma}^2_{\Omega}\sum_{t=1}^{T}\left[\left(\varrho_t^{im} - \Psi_{im} - \sum_{xh\neq jm}\varrho_{t-1}^{xh}[\boldsymbol{\Omega}]_{im,xh}\right)\varrho_{t-1}^{jl}\right] + \tilde{\mu}_{\Omega}\sigma^2_{\varrho}}{\tilde{\sigma}^2_{\Omega}\sum_{t=1}^{T}(\varrho_{t-1}^{jl})^2 + \sigma^2_{\varrho}}, \frac{\tilde{\sigma}^2_{\Omega}\sigma^2_{\varrho}}{\tilde{\sigma}^2_{\Omega}\sum_{t=1}^{T}(\varrho_{t-1}^{jl})^2 + \sigma^2_{\varrho}}\right), \tag{A16}$$

$$\sigma^2_{\varrho}|\boldsymbol{y}, \tilde{\boldsymbol{\varphi}}, \boldsymbol{\psi}_{-\sigma^2_{\varrho}} \sim \mathrm{IG}\left(\tilde{a}_{\varrho} + \frac{pkT}{2}, \tilde{b}_{\varrho} + \frac{1}{2}\sum_{t=1}^{T}\sum_{i=1}^{p}\sum_{m=1}^{k}\left(\varrho_t^{im} - \Psi_{im} - \boldsymbol{\varrho}_{t-1}^{T}[\boldsymbol{\Omega}]_{im,\cdot}\right)^2\right),$$

where $\tilde{\boldsymbol{\varphi}}$ is a vector of latent variables from Equation (8b) and $\boldsymbol{\psi}$ is a vector of static parameters updated to Equation (7). Depends on the cases f extended model, we have the following replacement of the posterioris from Appendix A.3

Case 1 Global factors $\mathbf{F}_t$ in the observation equation

$$\alpha_x|\boldsymbol{y}, \tilde{\boldsymbol{\varphi}}, \boldsymbol{\psi}_{-\alpha_x} \sim \mathcal{N}\left(\frac{\tilde{\sigma}^2_{\alpha}\sum_{t=1}^{T}\left(y_{x,t} - [\tilde{\mathbf{B}}_t]_{x,\cdot}^{T}\tilde{\boldsymbol{\varphi}}_t\right) + \tilde{\mu}_{\alpha}\sigma^2_{\varepsilon}}{\tilde{\sigma}^2_{\alpha}T + \sigma^2_{\varepsilon}}, \frac{\tilde{\sigma}^2_{\alpha}\sigma^2_{\varepsilon}}{\tilde{\sigma}^2_{\alpha}T + \sigma^2_{\varepsilon}}\right), \tag{A17}$$

$$\beta_x|\boldsymbol{y}, \tilde{\boldsymbol{\varphi}}, \boldsymbol{\psi}_{-\beta_x} \sim \mathcal{N}\left(\frac{\tilde{\sigma}^2_{\beta}\sum_{t=1}^{T}\left[y_{x,t} - \left(\alpha_x + \gamma_t^x + [\tilde{\mathbf{F}}_t]_{x,\cdot}^{T}\boldsymbol{\varrho}_t\right)\right]\kappa_t + \tilde{\mu}_{\beta}\sigma^2_{\varepsilon}}{\tilde{\sigma}^2_{\beta}\sum_{t=1}^{T}\kappa_t^2 + \sigma^2_{\varepsilon}}, \frac{\tilde{\sigma}^2_{\beta}\sigma^2_{\varepsilon}}{\tilde{\sigma}^2_{\beta}\sum_{t=1}^{T}\kappa_t^2 + \sigma^2_{\varepsilon}}\right) \tag{A18}$$

$$\sigma^2_{\varepsilon}|\boldsymbol{y}, \tilde{\boldsymbol{\varphi}}, \boldsymbol{\psi}_{-\sigma^2_{\varepsilon}} \sim \mathrm{IG}\left(\tilde{a}_{\varepsilon} + \frac{pT}{2}, \tilde{b}_{\varepsilon} + \frac{1}{2}\sum_{x=x_1}^{x_p}\sum_{t=1}^{T}\left[y_{x,t} - \left(\alpha_x + [\tilde{\mathbf{B}}_t]_{x,\cdot}T\tilde{\boldsymbol{\varphi}}_t\right)\right)^2\right] \tag{A19}$$

Case 2 Global factors $\mathbf{F}_t$ in the state equation of κ_t

$$\theta|\boldsymbol{y}, \tilde{\boldsymbol{\varphi}}, \boldsymbol{\psi}_{-\theta} \sim \mathcal{N}\left(\frac{\tilde{\sigma}^2_{\theta}\sum_{t=1}^{T}(\kappa_t - \kappa_{t-1} - \tilde{\mathbf{f}}_t^{T}\boldsymbol{\varrho}_t) + \tilde{\mu}_{\theta}\sigma^2_{\kappa}}{\tilde{\sigma}^2_{\theta}T + \sigma^2_{\kappa}}, \frac{\tilde{\sigma}^2_{\theta}\sigma^2_{\kappa}}{\tilde{\sigma}^2_{\theta}T + \sigma^2_{\kappa}}\right), \tag{A20}$$

$$\sigma^2_{\kappa}|\boldsymbol{y}, \boldsymbol{\varphi}, \boldsymbol{\psi}_{-\sigma^2_{\kappa}} \sim \mathrm{IG}\left(\tilde{a}_{\kappa} + \frac{T}{2}, \tilde{b}_{\kappa} + \frac{1}{2}\sum_{t=1}^{T}\left[\kappa_t - \left(\kappa_{t-1} + \theta + \tilde{\mathbf{f}}_t^{T}\boldsymbol{\varrho}_t\right)\right]^2\right) \tag{A21}$$

Case 3 Global factors $\mathbf{F}_t$ in the state equation of γ_t

$$\eta|\boldsymbol{y},\tilde{\boldsymbol{\varphi}},\boldsymbol{\psi}_{-\theta} \sim \mathcal{N}\left(\frac{\tilde{\sigma}_\eta^2 \sum_{t=1}^T (\gamma_t^{x_1} - \lambda\gamma_{t-1}^{x_1} - \varrho_t^T[\tilde{\mathbf{F}}_t]_{x_1,\cdot}) + \tilde{\mu}_\eta\sigma_\gamma^2}{\tilde{\sigma}_\eta^2 T + \sigma_\gamma^2}, \frac{\tilde{\sigma}_\eta^2\sigma_\gamma^2}{\tilde{\sigma}_\eta^2 T + \sigma_\gamma^2}\right), \tag{A22}$$

$$\lambda|\boldsymbol{y},\boldsymbol{\varphi},\boldsymbol{\psi}_{-\lambda} \sim \mathcal{N}_{[-1,1]}\left(\frac{\tilde{\sigma}_\lambda^2 \sum_{t=1}^T ((\gamma_t^{x_1} - \eta - \varrho_t^T[\tilde{\mathbf{F}}_t]_{x_1,\cdot})\gamma_{t-1}^{x_1}) + \tilde{\mu}_\lambda\sigma_\gamma^2}{\tilde{\sigma}_\lambda^2 \sum_{t=1}^T (\gamma_{t-1}^{x_1})^2 + \sigma_\gamma^2}, \frac{\tilde{\sigma}_\lambda^2\sigma_\gamma^2}{\tilde{\sigma}_\lambda^2 \sum_{t=1}^T (\gamma_{t-1}^{x_1})^2 + \sigma_\gamma^2}\right), \tag{A23}$$

$$\sigma_\gamma^2|\boldsymbol{y},\boldsymbol{\varphi},\boldsymbol{\psi}_{-\sigma_\gamma^2} \sim \mathrm{IG}\left(\tilde{a}_\gamma + \frac{T}{2}, \tilde{b}_\gamma + \frac{1}{2}\sum_{t=1}^T (\gamma_t^{x_1} - \lambda\gamma_{t-1}^{x_1})^2\right). \tag{A24}$$

Appendix A.5. Application of the Constraints

The constraints are applied for every iteration of the sampler. Let the current iteration be denoted by i, then the following procedures are performed:

1. The constraints of the vector $\boldsymbol{\beta}^{(i)}$ are applied after sampling the arbitrary vector of static parameters $\boldsymbol{\beta}^{(i)}$, the vector is mapped into a vector of transformed parameters, $\tilde{\boldsymbol{\beta}}^{(i)}$ by the following rescaling $\tilde{\boldsymbol{\beta}}^{(i)} = \frac{\boldsymbol{\beta}^{(i)}}{\sum_x \beta_x^{(i)}}$. Then we replace $\boldsymbol{\beta}^{(i)}$ with $\tilde{\boldsymbol{\beta}}^{(i)}$ and proceed to the next steps of the sampler.
2. The constraints for the latent processes $\kappa_t^{(i)}$ and γ_{t-x} are applied after the finalisation of Forward Backward. The arbitrary filtered estimates of the processes are transformed to $\tilde{\kappa}_t^{(i)} = \kappa_t^{(i)} - \bar{\kappa}^{(i)}$ and $\tilde{\gamma}_{t-x}^{(i)} = \gamma_{t-x}^{(i)} - \bar{\gamma}^{(i)}$ for $\bar{\kappa}^{(i)} = \frac{1}{N}\sum_{k=1}^N \kappa_{t_k}^{(i)}$ and $\bar{\gamma}^{(i)} = \frac{1}{N+p-1)}\sum_{c=t_1-x_p}^{t_N-x_1} \gamma_c^{(i)}$. Then we replace $\kappa_t^{(i)}$ with $\tilde{\kappa}_t^{(i)}$ and $\gamma_t^{(i)}$ with $\tilde{\gamma}_t^{(i)}$ and and proceed to the next steps of the sampler.

If one models the full cohort model the constraints of the vector $\boldsymbol{\beta}^\gamma$ are applied applied in the same fashion as for the vector $\boldsymbol{\beta}$. For a simplified cohort model, the vector of parameters is set to the vector of ones and is not sampled.

Appendix B. Description of Stochastic Mortality Models Utilizing Factor Extraction from European Demographic Data

Recalling the notation from the Equation (8), all models which utilize features extracted from Demographic data have the following the state-space representation

$$\boldsymbol{y}_t = \boldsymbol{\alpha} + \tilde{\mathbf{B}}_t\tilde{\boldsymbol{\varphi}}_t + \boldsymbol{\varepsilon}_t, \quad \boldsymbol{\varepsilon}_t \overset{iid}{\sim} \mathcal{N}(0, \sigma_\varepsilon^2\mathbb{I}_{21}), \tag{A25a}$$

$$\tilde{\boldsymbol{\varphi}}_t = \tilde{\boldsymbol{\Lambda}}\tilde{\boldsymbol{\varphi}}_{t-1} + \tilde{\boldsymbol{\Theta}} + \tilde{\omega}_t, \quad \tilde{\boldsymbol{\kappa}}_t \overset{iid}{\sim} \mathcal{N}(0, \tilde{\Upsilon}). \tag{A25b}$$

As we examine only **Case 1** defined in Section 3, the corresponding transition matrices of the observation and state equations are equal to

$$\tilde{\mathbf{B}}_{t\ 21\times(22+m)} = \left(\begin{array}{c|c} \mathbf{B}_{21\times 22} & \tilde{\mathbf{F}}_t \end{array}\right)$$

$$\tilde{\boldsymbol{\Lambda}}_{(22+m)\times(22+m)} = \left(\begin{array}{c|c} \boldsymbol{\Lambda}_{22\times 22} & \mathbf{0}_{22\times m} \\ \hline \mathbf{0}_{m\times 22} & \boldsymbol{\Omega}_{m\times m} \end{array}\right) \tag{A26}$$

where m is the dimensionality of the latent process vector ϱ_t which corresponds to the factor matrix $\tilde{\mathbf{F}}_t$. The structure of the matrix depends on the models what is further discussed in the next two subsections.

Appendix B.1. DFM-PC-B Model

The model is constructed as follow

Step 1: Take the first eigenvector of robustly standardized Birth counts which is of vector-type, country specific

$$[\mathbf{F}]_{\cdot,1} = \begin{bmatrix} f_{1,1}^{AUT} \\ \vdots \\ f_{21,1}^{UKR} \end{bmatrix};$$

Step 2: Take the mean across the countries (components of the first eigenvector vector) which is a scalar $\hat{f}$ and use a one per age group latent process to model additional supplementary information per age group;

Step 3: Incorporate $\hat{f}$ as elements of the diagonal matrix $\tilde{\mathbf{F}}$

$$\tilde{\mathbf{F}} = \begin{bmatrix} \hat{f} & 0 & 0 & \cdots & 0 \\ 0 & \hat{f} & 0 & \cdots & 0 \\ 0 & 0 & \ddots & 0 & 0 \\ 0 & 0 & 0 & \ddots & \vdots \\ 0 & 0 & 0 & 0 & \hat{f} \end{bmatrix}_{21\times 21}$$

The corresponding ϱ_t is age group specific vector, that is

$$\varrho_t = \left(\varrho_t^0, \ldots, \varrho_t^{95}\right)_{1\times 21}$$

Appendix B.2. The Models of the Class DFM-PC-D and DFM-PC-Mx

The models are constructed as follow

Step 1: Take the first eigenvector of robustly standardized corresponding data set which is of matrix-type, age and country specific

$$\mathbf{F} = \begin{bmatrix} f_{1,1}^{AUT} & \cdots & f_{1,28}^{UKR} \\ \vdots & \ddots & \vdots \\ f_{21,1}^{AUT} & \cdots & f_{21,28}^{UKR} \end{bmatrix}_{21\times 28}$$

Step 2: Notice that the matrix $\tilde{\mathbf{F}}$ is equal to $\mathbf{F}$

Step 3: Use a one per country latent process to model the impact of country specific vector;

The corresponding ϱ_t is country specific vector, that is

$$\varrho_t = \left(\varrho_t^{AUT}, \ldots, \varrho_t^{UKR}\right)_{1\times 28}$$

References

(Basilevsky 1994) Basilevsky, Alexander T. 1994. *Statistical Factor Analysis and Related Methods*. Hoboken: John Wiley & Sons, Inc.

(Cairns et al. 2009) Cairns, Andrew J. G., David Blake, Kewin Dowd, Guy D. Coughlan, David Epstein, Alen Ong, and Igor Balevich. 2009. A quantitative comparison of stochastic mortality models using data from England and Wales and the United States. *North American Actuarial Journal* 13: 1–35.

(Carter and Kohn 1994) Carter, Chris K., and Robert Kohn. 1994. On Gibbs sampling for state-space models. *Biometrika* 81: 541–53.

(Celeux et al. 2006) Celeux, G., F. Forbes, C. P. Robert, and D. M. Titterington. 2006. Deviance information criteria for missing data models. *Bayesian Anal* 1: 651–73.

(Davies 1987) Davies, P. Laurie 1987. Asymptotic Behaviour of S-Estimates of Multivariate Location Parameters and Dispersion Matrices. *The Annals of Statistics* 15: 1269–92.

(Dempster et al. 1977) Dempster, Arthur P., Nan M. Laird, and Donald B. Rubin. 1977. Maximum Likelihood from Incomplete Data via the EM Algorithm. *Journal of Royal Statistical Society. Series B (Methodological)* 39: 1–38.

(Diebold and Li 2006) Diebold, Francis X., and Canlin Li. 2006. Forecasting the term structure of government bond yields. *Journal of Econometrics* 130: 337–64.

(Erbas et al. 2010) Erbas, Bircan, Muhammed Akram, Dorota M. Gertig, Dallas English, John L. Hopper, Anne M. Kavanagh, and Rob Hyndman. 2010. Using functional data analysis models to estimate future time trends in age-specific breast cancer mortality for the United States and England-Wales. *Journal of Epidemiology* 20: 159–65.

(Frahm and Jaekel 2010) Frahm, Gabriel, and Uwe Jaekel. 2010. A generalization of Tyler's M-estimators to the case of incomplete data. *Computational Statistics & Data Analysis* 54: 374–93.

(Friedman and Tukey 1974) Friedman, Jerome H., and John W. Tukey. 1974. A Projection Pursuit Algorithm for Exploratory Data Analysis. *IEEE Transactions on Computers* C-23: 881–90.

(Fung et al. 2016) Fung, Man Chung, Gareth W. Peters, and Pavel V. Shevchenko. 2016. A unified approach to mortality modelling using state-space framework: Characterisation, identification, estimation and forecasting. *Annals of Actuarial Science* 1–47. doi:10.1017/S1748499517000069.

(Fung et al. 2017) Fung, Man Chung, Gareth William Peters, and Pavel V. Shevchenko. 2017 Cohort Effects in Mortality Modelling: A Bayesian State-Space Analysis. Available online: https://ssrn.com/abstract=2907868 (accessed on 31 January 2017).

(Gaille and Sherris 2015) Gaille, Sererine Arnold, and Michael Sherris. 2015. Causes-of-Death Mortality: What Do We Know on Their Dependence? *North American Actuarial Journal* 19:116–28.

(Gavrilov and Gavrilova 2015) Gavrilov, Leonid A., and Natalia S. Gavrilova. 2015. Predictors of Exceptional Longevity: Effects of Early-Life and Midlife Conditions, and Familial Longevity. *North America Actuarial Journal* 19: 174–86.

(Girosi and King 2008) Girosi, Federico, and Gary King. 2008. *Demographic Forecasting*. Princeton: Princeton University Press.

(Haberman and Renshaw 2011) Haberman, Steven, and Arthur Renshaw. 2011. A comparative study of parametric mortality projection models. *Insurance: Mathematics and Economics* 48: 35–55.

(Hanewald 2011) Hanewald, Katja 2011. Explaining Mortality Dynamics: The Role of Macroeconomic Fluctuations and Cause of Death Trends. *North American Actuarial Journal, Series B* 290–314.

(Huber 1964) Huber, Peter J. 1964. Robust Estimation of a Location Parameter. *The Annals of Mathematical Statistics* 35: 73–101.

(Huber and Ronchetti 2009) Huber, Peter J., and Elvezio M. Ronchetti. 2009. *Robust Statistics*. Wiley Series in Probability and Statistics. Hoboken: John Wiley & Sons, Inc., p. 380.

(Hunt and Villegas 2015) Hunt, Andrew, and Andres M. Villegas. 2015. Robustness and convergence in the Lee-Carter model with cohort effects. *Insurance: Mathematics and Economics* 64: 186–202.

(Hyndman and Yasmeen 2012) Hyndman, Rob J., and Farah Yasmeen. 2012. Common functional principal component models for mortality forecasting. In *Contributions in Infinite-Dimensional Statistics And Related Topics*. chp. 29, pp. 161–66.

(Jamshidian 1997) Jamshidian, Mortaza 1997. An EM Algorithm for ML Factor Analysis with Missing Data. In *Lecture Notes in Statistics*. New York: Springer, pp. 247–58.

(Jolliffe 2002) Jolliffe, I. T. 2002. *Principal Component Analysis* New York: Springer.

(Kogure and Kurachi 2010) Kogure, Atsuyuki, and Yoshiyuki Kurachi. 2010. A Bayesian approach to pricing longevity risk based on risk-neutral predictive distributions. *Insurance: Mathematics and Economics* 46: 162–72.

(Lee and Carter 1992) Lee, Ronald D., and Lawrence R. Carter. 1992. Modeling and forecasting US mortality. *Journal of the American Statistical Association* 87: 659–75.

(Little and Rubin 2002) Little, Roderick J. A., and Donald B. Rubin. 2002. *Statistical Analysis with Missing Data*, 2nd ed. Hoboken: John Wiley & Sons, Inc.

(Lopuhaa 1989) Lopuhaa, Hendrik P. 1989. On the Relation between S-Estimators and M-Estimators of Multivariate Location and Covariance. *The Annals of Statistics* 17: 1662–83.

(Maronna 1976) Maronna, Ricardo Antonio 1976. Robust M-Estimators of Multivariate Location and Scatter. *The Annals of Statistics* 4: 51–67.

(Murray and Lopez 1997) Murray, Christopher J. L., and Alan D. Lopez. 1997. Alternative projections of mortality and disability by cause 1990–2020: Global burden of disease study. *The Lancet* 1498–1504.

(Niu and Melenberg 2014) Niu, Geng, and Bertrand Melenberg. 2014. Trends in Mortality Decrease and Economic Growth. *Demography* 51: 1755–73.

(Pedroza 2006) Pedroza, Claudia 2006. A Bayesian forecasting model: predicting US male mortality. *Biostatistics* 7: 530–50.

(Renshaw and Haberman 2006) Renshaw, Arthur E., and Steven Haberman. 2006. A cohort-based extension to the Lee-Carter model for mortality reduction factors. *Insurance: Mathematics and Economics* 38: 556–70.

(Rousseeuw and Yohai 1984) Rousseeuw, Peter, and Victor Yohai. 1984. *Robust Regression by Means of S-Estimators*. Robust and Nonlinear Time Series Analysis, New York: Springer, pp. 256–72.

(Roweis 1998) Roweis, Sam T. 1998. EM Algorithms for PCA and SPCA. In *Advances in Neural Information Processing Systems*. Cambridge: MIT Press, pp. 626–32.

(Rubin and Thayer 1982) Rubin, Donald B., and Dorothy T. Thayer. 1982. EM algorithms for ML factor analysis. *Psychometrika* 47: 69–76.

(Shang and Hyndman 2016) Shang, Han Lin, and Rob J. Hyndman. 2016. Grouped functional time series forecasting: An application to age-specific mortality rates. *Journal of Computational and Graphical Statistics* 26: 330–43.

(Spiegelhalter et al. 2002) Spiegelhalter, David J., Nicola G. Best, and Bradley P. Carlin. 2002. Bayesian measures of model complexity and fit. *Journal of the Royal Statistical Society, Series B* 64: 583–639.

(Sun et al. 2016) Sun, Ying, Prabhu Babu, and Daniel P. Palomar. 2016. Robust Estimation of Structured Covariance Matrix for Heavy-Tailed Elliptical Distributions. *IEEE Transactions on Signal Processing* 64: 3576–90. [1506.05215].

(Tipping and Bishop 1999) Tipping, Michael E., and Christopher M. Bishop. 1999. Probabilistic Principal Component Analysis. *Journal of the Royal Statistical Society. Series B (Statistical Methodology)* 61: 611–22.

(Tyler 1987) Tyler, David E. 1987. A Distribution-Free M-Estimator of Multivariate Scatter. *The Annals of Statistics* 15: 234–51.

(Tyler 1987) Tyler, David E. 1987. Statistical Analysis for the Angular Central Gaussian Distribution on the Sphere. *Biometrika* 74: 579.

(Willets 2004) Willets, R. C. 2004. The cohort effect: insights and explanations. *British Actuarial Journal* 10: 833–77.

(Wilmoth et al. 2007) Wilmoth, J. R., K. Andreev, and D. Jdanov. 2007. *Methods Protocol for the Human Mortality Database*, Technical Report. Available online: http://www.mortality.org/Public/Docs/MethodsProtocol.pdf

risks

MDPI

Article

Optimal Time to Enter a Retirement Village

Jinhui Zhang *,†, Sachi Purcal [1,‡] and Jiaqin Wei [2,‡]

1 Department of Applied Finance and Actuarial Studies, Faculty of Business and Economics, Macquarie University, Sydney, NSW 2109, Australia; sachi.purcal@mq.edu.au

2 School of Statistics, Faculty of Economics and Management, East China Normal University, Shanghai 200241, China; jqwei@stat.ecnu.edu.cn

* Correspondence: colin.zhang@mq.edu.au; Tel.: +61-2-9850-8484

† Current address: Department of Applied Finance and Actuarial Studies, Faculty of Business and Economics, Macquarie University, Sydney, NSW 2109, Australia.

‡ These authors contributed equally to this work.

Academic Editor: Pavel Shevchenko

Received: 14 October 2016; Accepted: 18 March 2017; Published: 22 March 2017

Abstract: We consider the financial planning problem of a retiree wishing to enter a retirement village at a future uncertain date. The date of entry is determined by the retiree's utility and bequest maximisation problem within the context of uncertain future health states. In addition, the retiree must choose optimal consumption, investment, bequest and purchase of insurance products prior to their full annuitisation on entry to the retirement village. A hyperbolic absolute risk-aversion (HARA) utility function is used to allow necessary consumption for basic living and medical costs. The retirement village will typically require an initial deposit upon entry. This threshold wealth requirement leads to exercising the replication of an American put option at the uncertain stopping time. From our numerical results, active insurance and annuity markets are shown to be a critical aspect in retirement planning.

Keywords: retirement village; optimal control; optimal stopping, HARA, American put option; long-term care needs, costs and products for the elderly; disability/health state transitions; life-cycle modelling related to the retirement phase

---

1. Introduction

With the reduced mortality rate, life expectancy is continuing to increase globally [1]. In the next 40–50 years, the percentage of people aged over 60 years will nearly double all over the world. People are predicted to have longer lives and extended retirement living.

Australia has one of the longest life expectancies in the world, that is, 79.7 years for males and 84.2 years for females [2]. With the growing ageing population, Australia is now facing a profound ageing problem. The potential impact includes economy stagnation, high demand for pensions and increased aged care spending, which has caught Australian Government's attention [3].

As reported by the Australia Institute of Health and Welfare [4], 28.31% of the population aged 65 or over receive aged care services. This requires recurrent annual expenditure of more than A$13 billion for the Australian federal, state and territory governments. Almost 70% of the total spending on aged care is allocated to residential aged care services, that is, aged care homes [5]. The increasing demand for aged care has become a burden for the Australian government. Hence, improving wellness during retirement living has become a more profound topic.

For the growing senior population, retirement villages which are linked with "active ageing" and "community support" present an alternative high-quality retirement living option. From Glass and Skinner [6], a retirement village or retirement community can be defined as an organised residential place with a certain level of service for a voluntary age-specified retired or partially retired person.

The retirement village should provide its residents with shared activities and facilities in a community that offers secured living [7].

In the United States, a retirement village is usually called a retirement community. According to the size, scale, location, and facilities and activities provided, the retirement community can be classified into different categories, such as senior apartments, continuing-care retirement communities, leisure-oriented retirement communities, congregate housing, etc. [6]. In the United Kingdom (UK), the retirement village is now growing as a new growing long-term residential option for retirees [7].

It is well documented in the literature that residing in a retirement village can improve well-being. Factors that contribute to well-being include community facilities, accessibility features and 24-h emergency assistance [8], social contact [9,10], living independence [11] and organised group activity and exercise [12].

The Property Council of Australia [13] states that currently over 177,000 seniors aged 65 and over (i.e., only 5% of the total number) reside in an Australian retirement village. However, as stated by the Australian Bureau of Statistics [14], males have recently been stated to close the life expectancy gap. This prevailing tendency implies that retirees are expected to live a longer time as a part of a couple. As an alternative retirement living option for a spouse, retirement villages would attract more demand [6].

Optimal strategies have been widely studied for a variety of financial problems appearing in the literature. Merton [15,16] developed a well-known optimal asset allocation and consumption model for an investor with a fixed lifetime. In the model, utility is measured by a constant relative risk-aversion (CRRA) function and is maximised by the investor to determine her optimal strategy. Ding et al. [17] used put option replication to create a wealth threshold in Merton's model to allow for a luxury bequest. Noting the conclusion from Yaari [18] that investors benefit from a life annuity, Merton's model was extended in [19] by Richard in which investors were assumed to have a stochastic lifetime and access to the purchase of insurance products, that is, life insurance and life annuities.

Within the framework of Merton's model, Milevsky and Young [20] studied an optimal stopping problem for investors seeking a once-and-for-all annuitisation. Kingston and Thorp [21] extended the work of [20] to the more general case of hyperbolic absolute risk-aversion (HARA) utility. Dybvig and Liu [22], and Barucci and Marazzina [23] investigate the lifetime asset allocation problem for an investor who have stochastic labor income and can choose her retirement date.

Health status is another aspect which impacts on financial decision. Rosen and Wu [24] showed that self-rated health status is a profound indicator for portfolio choice. Bernheim et al. [25] studied the circumstances under which health status can initiate bequest motives. Edwards [26] explored the link between health status and portfolio selection. Specifically, in [26], the decline of financial risk observed after investors' retirement is partially explained by investors' health risk which usually increases along with age. Furthermore, the existence of medical costs associated with their health risk can vary retirees' financial strategy. Retirees who pay out-of-pocket medical costs consequently have less wealth [27] and tend to save more [28].

This arising ageing problem provided us with the motivation to develop a life-cycle model involving retirement living choices while considering asset allocation, consumption, bequests and insurance purchase, thus contributing to our understanding of the optimal financial behaviour of the ageing. In our model, retirees are found to have an increasing proportion of wealth invested in risky assets in line with their increasing age, when there is a wealth requirement threshold to enter a retirement village. This increasing proportion trend during retirement is also stated in Kingston and Fisher [29], Ding et al. [17] and Pfau and Kitces [30]. By allowing for dynamic health states, our model can be more suitable for the ageing problem.

In this paper, we study the retirees' optimal strategy models for different cases in Section 2. Numerical demonstrations (and parameters) are presented and discussed in Sections 3 and 4 and are followed by the conclusion in Section 5.

2. Model and Method

We assume that risky assets available in the market follow the geometric Brownian motion:

$$dX_t = \alpha X_t dt + \sigma X_t dB_t, \tag{1}$$

where α and σ are the expected return rate and volatility of the risky assets X_t and B_t is the standard Brownian motion.

In this paper, we use a HARA utility function for consumption, that is,

$$U_1(C) = \frac{(C-h)^\gamma}{\gamma},$$

where C is consumption, h is consumption of necessities for basic living (not including medical costs) and γ is a constant that reflects the individual's level of risk aversion.

Drawing on Haberman and Pitacco [31] and the theory of continuous-time Markov chains[1], we assume the retiree's health status is stochastic and is modelled by a continuous Markov chain process with the transition matrix shown as follows

$$\mathbf{Q} = \begin{pmatrix} q_{11} & q_{12} \\ q_{21} & q_{22} \end{pmatrix}, \tag{2}$$

where q_{11} is the intensity of staying in a healthy state, q_{12} is the intensity of becoming sick from a healthy state, q_{21} is the intensity of recovery from a sick state to a healthy state and q_{22} is the intensity of staying in a sick state. Here state 1 represents a healthy condition and state 2 represents a sick condition. For the homogeneity case, we have the transition probability of staying healthy, being sick from a healthy state, recovery from being sick to a healthy state and staying in a sick state, that is, $\tilde{P}_{11}$, $\tilde{P}_{12}$, $\tilde{P}_{21}$ and $\tilde{P}_{22}$

$$\tilde{P}_{11}(t,T) = \frac{1}{q_{12}+q_{21}}[q_{21} + q_{12}e^{-(q_{12}+q_{21})(T-t)}] \tag{3}$$

$$\tilde{P}_{12}(t,T) = 1 - \tilde{P}_{11}(t,T) \tag{4}$$

$$\tilde{P}_{21}(t,T) = 1 - \tilde{P}_{22}(t,T) \tag{5}$$

$$\tilde{P}_{22}(t,T) = \frac{1}{q_{12}+q_{21}}[q_{12} + q_{21}e^{-(q_{12}+q_{21})(T-t)}], \tag{6}$$

where $\tilde{P}_{ij}(t,T)$ is the transition probability from state i to state j with time interval (t,T).

In our model, a known distribution is assumed to describe the lifetime of retirees. The density function of mortality $f_x(t)$ is defined as follows,

$$f_x(t) = \mu(t) \cdot S(t),$$

where $\mu(t)$ is the force of mortality and $S(t)$ is the survival probability.

Further, retirees are assumed to have short-sighted or myopic vision about their future health state. That is, although their health state can continually change, reflected in the modelling above, our myopic agents make their plans assuming their current health state will continue indefinitely into the future. We make this assumption to reduce the complexity of our already complex model. Allowing agents to plan their future aware of future health changes is recognised as a mathematically difficult problem [33], and we leave this task for future research. Unlike Milevsky and Young [20],

---

[1] See, for example, Ross [32].

we do not explore asymmetric information between insured/annuitant and insurer, and so we assume insurers share the retirees' myopia.

With an assumed two-state health stochastic process $\{H(s),\ t \leq s \leq \tau\}$, the presence of myopic retirees making financial plans at some time t implies

$$\mu(s) = \begin{cases} \mu_1(s), & H(t) = h_t = 1,\ t \leq s \leq \tau \\ \mu_2(s), & H(t) = h_t = 2,\ t \leq s \leq \tau \end{cases} \tag{7}$$

with its corresponding $S(s)$, and so myopia implies $H(s) = h_t,\ t \leq s \leq \tau$, for some deterministic maximum age τ, and where h_t is the realisation of the individual's current health state at time t, $\mu_i(s)$ and its corresponding $S_i(s)$ are the future force of mortality and survival probability at time s for health state i. In this paper, state 1 represents the healthy state and state 2 represents the sick state. Hence, $\mu_1(s) \leq \mu_2(s)$ and $S_1(s) \geq S_2(2)$.

2.1. Case 1: No Bequest and Incomplete Insurance Market

In Australia, several types of housing are offered by retirement villages. One common type is the serviced apartment offered by a lease contract. These apartment-type residential options for seniors can also be found in other countries, such as in the UK and the United States. For this case, the retirees rent the apartment on a pay-as-you-go basis to move into a retirement village. According to [34], an owner-occupied house can be treated as a bequest. So, in the case of leased serviced apartments, as retirees do not own the residential property in the retirement village, some of these retirees will have no bequest motive. Focusing on such retirees, we further assume they have no access to insurance markets prior to their full annuitisation on their entry to the retirement village—with no bequest motive they have no interest in life insurance and to thwart their interest in annuitisation prior to entering a retirement village is an important consideration given the widespread incompleteness of annuity markets worldwide [35].

Meanwhile, retirees are assumed to maximise their utilities by consumption and investment before the optimal time $\tilde{\tau}$, that is, the chosen optimal time to enter retirement villages. At time $\tilde{\tau}$, retirees without a bequest motive would use all their remaining wealth to purchase a life annuity at the time they enter retirement villages.

Therefore, following [19,20], the value function of this optimal problem is as follows:

$$V = \max_{\pi,C,\tilde{\tau}} E\left\{ \int_t^{\tilde{\tau}} \frac{S(s)}{S(t)} e^{-\rho(s-t)} U_1(C(s))ds + \int_{\tilde{\tau}}^{\tau} \frac{S(s)}{S(t)} e^{-\rho(s-t)} U_1\left(\frac{W(\tilde{\tau})}{\bar{a}_{\tilde{\tau}}}\right) ds \middle| H(s) = h_t,\ t \leq s \leq \tau \right\} \tag{8}$$

$$= \max_{\pi,C,\tilde{\tau}} E\left\{ \int_t^{\tilde{\tau}} \frac{S(s)}{S(t)} e^{-\rho(s-t)} U_1(C(s))ds + e^{-\rho(\tilde{\tau}-t)} \frac{S(\tilde{\tau})}{S(t)} \bar{a}_{\tilde{\tau}} U_1\left(\frac{W(\tilde{\tau})}{\bar{a}_{\tilde{\tau}}}\right) \middle| H(s) = h_t,\ t \leq s \leq \tau \right\}, \tag{9}$$

with the wealth dynamics as

$$dW(t) = (rW(t) - D(t)W(t) - C(t) + (\alpha - r)\pi(t)W(t))dt + \sigma\pi(t)W(t)dB_t,$$

where t is the starting age, $\pi(t)$ is the proportion of total wealth invested in risky assets, $\bar{a}_t = \int_t^{\tau} \frac{S(s)}{S(t)} e^{-\rho(s-t)} ds$ is the annuity function and $D(t)$ is the medical cost represented by a percentage of wealth. As with the force of mortality and survival rate,

$$D(s) = D_{h_t}(s),\ t \leq s \leq \tau. \tag{10}$$

For simplicity, we set the time preference rate equal to the risk free rate, $\rho = r$.

As retirees in our model are assumed to be myopic with respect to their future health states, they develop their financial strategies ignoring future health dynamics. In another words, although retirees' health states can switch between different regimes, the view of a myopic retiree still will be limited to his or her current health condition and this is the reason for not including transition probabilities in our HJB equations. While our approach handles the regime switching environment within which it is set, we point to [36] as a reference for the generalised setting for regime switching environments.

From Milevsky and Young [20], and Kingston and Thorp [21], the optimal stopping time $\tilde{\tau}$ has been proven to be deterministic for CRRA utility and HARA utility. Based on Milevsky and Young [20], and Øksendal [37], the variational inequality is shown as follows,

$$\begin{aligned}(\rho+\mu(t))V \geq V_t + (r - D(t))W(t)V_W + \max_c[U_1(C(t)) - C(t)V_W] \\ + \max_\pi[(\alpha - r)\pi W(t)V_W + \frac{1}{2}\sigma^2\pi^2 W(t)^2 V_{WW}],\ t \in [0, \tilde{\tau}] \end{aligned} \tag{11}$$

and

$$V \geq \bar{a}_t U_1(\frac{W(t)}{\bar{a}_t}),\ t \in (\tilde{\tau}, \tau). \tag{12}$$

The form of solution for V is assumed to be

$$V = \frac{1}{\gamma}(W(t) - \hat{W}(t))^\gamma a(t)^{1-\gamma}, \tag{13}$$

where

$$\hat{W}(t) = \frac{h}{r - D(t)}(1 - e^{-(r-D(t))(\tau - t)})$$

is the 'floor' or 'protected' wealth, and $r - D(t)$ reflects the continuous compounding rate of interest to give the retirees an income stream covering health costs up to the maximum possible age τ. Such protection is needed as they are assumed to have no access to insurance markets prior to entry to the retirement village. Further note that $a(t)$ is health state dependent.

We also write $\tilde{W}(t) = W(t) - \hat{W}(t)$ as the difference between wealth and protected wealth which is known as 'surplus' wealth.

The derivatives of the value function are then

$$\begin{aligned} V_t &= \frac{1-\gamma}{\gamma}\tilde{W}(t)^\gamma a(t)^{-\gamma}a'(t) + \tilde{W}(t)^{\gamma-1}a(t)^{1-\gamma}h, \\ V_W &= \tilde{W}(t)^{\gamma-1}a(t)^{1-\gamma}, \\ \text{and} \quad V_{WW} &= (\gamma - 1)\tilde{W}(t)^{\gamma-2}a(t)^{1-\gamma}. \end{aligned} \tag{14}$$

Following Milevsky and Young [20], and Kingston and Thorp [21], we can use the first order derivative condition of Equation (11) to show that the optimal consumption $C^*(t)$ and optimal proportion invested in risky assets are

$$\begin{aligned} C^*(t) &= \tilde{W}(t)a(t)^{-1} + h, \\ \pi^*(t) &= \frac{\alpha - r}{\sigma^2(1-\gamma)}\frac{\tilde{W}(t)}{W(t)} \end{aligned} \tag{15}$$

and $C^*(t)$ depends on the current health state.

We substitute Equations (13)–(15) into (11) and (12): for $t \leq \tilde{\tau}$, we have

$$-1 \geq a'(t) + \frac{1}{1-\gamma}\Big[\gamma r - \gamma D(t) - \rho - \mu(t) + \frac{1}{2}\frac{(\alpha - r)^2\gamma}{\sigma^2(1-\gamma)}\Big]a(t),\ t \in [0, \tilde{\tau}], \tag{16}$$

while for $t > \tilde{\tau}$, we have

$$a(t) \geq \bar{a}_t,\ t \in (\tilde{\tau}, \tau). \tag{17}$$

We adopt the hypothesis from Milevsky and Young [20] which assumes the time before full annuitisation is of the form $(0, \tilde{\tau})$. With this hypothesis, $\tilde{\tau}$ is set to be deterministic and we write $\phi(t)$ as the solution of Equations (16) and (17) and let $\eta_1(t) = \frac{1}{1-\gamma}\left[\gamma r - \gamma D(t) - \rho - \mu(t) + \frac{1}{2}\frac{(\alpha-r)^2\gamma}{\sigma^2(1-\gamma)}\right]$. Hence, for $t \leq \tilde{\tau}$, we have

$$-1 = \phi'(t) + \eta_1(t)\phi(t). \tag{18}$$

Multiplying equation (18) by $e^{\int_0^t \eta_1(u)du}$, the equation can be shown as

$$-e^{\int_0^t \eta_1(u)du} = \phi'(t)e^{\int_0^t \eta_1(u)du} + \eta_1(t)\phi(t)e^{\int_0^t \eta_1(u)du}. \tag{19}$$

Integrating (19) from t to $\tilde{\tau}$, we can have

$$\int_t^{\tilde{\tau}} -e^{\int_0^s \eta_1(u)du} ds = \left[\phi(s)e^{\int_0^s \eta_1(u)du}\right]_t^{\tilde{\tau}}$$

and

$$\phi(t) = \bar{a}_{\tilde{\tau}} e^{\int_t^{\tilde{\tau}} \eta_1(u)du} + \int_t^{\tilde{\tau}} e^{\int_t^s \eta_1(u)du} ds. \tag{20}$$

For $t > \tilde{\tau}$, the solution ϕ is

$$\phi(t) = \bar{a}_{\tilde{\tau}}.$$

We re-write $\phi(t)$ as $\phi(t, \tilde{\tau})$, as it contains both t and $\tilde{\tau}$.

To find the optimal stopping time, we can differentiate the value function (13) with respect to $\tilde{\tau}$,

$$\frac{\partial V}{\partial \tilde{\tau}} = \frac{1-\gamma}{\gamma} W^{\gamma}(t)\phi^{-\gamma}(t, \tilde{\tau})\frac{\partial \phi(t, \tilde{\tau})}{\partial \tilde{\tau}},$$

and noting $\partial \bar{a}_{\tilde{\tau}} / \partial \tilde{\tau} = (\mu(\tilde{\tau}) + \rho)\bar{a}_{\tilde{\tau}} - 1$ and $\partial \phi(t, \tilde{\tau})/\partial \tilde{\tau} = [(\mu(\tilde{\tau}) + \rho)\bar{a}_{\tilde{\tau}}]e^{\int_t^{\tilde{\tau}} \eta_1(u)du} + \bar{a}_{\tilde{\tau}} e^{\int_t^{\tilde{\tau}} \eta_1(u)du}\eta_1(\tilde{\tau})$, with $W(t)$, $\phi(t)$ and $\bar{a}_{\tilde{\tau}}$ always positive, then

$$\frac{\partial V}{\partial \tilde{\tau}} \propto \mu(\tilde{\tau}) + \rho + \eta_1(\tilde{\tau})$$

and the optimal stopping time is given when this expression is zero.

2.2. *Case 2: With Bequest and Complete Insurance Market*

The most common housing type offered by retirement villages in Australia is the resident-funded unit. Retirees need to purchase a licence to reside in the retirement village and can sell the licence when they exit. This type of agreement is similar to a purchase in the real-estate market. Retirees who have a licence to live in a resident-funded unit can be regarded as house owners. Similarly, in the UK, retirees can purchase retirement housing on a leasehold basis[2] or as a property owner. In the United States, it is also common for retirees to purchase properties in leisure-oriented retirement communities for retirement living. Following the assumption by [34]—that the owner-occupied house can be treated

2 Retirees need to pay a large amount in upfront fees to live in such a community and have the right to re-sell the occupation rights of the property.

as a bequest—we can assume that those retirees have bequest motives and access to the insurance market prior to full annuitisation.

In this case, retirees are assumed to have bequest motives from time t to $\tilde{\tau}$. We use a power utility function for the bequest motive U_2, that is

$$U_2(L(t)) = m(t)^{1-\gamma}\frac{L(t)^{\gamma}}{\gamma},$$

where $L(t)$ is the legacy amount and, following the argument in [38], with $m(t) = \frac{2}{3}\int_t^{\tau} e^{-r(u-t)}du$. In our calculation, we use τ to represent the deterministic maximum age.

We also assume that insurance products, that is, life insurance and annuities, are available in the market. Before the optimal time to enter a retirement village $\tilde{\tau}$, retirees use consumption, bequests and the purchase of insurance products to maximise their utility. From Richard [19], the insurance premium is related to $L(t)$ and wealth W_t and given by[3]

$$P(t) = \mu(t)[L(t) - W(t)]$$

and where both $P(t)$ and $L(t)$ depend on the current health state.

At time $\tilde{\tau}$, retirees split their wealth into two parts: $vW_{\tilde{\tau}}$ and $(1-v)W_{\tilde{\tau}}$. The first part, $vW_{\tilde{\tau}}$, is used to purchase lifetime annuity products, with this being similar to the behaviour of retirees without a bequest motive. The second part, $(1-v)W_{\tilde{\tau}}$, reflects their altruism, with this sum to be delivered to their heirs at time $\tilde{\tau}$ as an inter vivos transfer. Hence, the value function is

$$\begin{aligned}
V = & \max_{\pi,C,L,\tilde{\tau}} E\Big\{ \int_t^{\tilde{\tau}} \frac{S(s)}{S(t)} e^{-\rho(s-t)} \left[U_1(C(s)) + \mu(s)U_2(L(s))\right] ds \\
& + \int_{\tilde{\tau}}^{\tau} \frac{S(s)}{S(t)} e^{-\rho(s-t)} U_1(\frac{vW(\tilde{\tau})}{\bar{a}_{\tilde{\tau}}}) ds + \frac{S(\tilde{\tau})}{S(t)} e^{-\rho(\tilde{\tau}-t)} U_2((1-v)W(\tilde{\tau})) \Big| H(s) = h_t,\ t \le s \le \tau \Big\} \\
= & \max_{\pi,C,L,\tilde{\tau}} E\Big\{ \int_t^{\tilde{\tau}} \frac{S(s)}{S(t)} e^{-\rho(s-t)} \left[U_1(C(s)) + \mu(s)U_2(L(s))\right] ds + e^{-\rho(\tilde{\tau}-t)} \frac{S(\tilde{\tau})}{S(t)} \bar{a}_{\tilde{\tau}} U_1(\frac{vW(\tilde{\tau})}{\bar{a}_{\tilde{\tau}}}) \\
& + \frac{S(\tilde{\tau})}{S(t)} e^{-\rho(\tilde{\tau}-t)} U_2((1-v)W(\tilde{\tau})) \Big| H(s) = h_t,\ t \le s \le \tau \Big\}
\end{aligned}$$

with the wealth dynamics

$$dW(t) = (rW(t) - D(t)W(t) - C(t) + (\alpha - r)\pi(t)W(t) - P(t))dt + \sigma\pi(t)W(t)dB_t.$$

The variational inequality is then shown as

$$\begin{aligned}
(\rho + \mu(t))V \ge & V_t + rWV_W - P(t)V_W + \max_{C,L}[U_1(C(t)) + \mu(t)U_2(L(t)) - C(t)V_W] \\
& + \max_{\pi}[(\alpha - r)\pi W(t)V_W + \frac{1}{2}\sigma^2\pi^2 W(t)^2 V_{WW}],\ t \in [0, \tilde{\tau}]
\end{aligned} \tag{21}$$

and

$$V \ge \frac{(v\frac{W(t)}{\bar{a}_{\tilde{\tau}}})^{\gamma}}{\gamma}\bar{a}_{\tilde{\tau}} + \frac{((1-v)W(t))^{\gamma}m(t)}{\gamma},\ t \in (\tilde{\tau}, \tau). \tag{22}$$

Similar to the case in Section 2.1, we have

---

3 Note that $P(t) > 0$ reflects the retiree (continuously) purchasing life insurance, while $P(t) < 0$ indicates the retiree has entered into something akin to a (instantaneous) variable annuity contract with an insurer [38].

$$V = \frac{1}{\gamma}(W(t) - \hat{W}(t))^{\gamma} a(t)^{1-\gamma},$$

where

$$\hat{W}(t) = h \int_t^{\tau} \frac{S(s)}{S(t)} e^{-(r-D(t))(s-t)} ds.$$

For the time $t \leq \tilde{\tau}$, the value function reduces to Richard's model [19] in which the optimal consumption $C^*(t)$, optimal legacy amount $L^*(t)$, optimal proportion invested in risky assets $\pi^*(t)$ and optimal insurance premium $P^*(t)$ are shown as follows

$$\begin{aligned} C^*(t) &= \tilde{W}(t)a(t)^{-1} + h, \\ L^*(t) &= m(t)\tilde{W}(t)a(t)^{-1}, \\ \pi^*(t) &= \frac{\alpha - r}{\sigma^2(1-\gamma)} \frac{\tilde{W}(t)}{W(t)}, \\ P^*(t) &= (L^*(t) - W(t))\mu(t) \\ &= \mu(t)m(t)\tilde{W}(t)a(t)^{-1} - \mu(t)W(t) \end{aligned} \tag{23}$$

and where all controls, apart from $\pi^*(t)$ depend on the health state at time t. The utility function with optimal consumption and optimal legacy is then shown as

$$\begin{aligned} U_1(C^*) &= \frac{\tilde{W}(t)^{\gamma} a(t)^{-\gamma}}{\gamma}, \\ U_2(L^*) &= \frac{m(t)\tilde{W}(t)^{\gamma} a(t)^{-\gamma}}{\gamma}. \end{aligned} \tag{24}$$

By substituting Equations (13), (14), (23) and (24) into Equations (21) and (22), for $t \leq \tilde{\tau}$, we have

$$-(1 + \mu(t)m(t)) \geq a'(t) + \left[\frac{\gamma}{1-\gamma}(r - D(t)) - \frac{1}{1-\gamma}\rho - \mu(t) + \frac{1}{2}\frac{(\alpha - r)^2\gamma}{(1-\gamma)^2\sigma^2}\right]a(t) \tag{25}$$

and for $t > \tilde{\tau}$, we have

$$a(t) \geq \left[v^{\gamma}\bar{a}_t^{1-\gamma} + (1-v)^{\gamma} m(t)\right]^{\frac{1}{1-\gamma}}. \tag{26}$$

We write ϕ as the solution of this problem and $\eta_2 = \frac{\gamma}{1-\gamma}(r - D(t)) - \frac{1}{1-\gamma}\rho - \mu(t) + \frac{1}{2}\frac{(\alpha-r)^2\gamma}{(1-\gamma)^2\sigma^2}$. Hence, for $t \leq \tilde{\tau}$,

$$-(1 + \mu(t)m(t)) = \phi'(t) + \eta_2(t)\phi(t). \tag{27}$$

Multiplying Equation (27) by $e^{\int_0^t \eta_2(u)du}$, it can be shown as

$$-(1 + \mu(t)m(t))e^{\int_0^t \eta_2(u)du} = \phi'(t)e^{\int_0^t \eta_2(u)du} + \eta_2(t)\phi(t)e^{\int_0^t \eta_2(u)du}. \tag{28}$$

Integrating Equation (28) from time t to $\tilde{\tau}$, the equation can be shown as

$$-\int_t^{\tilde{\tau}} (1 + \mu(s)m(s))e^{\int_0^s \eta_2(u)du} ds = \left[\phi(s)e^{\int_0^s \eta_2(u)du}\right]_t^{\tilde{\tau}}.$$

and

$$\phi(t) = \left[v^{\gamma}\bar{a}_{\tilde{\tau}}^{1-\gamma} + (1-v)^{\gamma} m(\tilde{\tau})\right]^{\frac{1}{1-\gamma}} e^{\int_t^{\tilde{\tau}} \eta_2(u)du} + \int_t^{\tilde{\tau}} [1 + \mu(s)m(s)]e^{\int_t^s \eta_2(u)du} ds. \tag{29}$$

For $t > \tilde{\tau}$, the solution ϕ is

$$\phi(t) = \left[v^{\gamma}\bar{a}_t^{1-\gamma} + (1-v)^{\gamma}m(t)\right]^{\frac{1}{1-\gamma}}. \tag{30}$$

We re-write $\phi(t)$ as $\phi(t, \tilde{\tau})$, as it contains both t and $\tilde{\tau}$.

To find the optimal stopping time, we can differentiate the value function with respect to $\tilde{\tau}$,

$$\frac{\partial V}{\partial \tilde{\tau}} = \frac{1-\gamma}{\gamma}\tilde{W}^{\gamma}(t)\phi^{-\gamma}(t,\tilde{\tau})\frac{\partial \phi(t,\tilde{\tau})}{\partial \tilde{\tau}},$$

where

$$\begin{aligned} ll\frac{\partial \phi(t,\tilde{\tau})}{\partial \tilde{\tau}} &= \eta_2(\tilde{\tau})[v^{\gamma}\bar{a}_{\tilde{\tau}}^{1-\gamma} + (1-v)^{\gamma}m(\tilde{\tau})]^{\frac{1}{1-\gamma}}e^{\int_t^{\tilde{\tau}}\eta_2(u)du} + [1+\mu(\tilde{\tau})m(\tilde{\tau})]e^{\int_t^{\tilde{\tau}}\eta_2(u)du} \\ &+ \frac{1}{1-\gamma}[v^{\gamma}\bar{a}_{\tilde{\tau}}^{1-\gamma} + (1-v)^{\gamma}m(\tilde{\tau})]^{\frac{\gamma}{1-\gamma}}\Big\{v^{\gamma}(1-\gamma)\bar{a}_{\tilde{\tau}}^{-\gamma}[(\mu(\tilde{\tau})+\rho)\bar{a}_{\tilde{\tau}} - 1] \\ &+ (1-v)^{\gamma}[rm(\tilde{\tau}) - \frac{2}{3}]\Big\}e^{\int_t^{\tilde{\tau}}\eta_2(u)du}. \end{aligned}$$

It then follows, noting our approach for case 1 above, that

$$\frac{\partial V}{\partial \tilde{\tau}} \propto \frac{\partial \phi(t,\tilde{\tau})}{\partial \tilde{\tau}} \tag{31}$$

and so we can determine our optimal stopping time.

2.3. *Case 3: With Bequest, Complete Insurance Market and Wealth Floor*

In addition to resident-funded unit and serviced apartment, some non-profit Australian retirement villages offer a type of unit housing type with an entry contribution. To reside in such place, retirees are required to make a contribution deposit. This deposit might contribute to the maintenance or improvement of a retirement village. In the United States, an entry contribution with monthly fees is a payment option for continuing-care retirement community living. We can treat this contribution requirement as a threshold for the wealth level for retirees to enter a retirement village, that is,

$$W(\tilde{\tau}) \geq R,$$

where R is the certain level of wealth required for retirees to enter a retirement village. This R can be explained as a combination of the management fee, upfront loading fee of the retirement village or the transaction cost of asset relocation.

We assume that retirees would still follow the optimal strategy of consumption, bequest and entering retirement village but change the proportion of wealth invested in the risky asset.

In letting $W(t)$ can fulfil such requirement, we are inspired by Ding et al. [17] and assume that retirees would separate their wealth into two parts: surplus wealth $\tilde{W}(t)$ and protected wealth $\hat{W}(t)$:

$$W(t) = \hat{W}(t) + \tilde{W}(t),$$

where $\hat{W}(t) = h\bar{a}_t$. The protected wealth is used for necessity consumption h, which can be basic living costs and medical costs.

In terms of their surplus wealth, retirees can use it for consumption and bequest purposes. To ensure that $\tilde{W}(t)$ is greater than the certain required level R, retirees can replicate a put option by separating their surplus wealth into two parts:

$$\tilde{W}(t) = \tilde{W}_{\kappa}(t) + \mathcal{P}(\tilde{W}_{\kappa}(t), R, t). \tag{32}$$

The first part $\tilde{W}_\kappa(t)$ is the remaining wealth used for consumption, investment and insurance and the second part is used to replicate an American put option: $\mathcal{P}(W_\kappa(t), R, t))$, with the underlying asset $W_\kappa(t)$ and strike price R.

At the optimal time of entering a retirement village, retirees will then exercise the option to let wealth $W(t)$ have the minimum value R:

$$\tilde{W}(t) = \tilde{W}_\kappa(t) + \max(0, R - \tilde{W}_\kappa(t)) = \max(\tilde{W}_\kappa(t), R).$$

We now define the value function as

$$\begin{aligned} V = & \max_{\pi, \tilde{C}_\kappa, \tilde{L}_\kappa, \tilde{\tau}} \left\{ \int_t^{\tilde{\tau}} \frac{S(s)}{S(t)} e^{-\rho(s-t)} \left[U_1(\tilde{C}_\kappa(s)) + \mu(s) U_2(\tilde{L}_\kappa(s)) \right] ds \right. \\ & \left. + \int_{\tilde{\tau}}^{\infty} \frac{S(s)}{S(t)} e^{-\rho(s-t)} U_1\left(\frac{v\tilde{W}_\kappa(\tilde{\tau})}{\bar{a}_{\tilde{\tau}}}\right) ds + \frac{S(\tilde{\tau})}{S(t)} e^{-\rho(\tilde{\tau}-t)} U_2((1-v)\tilde{W}_\kappa(\tilde{\tau})) \middle| H(s) = h_t,\, t \le s \le \tau \right\} \\ = & \max_{\pi, \tilde{C}_\kappa, \tilde{L}_\kappa, \tilde{\tau}} \left\{ \int_t^{\tilde{\tau}} \frac{S(s)}{S(t)} e^{-\rho(s-t)} \left[U_1(\tilde{C}_\kappa(s)) + \mu(s) U_2(\tilde{W}_\kappa(s)) \right] ds + e^{-\rho(\tilde{\tau}-t)} \frac{S(\tilde{\tau})}{S(t)} \bar{a}_{\tilde{\tau}} U_1\left(\frac{v\tilde{W}_\kappa(\tilde{\tau})}{\bar{a}_{\tilde{\tau}}}\right) \right. \\ & \left. + \frac{S(\tilde{\tau})}{S(t)} e^{-\rho(\tilde{\tau}-t)} U_2((1-v)\tilde{W}_\kappa(\tilde{\tau})) \middle| H(s) = h_t,\, t \le s \le \tau \right\} \end{aligned}$$

with the wealth dynamics

$$d\tilde{W}_\kappa(t) = (r\tilde{W}_\kappa(t) - D(t)\tilde{W}_\kappa(t) - \tilde{C}_\kappa(t) + (\alpha - r)\pi(t)\tilde{W}_\kappa(t) - \tilde{P}_\kappa(t))dt + \sigma\pi(t)\tilde{W}_\kappa(t)dB_t,$$

where $\tilde{C}_\kappa(t)$ and $\tilde{P}_\kappa(t)$ are the consumption and insurance premium at time t by using the surplus wealth $\tilde{W}_\kappa(t)$. The form of the value function is assumed be

$$V = \frac{1}{\gamma} \tilde{W}_\kappa(t)^\gamma a(t)^{1-\gamma},$$

in which the solution of a is in Equations (29) and (30). Then for $\tilde{W}_\kappa(t)$ the optimal consumption $C_\kappa^*(t)$, optimal legacy amount $L_\kappa^*(t)$, optimal proportion invested in risky assets $\pi_\kappa^*(t)$ and optimal insurance premium $P_\kappa^*(t)$ are shown as follows

$$\begin{aligned} C_\kappa^*(t) &= \tilde{W}_\kappa(t) a(t)^{-1} + h, \\ L_\kappa^*(t) &= m(t) \tilde{W}_\kappa(t) a(t)^{-1}, \\ \pi_\kappa^*(t) &= \frac{\alpha - r}{\sigma^2(1-\gamma)} \frac{\tilde{W}(t)}{\hat{W}(t) + \tilde{W}_\kappa(t)}, \\ P_\kappa^*(t) &= (L_\kappa^*(t) - \hat{W}(t) - \tilde{W}_\kappa(t))\mu(t) \end{aligned}$$

and where all controls, apart from $\pi_\kappa^*(t)$, depend on the health state at time t.

To replicate an American put option, we use the delta hedging defined in Huang et al. [39],

$$Delta = \frac{\partial \mathcal{P}}{\partial X} = -N(-d_1(X, K, T-t)) - \int_t^T \frac{r}{\sigma\sqrt{2\pi u}} e^{-\frac{d_1}{2}} du, \tag{33}$$

where $\tilde{d}_1 = \left(\ln \frac{X}{\mathcal{B}} + (r + \frac{\sigma^2}{2})u\right) / \sigma\sqrt{u}$ and $\mathcal{B}(t)$ is defined as the optimal exercise price for underlying asset X. Please see the appendix for details on how to obtain values of $\mathcal{B}(t)$ by using the front-fixing finite difference method. Finally, the value of $\tilde{\tau}$ can be found by following the procedures outlined at the end of our discussion of case 2 above.

3. Parameter Values

In this paper we calibrate our parameters to Australian data to obtain numerical results for a starting age of $t = 65$ to a maximum age of $\tau = 109$. These and other parameters are presented in Table 1 below, and we now turn to a discussion of each. Survival probabilities and the force of mortality are from the [40]. In particular, we use the tabulated values from [40] for $S_1(s)$ and $\mu_1(s)$. To determine survival rates and force of mortality for the sick state, we adopt the frailty model from Su and Sherris [41]. For $S_2(s)$ and $\mu_2(s)$, we simply set $S_2(s) = S_1^u(s)$ and $\mu_2(s) = u \times \mu_1(s)$, where u is defined as a frailty factor and is assumed to be a constant here.

The risky return rate, $\alpha = 8.112\%$, and volatility of risky assets, $\sigma = 0.15685$, are based on the 5-year average rate (from 2009 to 2014) of the ASX 200 (http://www.asx.com.au/). We use the 5-year cash rate (from 2009 to 2014) from the Reserve Bank of Australia (http://www.rba.gov.au/statistics/cash-rate/) as our risk free rate, that is, $r = 3.4\%$. As was done by [20,21], we set the rate of time preference to be equal to the risk-free rate, $\rho = r$. The average annual income, $Y =$ AUD\$47,736, is from [42], and retirees in our model are assumed to have total initial wealth of $10Y$ from previous savings and have no future income. Following [38], the risk-aversion parameter γ is set to be -0.5. In this paper, retirees with bequest motives are assumed to use 80% of their wealth, $v = 0.8$, to annuitise and use the rest as an inter vivos transfor at the time of entering the retirement village. The frailty factor u to be 1.2. Medical costs are assumed to be 1% of total wealth for agents in the healthy state and be 2% of total wealth for agents in the sick state, that is, $D_1 = 0.01$ and $D_2 = 0.02$, respectively. With expenditure as estimated by [43], the necessary consumption amount h is set to be AUD\$12,000 per annum. As mentioned above, we set the maximum survival age to 109.

Table 1. Parameters used in the numerical simulation.

$t = 65$	$\tau = 109$
$q_{12} = 0.04$	$q_{21} = 0.4$
$\alpha = 0.08112$	$r = 0.034$
$\rho = 0.034$	$\sigma = 0.15685$
$Y =$ AUD\$47,736	$\gamma = -0.5$
$v = 0.8$	$u = 1.2$
$D_1 = 0.01$	$D_2 = 0.02$
$h =$ AUD\$12,000 p.a.	

4. Numerical Results and Discussion

In our numerical demonstration, three cases are studied. For the serviced apartment case (case 1), there is no bequest motive and agents have no access to the insurance market prior to entering the retirement village; retirees can purchase neither life insurance nor a variable annuity. Retirees are assumed to be fully annuitisated (purchase of a fixed annuity) at the time of entering the retirement village. For the resident-funded unit case (case 2) and the early contribution unit case (case 3), retirees have bequest motives and can purchase life insurance or a variable annuity in the insurance market prior to entering the retirement village. In addition, retirees are assumed to leave part of their wealth as a pre-inheritance disbursement and use the rest for full annuitisation when entering the retirement village. Furthermore, in the entry contribution case (case 3), a minimum wealth requirement is a prerequisite for retirement village entry. These retirees are then assumed to replicate an American put option to clear this financial hurdle.

We present the expected consumption path for case 1 in Figure 1. From the plot, we see the expected consumption path is hump-shaped—similar to consumption observed in empirical studies [44,45]. This phenomenon can be attributed to both market incompleteness (lack of access to insurance markets) and low wealth levels in the later life stages.

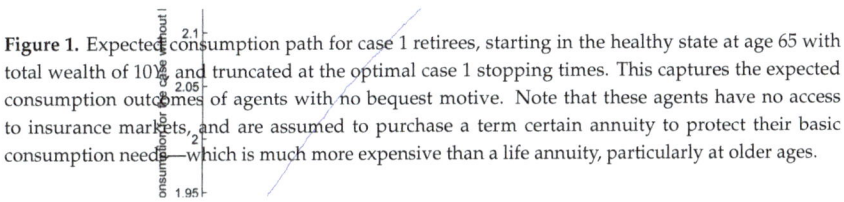

Figure 1. Expected consumption path for case 1 retirees, starting in the healthy state at age 65 with total wealth of $10Y$, and truncated at the optimal case 1 stopping times. This captures the expected consumption outcomes of agents with no bequest motive. Note that these agents have no access to insurance markets, and are assumed to purchase a term certain annuity to protect their basic consumption needs—which is much more expensive than a life annuity, particularly at older ages.

In Figure 2, the expected consumption for cases 2 and 3 rises in line with increasing age. Due to uncertainty arising from the unknown future health state, the market is not entirely complete and thus expected consumption is slightly convex. Compared to Figure 1, Figure 2 reflects the ability of retirees in cases 2 and 3 who have bequest motives to spend more on consumption as they have access to an active insurance market to carry out annuitisation or to purchase insurance. Figure 2 also shows that retirees in case 3 have less consumption than those in case 2, due to the cost of replication of the American put option to ensure they can clear the wealth hurdle required for entry.

Figure 2. Expected consumption, truncated at optimal stopping times, for case 2 and case 3 agents commencing at age 65 in the healthy state with total wealth of $10Y$. The figure captures the expected consumption paths for agents with bequest motives. These agents, in contrast to case 1, have access to perfect insurance markets.

Our calculations indicate health changes impact optimal consumption decisions. As one would expect, agents in the poorer health state consume more than those in the healthy state.

We display the expected wealth path for cases 1, 2 and 3 in Figure 3. For most of time, retirees in case 1 are in possession of more expected wealth than those in case 2 and case 3. As there is no active insurance market in case 1, self-insurance due to precautionary motives is found to be another driver for holding wealth [46]. Hence, Figure 3, suggests retirees tend to draw on their wealth more cautiously when there is no active insurance market. Moreover, the wealth floor requirement in case 3 demands more outgoes and results in less wealth.

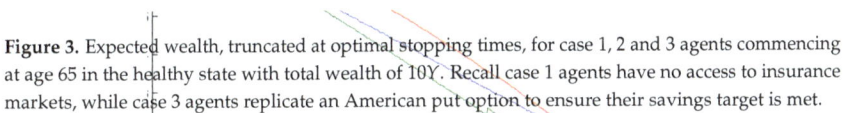

Figure 3. Expected wealth, truncated at optimal stopping times, for case 1, 2 and 3 agents commencing at age 65 in the healthy state with total wealth of $10Y$. Recall case 1 agents have no access to insurance markets, while case 3 agents replicate an American put option to ensure their savings target is met.

The expected insurance premiums for life insurance or receipt of variable annuity income for cases 2 and 3 are displayed in Figure 4. A positive or negative premium value is linked to the demand for life insurance or a variable annuity, respectively. In Figure 4, retirees in cases 2 and 3 are shown to purchase a variable annuity in order to maximise utility. Compared to those in case 2, retirees in case 3 have a lower annuitisation amount, reflecting the resources they have to put toward replicating the American put option to secure their retirement village entry.

We calculate the proportions of total wealth in risky assets for cases 2 and 3, and display the expected paths of the proportion of surplus wealth, $\tilde{W}$, invested in the risky assets in Figure 5. Retirees in case 2 appear to invest a constant proportion of surplus wealth in risky assets, very much in line with the Merton ratio [15,16]. Indeed, the high values seen are characteristic of the Merton ratio for the parameters chosen and also reflect the lack of short-selling/borrowing restrictions in the modelling. The situation is very different for retirees in case 3 who are target savers and who are assumed to replicate an American put option to meet their target. These retirees, who want to

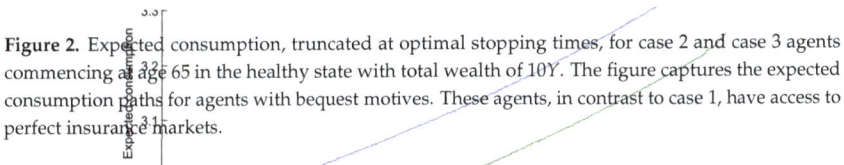

hedge risk, are encouraged to have an increasing risk exposure while they are ageing[4]. In Figure 5, the proportion of surplus wealth for case 3 rises along with age, producing a convex shape. This trend is similar to that reported in the study by Ding et al. [17], in which retirees are assumed to replicate a European put option for their wealth requirement.

Health changes are seen not to impact investment decisions for our health myopic agents as we chose a level of risk aversion, γ, that was constant between health states. It should be clear from our myopic health modelling above that if this value differed between states then this would lead to investment behaviour that differed between states. That is, if investors were more risk averse in the sick state, then they would also invest less in the risky assets (compare Merton ratios).

Figure 4. Expected insurance premiums paid by case 2 and case 3 agents, truncated at optimal stopping times, for those commencing at age 65 in the healthy state with a total wealth of $10Y$. Negative insurance premiums mean the agents are receiving funds from the insurers, that is, they are in receipt of an annuity.

Figure 5. Expected proportion of surplus wealth, $\tilde{W}$, invested in the risky assets, or $\pi^* W/\tilde{W}$, by agents starting at age 65 in the healthy state with a total wealth of $10Y$. The expected paths are truncated at the optimal stopping times for case 2 and case 3, respectively. The differing behaviour of the case 3 target savers is clear.

We also test the impacts of some variables on optimal stopping times. As shown in Table 2, we try different risk-aversion parameter values for case 1, that is, no bequest motive and an incomplete insurance market, and case 2, that is, with bequest motives and a complete insurance market, respectively. With an increasing risk-aversion level for both cases, retirees are shown to be more afraid of potential risks in the markets and prefer an earlier stopping time. The stopping times for case 2 are more sensitive to change in the risk-aversion parameter value. This phenomenon can be explained by the extra risk aversion generated by the bequest motive utility function.

Table 2. Expected stopping times by level of risk aversion for case 1 and case 2 agents aged 65, in the healthy state, and with total wealth of $10Y$—and other parameters as given in Table 1. Increasing levels of risk aversion lead to falling stopping times. Also, the bequest motives of case 2 agents produce results much more sensitive to the level of risk aversion. Indeed, at $\gamma = -0.5$ case 2 agents abandon their conservative behaviour and embrace the risky investment environment.

	Expected Stopping Time (Years)	
Gamma	**Case 1**	**Case 2**
−0.5	11.65	13.22
−0.6	11.04	10.53
−0.7	10.56	8.28
−0.8	10.04	6.23
−0.9	9.54	4.50
−1	9.13	2.99

Table 3 shows the results of our tests on the impact of excess returns, $\alpha - r$, on the stopping time for case 1, that is, no bequest motive and an incomplete insurance market, and case 2, that is, with bequest motives and a complete insurance market, respectively. As we expected, higher excess returns are more attractive to retirees and defer the stopping time for both cases. This trend can be also found in [21].

[4] Retirees are also found to use increasing risk exposure to hedge against risk in other studies, such as Hulley et al. [47] and Thorp et al. [48].

Table 3. Expected stopping times by level of equity premium for case 1 and case 2 agents aged 65, in the healthy state, and with total wealth of 10Y—and other parameters as given in Table 1. Increasing the equity premium results in longer stopping times, as agents exploit the more profitable investment environment. The situation illustrated is for agents with risk aversion of $\gamma = -0.5$, where case 2 agents are less conservative than case 1 agents. With more risk averse agents, this boldness of agents with bequest motives over those without is reversed.

	Expected Stopping Time (Years)	
$\alpha - r$	**Case 1**	**Case 2**
0.02	5.49	6.38
0.03	7.76	9.02
0.04	10.07	11.60
0.05	12.27	13.87
0.06	14.31	16.06

The impact of volatility, σ, on the stopping time for case 1 and case 2 is demonstrated in Table 4. For both two cases, retirees are seen to enter the retirement village earlier when the market is more volatile.

As shown in Table 5, we also study the impact of the frailty factor on the stopping time. In both case 1 and case 2, when retirees are more frail in the sick state, and consequently have more mortality risk, they intend to stop earlier. These findings are in line with [49], who uses a very different (actuarial) approach, to discover that retirees entering retirement villages when they are younger and healthier are financially better off.

Table 4. Expected stopping times by level of market volatility for case 1 and case 2 agents aged 65, in the healthy state, and with total wealth of 10Y—and other parameters as given in Table 1. Increasing market volatility results in shorter stopping times, as agents shy away from the riskier environment. The situation illustrated is for agents with risk aversion of $\gamma = -0.5$, where case 2 agents are less conservative than case 1 agents. With more risk averse agents, this boldness of agents with bequest motives over those without is reversed.

	Expected Stopping Time (Years)	
σ	**Case 1**	**Case 2**
0.12	14.62	16.45
0.13	13.67	15.46
0.14	13.44	14.51
0.15	12.10	13.70
0.16	11.42	12.99

Table 5. Expected stopping times by frailty factor u for case 1 and case 2 agents aged 65, in the healthy state, and with total wealth of 10Y—and other parameters as given in Table 1. Increasing frailty results in shorter stopping times, as less healthy agents choose the safer retirement village world sooner. The situation illustrated is for agents with risk aversion of $\gamma = -0.5$, where case 2 agents are less conservative than case 1 agents. With more risk averse agents, this boldness of agents with bequest motives over those without is reversed.

	Expected Stopping Time (Years)	
u	**Case 1**	**Case 2**
1.1	13.40	14.15
1.2	11.65	13.22
1.3	10.15	12.38
1.4	8.85	11.58

5. Conclusions

This paper provides an innovative contribution in its investigation of several cases of retirees entering retirement villages by using Richard's model with a HARA utility function and dynamic health states. In our research, in which the time of entering the retirement village is the stopping time, we study the optimal strategy with the optimal stopping time for retirees.

We make several different assumptions for bequest motives and the insurance market to mimic the options faced by retirees when entering retirement villages in the real world. In studying these problems we obtain numerical results of consumption, wealth, insurance premiums and stopping times. In our generalised model retirees are assumed to have require a minimum level of consumption as well as facing a future of dynamic health changes and medical costs.

Retirees are found to have divergent consumption and stopping time trends, when the assumptions of bequest motives and the insurance market change. If retirees are assumed to have a bequest motive and access to insurance and annuity products, they are found to annuitise their excess wealth and to have a higher level of consumption. Otherwise, retirees are shown to have less consumption and to hold more wealth for precautionary purposes. Our numerical results indicate the importance of complete insurance markets for self-reliance in retirement—for increasing the consumption level prior to full annuatisation. This finding implies that the existence of a life insurance market for retirees is essential and critical for retirees' financial strategy. Our finding supports the argument of Blake [35] and others for deepening insurance and annuity markets. A new research direction is then suggested in the insurance market in relation to the ageing problem. Stopping times are also impacted by the risk-aversion parameter, excess returns and the frailty factor.

In this paper, we also study the investment proportion in risky assets. In the case where there is a wealth requirement (wealth floor), retirees are assumed to replicate an American put option. In our numerical results, retirees are shown to be more conservative and have an increasing proportion of wealth invested in risky assets in line with their increasing age. This result once again verifies the findings in the existing literature.

Acknowledgments: The authors thank the reviewers for their valuable suggestions. Jinhui Zhang is grateful for research funds from the Faculty of Business and Economics at Macquarie University, Australia. The work of Jiaqin Wei is supported by National Natural Science Foundation of China (11601157).

Author Contributions: Jinhui Zhang and Sachi Purcal conceived and designed the experiments; Jinhui Zhang performed the experiments; Jinhui Zhang and Sachi Purcal analyzed the data; Jiaqin Wei contributed to the mathematical derivations; Jinhui Zhang wrote the paper.

Conflicts of Interest: The authors declare no conflict of interest.

Appendix A. Optimal Exercise Price

Based on the definition of $\mathcal{B}(t)$, that is, the optimal exercise price, the dynamics of the American put option price are the same as those for the price of the European put option, when the $S(t)$ is greater than $\mathcal{B}(t)$. Hence, from Black and Scholes [50], we have

$$\frac{\partial \mathcal{P}}{\partial t} + \frac{1}{2}\sigma^2 X_t^2 \frac{\partial^2 \mathcal{P}}{\partial X_t^2} + rS_{\tilde{t}} - r\mathcal{P} = 0,\ X \in (\mathcal{B}(t), \infty). \tag{A1}$$

The American put options should be exercised at the strike price K when the $S(t)$ is less than $\mathcal{B}(t)$

$$\mathcal{P}(X(t), K, t) = K - X(t), X \in (0, \mathcal{B}(t)). \tag{A2}$$

The boundary condition of the American put option is

$$\lim_{X(t)\to\infty} \mathcal{P}(X(t), K, t) = 0. \tag{A3}$$

The American put option price $\mathcal{P}(X_t, K, t)$ also have the following conditions at the fixed exercise boundary $\mathcal{B}(t)$,

$$\mathcal{P}(\mathcal{B}(t), K, t) = K - \mathcal{B}(t), \quad \frac{\partial \mathcal{P}(\mathcal{B}(t), K, t)}{\partial X} = -1. \tag{A4}$$

At the time of expiration, all unexercised American put options will be exercised or expired. As $\mathcal{B}(\tilde{\tau})$ is the optimal exercise price, the terminal condition is provided by

$$\mathcal{P}(\mathcal{B}(\tilde{\tau}), \tilde{\tau}, K) = 0, \ X \in (\mathcal{B}(\tilde{\tau}), \infty) \text{ with } \tilde{\tau} = 0 \text{ and } \mathcal{B}(0) = K. \tag{A5}$$

To obtain the optimal exercise price $\mathcal{B}(t)$, we use the front fixing finite difference method from Wu and Kwok [51]. We transform the option price $\mathcal{P}(S_t, K, t)$, asset price S_t and the fixed boundary $\mathcal{B}(t)$ respectively, as follows

$$\tilde{\mathcal{P}} = \frac{\mathcal{P}}{K}, \ \tilde{\mathcal{B}}(\tilde{\tau}) = \frac{\mathcal{B}(t)}{K}, \ \tilde{X}(t) = \frac{X(t)}{K}, \ \tilde{K} = \frac{K}{K} = 1,$$

where $\mathcal{P}$ represents the American put option price $\mathcal{P}(X(t), t, K)$ and $\tilde{\mathcal{P}}$ represents the transformed American put option price at time $\tilde{\tau}$ about the underlying asset $\tilde{X}(t)$ and the strike price $\tilde{K}$.

Here the dynamics of $\tilde{\mathcal{P}}$ are described by Equations (A1) and (A2) with $K = 1$. Equations (A3)–(A5) still hold for $\tilde{\mathcal{P}}$, $\tilde{X}$ and $\tilde{\mathcal{B}}$ with $K = 1$.

In Wu and Kwok [51], a new variable $\tilde{y}$ at time $\tilde{\tau}$ which was introduced to transform the the unknown boundary to a known fixed one is defined as

$$\tilde{y}(t) = \ln \frac{\tilde{X}(t)}{\tilde{\mathcal{B}}(t)}. \tag{A6}$$

The process of $\tilde{y}$ is shown as follows:

$$\begin{aligned}
\tilde{y}(t) &= \ln\tilde{X}(t) - \ln\tilde{\mathcal{B}}(t), \\
d\tilde{y}(t) &= d\ln\tilde{X}(t) - d\ln\tilde{\mathcal{B}}(t) \\
&= \left(r - \frac{\sigma^2}{2} + \frac{\tilde{\mathcal{B}}'(t)}{\tilde{\mathcal{B}}(t)} \right) dt + \sigma dB_t.
\end{aligned}$$

Following Wu and Kwok [51], the partial differential equation (PDE) of the new variable $\tilde{y}$ is obtained by forming a direct substitution to Equation (A1):

$$\frac{\partial \tilde{\mathcal{P}}}{\partial t} + \frac{\sigma^2}{2} \frac{\partial^2 \tilde{\mathcal{P}}}{\partial y^2(t)} + (r - \frac{\sigma^2}{2}) \frac{\partial \tilde{\mathcal{P}}}{\partial y(t)} - r\tilde{\mathcal{P}} + \frac{\tilde{\mathcal{B}}'(t)}{\tilde{\mathcal{B}}(t)} \frac{\partial \tilde{\mathcal{P}}}{\partial y(t)} = 0. \tag{A7}$$

Equation (A7) is the PDE of a transformed American put option price $\tilde{\mathcal{P}}$ with fixed boundary $\tilde{\mathcal{B}}(t)$. Using the finite difference scheme defined in Wu and Kwok [51], we can explicitly solve Equation (A7) and obtain the numerical result for $\mathcal{B}(t)$.

Substituting the $\mathcal{B}(t)$ value into equation (33), we can obtain the delta value of an American put option. With this delta value, an American put option can be replicated by risky assets in the market.

References

1. World Health Organization (WHO). World Report on Ageing and Health. 2015. Available online: http://apps.who.int/iris/bitstream/10665/186463/1/9789240694811_eng.png?ua=1 (accessed on 4 July 2016).

2. Australian Institute of Health and Welfare. Australia's Welfare 2013: In Brief. 2013. Available online: http://www.aihw.gov.au/WorkArea/DownloadAsset.aspx?id=60129544075 (accessed on 5 July 2016).
3. Australian Government. Australia's Demographic Challenges. 2004. Available online: http://demographics.treasury.gov.au/content/discussion.asp (accessed on 4 July 2016).
4. Australian Institute of Health and Welfare. Patterns in Use of Aged Care: 2002–03 to 2010–11. 2014. Available online: http://www.aihw.gov.au/WorkArea/DownloadAsset.aspx?id=60129548006 (accessed on 5 July 2016).
5. Australian Institute of Health and Welfare. The Residential Aged Care and Aged Care Packages in the Community 2012–13 Web Report. 2014. Available online: http://www.aihw.gov.au/aged-care/residential-and-community-2012-13/ (accessed on 5 July 2016).
6. Glass, A.P.; Skinner, J. Retirement communities: We know what they are ... or do we? *J. Hous. Elderly* **2013**, *27*, 61–88.
7. Bernard, M.; Bartlam, B.; Sim, J.; Biggs, S. Housing and care for older people: Life in an English purpose-built retirement village. *Ageing Soc.* **2007**, *27*, 555–578.
8. Property Council of Australia. Retirement Villages and Residential Aged Care Facilities Compared. 2013. Available online: http://www.retirementliving.org.au/industry/services/facts/ (accessed on 5 July 2016).
9. McDonald, J. Community participation in an Australian retirement village. *Aust. J. Ageing* **1996**, *15*, 167–171.
10. Buys, L.R. Life in a retirement village: Implications for contact with community and village friends. *Gerontology* **2000**, *47*, 55–59.
11. Kingston, P.; Bernard, M.; Biggs, S.; Nettleton, H. Assessing the health impact of age-specific housing. *Health Soc. Care Community* **2001**, *9*, 228–234.
12. Lord, S.R.; Castell, S.; Corcoran, J.; Dayhew, J.; Matters, B.; Shan, A; Williams, P. The effect of group exercise on physical functioning and falls in frail older people living in retirement villages: A randomized, controlled trial. *J. Am. Geriatr. Soc.* **2003**, *51*, 1685–1692.
13. Property Council of Australia. Retirement Village Resident Profile. 2013. Available online: http://www.retirementliving.org.au/industry/services/facts/ (accessed on 5 July 2016).
14. Australian Bureau of Statistics. Gender Indicators, Australia, Jan 2013. Available online: http://www.abs.gov.au/ausstats/abs@.nsf/Lookup/4125.0main+features3110Jan%202013 (accessed on 5 July 2016).
15. Merton, R.C. Lifetime portfolio selection under uncertainty: The continuous-time case. *Rev. Econ. Stat.* **1969**, *51*, 247–257.
16. Merton, R.C. Optimum consumption and portfolio rules in a continuous-time model. *J. Econ. Theory* **1971**, *3*, 373–413.
17. Ding, J.; Kingston, G.; Purcal, S. Dynamic asset allocation when bequests are luxury goods. *J. Econ. Dyn. Control* **2014**, *38*, 65–71.
18. Yaari, M.E. Uncertain lifetime, life insurance, and the theory of the consumer. *Rev. Econ. Stud.* **1965**, *32*, 137–150.
19. Richard, S.F. Optimal consumption, portfolio and life insurance rules for an uncertain lived individual in a continuous time model. *J. Financ. Econ.* **1975**, *2*, 187–203.
20. Milevsky, M.A.; Young, V.R. Annuitization and asset allocation. *J. Econ. Dyn. Control* **2007**, *31* 3138–3177.
21. Kingston, G.; Thorp, S. Annuitization and asset allocation with HARA utility. *J. Pension Econ. Financ.* **2005**, *4*, 225–248.
22. Dybvig, P. H.; Liu, H. Lifetime consumption and investment: retirement and constrained borrowing. *J. Econ. Theory* **2010**, *145*, 885–907.
23. Barucci, E.; Marazzina, D. Optimal investment, stochastic labor income and retirement. *Appl. Math. Comput.* **2012**, *218*, 5588–5604.
24. Rosen, H.S.; Wu, S. Portfolio choice and health status. *J. Financ. Econ.* **2004**, *72*, 457–484.
25. Bernheim, B.D.; Shleifer, A.; Summers, L.H. The strategic bequest motive. *J. Political Econ.* **1985**, *93*, 1045–1076.
26. Edwards, R.D. Health risk and portfolio choice. *J. Bus. Econ. Stat.* **2008**, *26*, 472–485.
27. Yogo, M. Portfolio choice in retirement: Health risk and the demand for annuities, housing, and risky assets. *J. Monet. Econ.* **2009**, *80*, 17–34.
28. De Nardi, M.; French, E.; Jones, J.B. Why do the elderly save? The role of medical expenses. *J. Political Econ.* **2010**, *118*, 39–75.
29. Kingston, G.; Fisher, L. Down the retirement risk zone with gun and camera. *Econ. Pap.* **2014**, *33*, 153–162.

30. Pfau, W.D.; Kitces, M.E. Reducing Retirement Risk With a Rising Equity Glide-Path (12 September 2013). Available online: http://ssrn.com/abstract=2324930 (accessed on 5 July 2016).
31. Haberman, S.; Pitacco, E. *Actuarial Models for Disability Insurance*; Chapman & Hall/CRC: New York, NY, USA, 1999.
32. Ross, S.M. *Introduction to Probability Models*; Academic Press: New York, NY, USA, 2007.
33. Guo, X. An explicit solution to an optimal stopping problem with regime switching. *J. Appl. Prob.* **2001**, *38*, 464–481.
34. Iskhakov, F.; Thorp, S.; Bateman, H. Optimal annuity purchases for Australian retirees. *Econ. Rec.* **2015**, *91*, 139–154.
35. Blake, D. Annuity markets: Problems and solutions. *Geneva Pap. Risk Ins. Issues Pract.* **1999**, *24*, 358–375.
36. Zhu, J. Dividend Optimization For A Regime-Switching Diffusion Model With Restricted Dividend Rates. *ASTIN Bull.* **2014**, *44*, 459–494.
37. Øksendal, B. *Stochastic Differential Equations*, 5th ed.; Springer Series; Springer: New York, NY, USA, 2003.
38. Purcal, S.; Piggott, J. Explaining low annuity demand: An optimal portfolio application to Japan. *J. Risk Insur.* **2008**, *75*, 493–516.
39. Huang, J.Z.; Subrahmanyam, M.G.; Yu, G.G. Pricing and hedging American options: A recursive investigation method. *Rev. Financ. Stud.* **1996**, *9*, 277–300.
40. Australian Government Actuary. Australian Life Tables 2010–12: Males. Available online: http://www.aga.gov.au/publications/life_table_2010-12/default.asp (accessed on 5 July 2016).
41. Su, S.; Sherris, M. Heterogeneity of Australian population mortality and implications for a viable life annuity market. *Insur. Math. Econ.* **2012**, *51*, 322–332.
42. Australian Bureau of Statistics. Household Income and Income Distribution, Australia, 2011–12. Available online: http://www.abs.gov.au/AUSSTATS/abs@.nsf/DetailsPage/6523.02011-12?OpenDocument (accessed on 5 July 2016).
43. Australian Bureau of Statistics. Household Expenditure Survey, Australia: Summary of Results, 2009–10. Available online: http://www.abs.gov.au/AUSSTATS/abs@.nsf/DetailsPage/6530.02009-10?OpenDocument (accessed on 5 July 2016).
44. Gourinchas, P.O.; Parker, J.A. Consumption over the life cycle. *Econometrica* **2002**, *70*, 47–89.
45. Fernández-Villaverde, J.; Krueger, D. Consumption over the life cycle: Facts from consumer expenditure survey data. *Rev. Econ. Stat.* **2007**, *89*, 552–565.
46. Ameriks, J.; Caplin, A.; Laufer, S.; Van Nieuwerburgh, S. The joy of giving or assisted living? Using strategic surveys to separate public care aversion from bequest motives. *J. Financ.* **2011**, *66*, 519–561.
47. Hulley, H.; Mckibbin, R.; Pedersen, A.; Thorp, S. Means-tested public pensions, portfolio choice and decumulation in retirement. *Econ. Rec.* **2013**, *89*, 31–51.
48. Thorp, S.; Kingston, G.; Bateman, H. Financial engineering for Australian annuitants. In *Retirement Provision in Scary Markets*; Bateman, H., Ed.; Edward Elgar: Cheltenham, UK; Northampton, MA, USA, 2007; pp. 123–144.
49. Kyng, T.; Stolz, B. *An Actuarial Analysis of Australian Retirement Village Contracts: Consumer Perspective*; Unpublished Paper; Macquarie University: Sydney, Australia, 2016.
50. Black, F.; Scholes, M. The pricing of options and corporate liabilities. *J. Political Econ.* **1973**, *81*, 637–654.
51. Wu, L.; Kwok, Y.K. A front-fixing finite difference method for the valuation of American options. *J. Financ. Eng.* **1997**, *6*, 83–97.

risks

MDPI

Article

Assessment of Policy Changes to Means-Tested Age Pension Using the Expected Utility Model: Implication for Decisions in Retirement

Johan G. Andréasson [1,2,*] and Pavel V. Shevchenko [3]

1. School of Mathematical and Physical Sciences, University of Technology, Sydney, Broadway, PO Box 123, NSW 2007, Australia
2. Data61 CSIRO, Australia
3. Department of Applied Finance and Actuarial Studies, Macquarie University, Sydney, NSW 2109, Australia; pavel.shevchenko@mq.edu.au

* Correspondence: johan.andreasson@uts.edu.au

Academic Editor: Mogens Steffensen
Received: 7 July 2017; Accepted: 6 September 2017; Published: 9 September 2017

Abstract: Means-tested pension policies are typical for many countries, and the assessment of policy changes is critical for policy makers. In this paper, we consider the Australian means-tested Age Pension. In 2015, two important changes were made to the popular Allocated Pension accounts: the income means-test is now based on deemed income rather than account withdrawals, and the income-test deduction no longer applies. We examine the implications of the new changes in regard to optimal decisions for consumption, investment and housing. We account for regulatory minimum withdrawal rules that are imposed by regulations on Allocated Pension accounts, as well as the 2017 asset-test rebalancing. The policy changes are considered under a utility-maximising life cycle model solved as an optimal stochastic control problem. We find that the new rules decrease the advantages of planning the consumption in relation to the means-test, while risky asset allocation becomes more sensitive to the asset-test. The difference in optimal drawdown between the old and new policy is only noticeable early in retirement until regulatory minimum withdrawal rates are enforced. However, the amount of extra Age Pension received by many households is now significantly higher due to the new deeming income rules, which benefit wealthier households who previously would not have received Age Pension due to the income-test and minimum withdrawals.

Keywords: dynamic programming; stochastic control; optimal policy; retirement; means-tested age pension; defined contribution pension

JEL Classification: D14 (Household Saving; Personal Finance); D91 (Intertemporal Household Choice; Life Cycle Models and Saving); G11 (Portfolio Choice; Investment Decisions); C61 (Optimization Techniques; Programming Models; Dynamic Analysis)

1. Introduction

Means-tested pension policies become more important globally, as the general population ages and the life expectancy improves. The policies are country-specific to meet government budgets and are updated regularly. Since the Australian retirement system is relatively young, the long-term effects of this new pension system are not yet known. Changes to policy, means-tests and tax rules are expected to occur frequently due to fiscal reasons and once the effects of policy changes to a retiree's personal wealth (and the economy in general) become evident. Variables directly related to the means-test such as entitlement age, means-test thresholds, taper rates and pension payments can all be adjusted to meet budget needs by the government. On a larger scale, regulatory changes may include whether the family home is included in the means-tested assets, the elimination of minimum withdrawal[1] rules, changes in mandatory savings rates or additional taxes on superannuation savings. From a mathematical modelling perspective, this poses difficulties in terms of future model validity, as regulatory risk and policy changes can quickly make a model obsolete if it is not modified to account for the new rules.

The Australian pension system is based on the compulsory superannuation[2] guarantee (paid by employers), private savings, and a government-provided means-tested Age Pension. The superannuation guarantee, supporting both defined-benefit and defined-contribution pension plans, mandates that employers contribute a fixed percentage of the employee's gross earnings to a superannuation fund, which accumulates and is invested until retirement. The current contribution rate is set to 9.5%, and additional contributions attract certain tax benefits. Private savings are comprised of these additional contributions, but also include savings outside the superannuation fund such as investment accounts, dwelling and other assets. Finally, the Age Pension is a government-managed safety net, which provides the retiree with a means-tested Age Pension. This means-test determines whether the retiree qualifies for full, partial or no Age Pension once the entitlement age is reached. In this means-test, income and assets are evaluated individually, and a certain taper rate reduces the maximum payments once income or assets surpass certain thresholds (which are subject to family status and home-ownership). Income from different sources is also treated differently; financial assets are expected to generate income at the so-called deeming rate, while income streams such as labour and annuity payments that are not from a pension account are assessed based on their nominal value.

The motivation for this paper was the recent changes for Allocated Pension accounts, where assets are now assumed to generate a deemed income and no longer have an income-test deduction. Account-based pensions (such as Allocated Pension accounts) are accounts that have been purchased with superannuation and generate an income stream throughout retirement. Such an account does not have tax on investment earnings and is subject to regulatory minimum withdrawal rates each year, which increase with age. Prior to 2015, these types of accounts allowed for an income-test deduction that was determined upon account opening, and withdrawals were considered to be income in the means-test. The income-test deduction allowed the retiree to withdraw slightly more every year without missing out on Age Pension. However, in 2015, the rules changed. Existing accounts were 'grandfathered' and will continue to be assessed under the old rules, while the new rules will be applied to any new accounts. The arguments for the changes were simplicity (people with the same level of assets should be treated the same, regardless of how the assets are invested), to increase incentive to maximise total disposable income rather than maximising Age Pension payments and to simplify how capital growth and interest-paying investments are assessed (Department of Social Services 2017). From a fiscal point of view, the recommendation to introduce the new rules was based on estimated unchanged costs[3] (Henry 2009); however, the 2015–2016 budget stated expected savings of $57 million for 2015–2016 and $129 million and $136 million for subsequent years (The Commonwealth of Australia 2015). The allocation to Age Pension in the 2015–2016 budget includes all changes to the Age Pension in a combined viewpoint, so the specific impact of the deeming rule changes on the government is not known.

1 Certain account types for retirement savings have a minimum withdrawal rate once the owner is retired.
2 The pension system in Australia is called 'superannuation'.
3 The recommendations to introduce deeming was made in Henry (2009), where the fiscal sustainability is evaluated with the general equilibrium model 'KPMG Econtech MM900' (KPMG 2010). The model shows the estimation over a 10-year window; hence, we do not know the short-term or year-to-year estimates. In addition to this, the model includes additional suggested tax- and budget-related changes; hence, the effect of introducing deeming rates cannot be isolated.

Problems with decisions that span over multiple time periods are typically modelled with life cycle models and solved with backwards recursion (Cocco et al. 2005; Cocco and Gomes 2012; Blake et al. 2014, to name a few). Life cycle modelling based on utility theory originates from Fisher (1930) and was later updated by Modigliani and Brumberg (1954), who observed that individuals make consumption decisions based on resources available at the current time, as well as over the course of their lifetimes. The key work for early models was laid out by Yaari (1964, 1965), who extended the model with uncertain lifetime and studied the optimal choice of life insurance and annuities, while Samuelson (1969) and Merton (1969, 1971) studied the problem in relation to optimal portfolio allocation. Nowadays, there are extended theories available such as prospect theory (Kahneman and Tversky 1979) or stochastic dominance theory (Kopa et al. 2016; Levy 2006). While prospect theory is based on the findings that individuals often violate expected utility maximization, the stochastic dominance is developed on the foundation of the expected utility paradigm. There is a plethora of research on retirement modelling internationally (Boender et al. 1997; Dupačová and Polívka 2009; Hilli et al. 2007; Vitali et al. 2017, to name a few), but there is still rather limited research modelling the Australian Age Pension, and even less that enforces the minimum withdrawal rules. The model in Ding (2014) does not constrain drawdown with minimum withdrawal, which would limit the author from finding a semi-closed form solution. Similarly, other authors that focus on means-tested pension also do not enforce minimum withdrawal rates, such as Hulley et al. (2013), who use Constant Relative Risk Aversion (CRRA) utility to understand consumption and investment behaviour, or Iskhakov et al. (2015), who investigate how annuity purchases change in relation to Age Pension. It should be noted that their assumptions do not include Allocated Pension accounts; thus, minimum withdrawal rates may not apply. However, as the majority of Australian retirees own an Allocated Pension account (or similar phased withdrawal products), there is surprisingly limited research conducted on the implications of the regulatory minimum withdrawal rates (Andreasson et al. 2017). The exception is Bateman et al. (2007), who compare the welfare of retirees when the current minimum withdrawal rates were introduced in 2007 against the previous rules and alternative drawdown strategies. The authors use a rather simple CRRA model to examine the effect of different risk aversion and investment strategies, but find that the minimum withdrawal rules increase the welfare for retirees, though slightly less than optimal drawdown does. In Andreasson et al. (2017), the minimum withdrawal rules are included in part of the model outcome, but are by no means exhaustive and only provide a brief introduction to the effects. These rules are designed to exhaust the retiree's account around Year 100; however, it is empirically observed that after Year 85 (subject to investment returns), the withdrawn dollar amount starts decreasing quickly. In a recent report from Plan For Life (2016), it is identified that only 5% of retirees exhaust their accounts completely, though this number is expected to increase as life expectancy increases and the population ages. They find that retirees tend to follow the minimum withdrawal rules as guidelines for their own withdrawal, as few withdraw more than the minimum amount. This is further confirmed in Shevchenko (2016). However, Rice Warner (2015) argues that the minimum withdrawal rates should be cut by 25–50% to prevent retirees from exhausting their superannuation prematurely due to increased longevity. They suggest that the current rates are simply too high for many retirees, thus not sustainable for people living longer than the average life expectancy, and are significantly higher than what is optimal in Andreasson et al. (2017). In addition, it has been discussed in the media whether deeming rates are set too high, and as retirees tend to have a low proportion of risky assets while in retirement (Spicer et al. 2016), this often results in lower returns on assets than what is assumed in the income-test. The Australian term rates[4] are below the upper deeming rate; hence, the effective return on the portfolio is generally lower than the deeming rate. This, in turn, will affect the Age Pension payments for the retiree.

[4] As of 4 May 2017, the current three-month rate offered by Commonwealth Bank is 2.05% (https://www.commbank.com.au/personal/accounts/term-deposits/rates-fees.html, accessed on June 8, 2017).

In this paper, we demonstrate how the assessment of policy changes can be done via an expected utility model in the Australian pension system. We adapt the model previously developed in Andreasson et al. (2017) to examine the impact of this policy change on an individual retiree. This model captures retirement behaviour in the decumulation phase of Australian retirees subject to consumption, housing, investment, bequest and government-provided means-tested Age Pension and is an extension with stochastic factors (mortality, risky investments and sequential family status) to what was originally presented in Ding (2014); Ding et al. (2014). The contribution of this paper is to improve the understanding of the effect deeming rate-based policies have on a typical retiree's optimal decisions, both in terms of how the optimal behaviour changes and whether the retiree is better or worse off. We also examine the impact high and low risky returns have on the retiree in relation to deeming rates. We then examine the differences in optimal decisions between an Allocated Pension account opened prior to 2015 with the one opened after 2015, as well as compare the results with the recent 2017 asset-test adjustments. The paper is structured as follows: In Section 2, we summarise the model and present the Age Pension function, as well as explain the parameterization and policies. Section 3 contains a discussion of the results. Finally, in Section 4, we present our concluding remarks.

2. Model

We begin with the setup of the utility model framework for the retirement phase. We adopt the model from Andreasson et al. (2017), where the Age Pension function has been adjusted to account for the policy changes in 2015. For a complete description of the model, its calibration to the data and numerical solution and a discussion of the construction and assumptions, please see that reference.

The objective of the retiree is to maximise expected utility generated from consumption, housing and bequest. The retiree starts off with a total wealth W and, at the year of retirement $t = t_0$, is given the option to allocate wealth into housing H (if he/she is already a homeowner, he/she has the option to adjust current allocation by up- or down-sizing). The remaining (liquid) wealth $W_{t_0} = \mathrm{W} - H$ is placed in an Allocated Pension account, which is a special type of account that does not have a tax on investment earnings and is subject to the regulatory minimum withdrawal rates. A retiree can either start as a couple or single household, where this information is contained in a family status random variable:

$$G_t \in \mathcal{G} = \{\Delta, 0, 1, 2\}, \tag{1}$$

where Δ corresponds to the agent already deceased at time t, 0 corresponds to the agent who died during $(t-1, t]$ and 1 and 2 correspond to the agent being alive at time t in a single or couple household, respectively. Evolution in time of the family state variable G_t is subject to survival probabilities. In the case of a couple household, there is a risk each time period that one of the spouses passes away, in which case, it is treated as a single household model for the remaining years.

At the start of each year $t = t_0, t_0 + 1, ..., T-1$, the retiree will receive a means-tested Age Pension P_t and will decide what amount of saved liquid wealth W_t will be used for consumption (defined as proportion drawdown α_t of liquid wealth). Consumption each period equals received Age Pension and drawdowns:

$$C_t = P_t + \alpha_t W_t. \tag{2}$$

Any remaining liquid wealth after drawdown can be invested in a risky or a risk-free asset, where δ_t determines the proportion invested in the risky asset. Then, the change in wealth after the decision to the next period is given by:

$$W_{t+1} = [W_t - \alpha_t W_t]\left[\delta_t e^{Z_{t+1}} + (1-\delta_t)e^{r_t}\right], \tag{3}$$

where Z_{t+1} is the stochastic return on risky assets modelled as independent and identically distributed random variables from a normal distribution $\mathcal{N}(\mu, \sigma)$ with mean μ defined in real[5] terms and variance σ^2. Any wealth not allocated to risky assets is assumed to generate a deterministic real risk-free return r_t (risk-free interest rate adjusted for inflation). Each period the agent receives utility based on the current state of family status G_t:

$$R_t(W_t, G_t, \alpha_t, H) = \begin{cases} U_C(C_t, G_t, t) + U_H(H, G_t), & \text{if } G_t = 1, 2, \\ U_B(W_t, H), & \text{if } G_t = 0, \\ 0, & \text{if } G_t = \Delta. \end{cases} \quad (4)$$

That is, if the agent is alive, he/she receives reward (utility) based on consumption U_C and housing U_H, if he/she died during the year, the reward comes from the bequest U_B, and if he/she is dead, there is no reward. Note that the reward received when the agent is alive depends on whether the family state is a couple or single household due to different utility parameters and Age Pension thresholds.

Finally, $t = T$ is the maximum age of the agent beyond which survival is deemed impossible, and the terminal reward function is given as:

$$\widetilde{R}(W_T, G_T, H) = \begin{cases} U_B(W_T, H), & \text{if } G_T \geq 0, \\ 0, & \text{if } G_T = \Delta. \end{cases} \quad (5)$$

The retiree has to find the decisions that maximise expected utility with respect to the decisions for consumption, investment and housing. This is defined as a stochastic control problem, where decisions (controls) at time t depend on the realisation of stochastic state variables W_t and G_t at time t with unknown future realisations. Then, the overall problem of maximization of expected utility is defined as:

$$\max_H \left[\sup_{\alpha,\delta} \mathbb{E}_{t_0}^{\alpha,\delta} \left[\beta_{t_0,T} \widetilde{R}(W_T, G_T, H) + \sum_{t=t_0}^{T-1} \beta_{t_0,t} R_t(W_t, G_t, \alpha_t, H) \,\middle|\, W_{t_0}, G_{t_0} \right] \right], \quad (6)$$

where $\mathbb{E}_{t_0}^{\alpha,\delta}[\cdot]$ is the expectation with respect to the state variables W_t and G_t for $t = t_0 + 1, ..., T$, conditional on the state variables at time $t = t_0$ if we use controls $\boldsymbol{\alpha} = (\alpha_{t_0}, \alpha_{t_0+1}, ..., \alpha_{T-1})$ and $\boldsymbol{\delta} = (\delta_{t_0}, \delta_{t_0+1}, ..., \delta_{T-1})$ for $t = t_0, t_0 + 1, ..., T - 1$. The subjective discount rate $\beta_{t,t'}$ is a proxy for personal impatience between time t and t'. Note that the death probabilities are not explicit in the objective function, but affect the evolution of the family status and, thus, are involved in the calculation of the conditional expectation. This problem can be solved numerically with dynamic programming by using backwards induction of the Bellman equation. The state variables W and H are discretized on a grid, and the Gaussian quadrature method is used for integration between periods; for details, see Andreasson et al. (2017).

2.1. Utility Functions

Utility in the model is measured with time-separable additive functions based on the commonly-used Hyperbolic Absolute Risk Aversion (HARA) utility function, subject to different utility parameters for singles and couples, as follows.

---

5 By defining the model in real terms (adjusted for inflation), time-dependent variables do not have to include inflation, which otherwise would be an additional stochastic variable.

- Consumption preferences: It is assumed that utility comes from consumption exceeding the consumption floor, weighted with a time-dependent "health" status proxy[6]. The utility function for consumption is defined as:

$$U_C(C_t, G_t, t) = \frac{1}{\psi^{t-t_0}\gamma_d}\left(\frac{C_t - \overline{c}_d}{\zeta_d}\right)^{\gamma_d}, \quad d = \begin{cases} \mathrm{C}, & \text{if } G_t = 2 \quad \text{(couple)}, \\ \mathrm{S}, & \text{if } G_t = 1 \quad \text{(single)}, \end{cases} \tag{7}$$

  where $\gamma_d \in (-\infty, 0)$ is the risk aversion and $\overline{c}_d$ is the consumption floor parameters. The scaling factor ζ_d normalises the utility a couple receives in relation to a single household. The utility parameters γ_d, $\overline{c}_d$ and ζ_d are subject to family state G_t; hence, they will have different values for couple and single households. Furthermore, $\psi \in [1, \infty)$ is the utility parameter for the "health" status proxy, which controls the declining consumption between current time t and time of retirement t_0.

- Bequest preferences: Utility is also received from luxury bequest, where the utility function for bequest is then defined as:

$$U_B(W_t, H) = \left(\frac{\theta}{1-\theta}\right)^{1-\gamma_S} \frac{\left(\frac{\theta}{1-\theta}a + W_t + H\right)^{\gamma_S}}{\gamma_S}. \tag{8}$$

  Here, W_t is the liquid assets available for bequest; H is the value of the home and γ_S the risk aversion parameters for single households[7]. The parameter $\theta \in [0, 1)$ is the degree of altruism, which controls the preference of bequest over consumption, and $a \in \mathbb{R}^+$ is the threshold for luxury bequest up to where the retiree leaves no bequest[8].

  Note that the inclusion of housing in the bequest function simply adjusts the threshold for luxury bequest, as the allocation to housing is a one-off decision and remains constant after retirement. Because of this, if the retiree is a homeowner, then the marginal utility of bequest will be lower for a given liquid wealth; hence, additional consumption is preferred. The optimal consumption with respect to liquid wealth will have the same shape, although be slightly higher with higher house values. This justifies the simplification in Andreasson et al. (2017), where housing has been dropped from the bequest, as it is conceptually the same and avoids an extra state variables, while the impact on optimal control is marginal.

- Housing preferences: The utility from owning a home comes in the form of preferences over renting, but is approximated by the home value. The housing utility is defined as:

$$U_H(H, G_t) = \frac{1}{\gamma_H}\left(\frac{\lambda_d H}{\zeta_d}\right)^{\gamma_H}, \tag{9}$$

  where γ_H is the risk aversion parameter for housing (allowed to be different from risk aversion for consumption and bequest), ζ_d is the same scaling factor as in Equation (7), $H > 0$ is the market value of the family home at time of purchase t_0 and $\lambda_d \in (0, 1]$ is the preference of housing defined as a proportion of the market value.

---

6 Note that the purpose is not to model health among the retirees, but rather to explain decreasing consumption with age.

7 The risk aversion is considered to be the same as consumption risk aversion for singles since a couple is expected to become a single household before bequeathing assets.

8 Because the marginal utility is constant for the bequest utility with zero wealth, in a model with perfect certainty and CRRA utility, the optimal solution will suggest consumption up to level a before it is optimal to save wealth for bequest (Lockwood 2014).

2.2. Policies and Scenarios

We apply the model under three different policies that represent recent changes in the Australian Age Pension system, as well as high and low expected risky asset return scenarios. The expected return is chosen in such a way that a typical retirement portfolio will either generate larger or smaller asset growth than assumed by the deeming rates. A summary of the policies with the Age Pension rates and means-test assumption is shown in Table 1.

Policy 1, Pre-January 2015 (PRE2015): The first policy reflects the means-test and policy rules prior to 1 January 2015, which is what the majority of Australian retirees are being tested under. Any drawdown from the Allocated Pension account is counted towards the income-test, where minimum withdrawal rates impose a lower bound on optimal consumption (withdrawals from liquid wealth must be larger or equal to these rates).

Policy 2, Post-January 2015 (POST2015): This policy focuses on the changes for the income-test of Allocated Pension accounts. The income-test now uses deemed income rather than drawdown; thus, the liquid wealth is used in both the asset and income-test. The retiree can therefore withdraw more liquid wealth without missing out on Age Pension payments.

Policy 3, asset-test changes January 2017 (POST2017): On 1 January 2017, the thresholds of the asset-test were 'rebalanced', hence changed significantly. The thresholds for the asset-test increased, and the taper rate doubled. This effectively means that retirees will now receive full Age Pension for a higher level of wealth, but once the asset-test binds, the partial Age Pension will decrease twice as fast, causing them to receive no Age Pension at a lower level of wealth than before. No adjustments were made to the full Age Pension or income-test threshold.

Table 1. Age Pension rates, thresholds and taper rates used in the means-test for each policy variation.

	PRE2015	POST2015	POST2017
Full Age Pension singles (P^S_{max})	\$22,721	\$22,721	\$22,721
Full Age Pension couples (P^C_{max})	\$34,252	\$34,252	\$34,252
Income-Test	Drawdown	Deemed	Deemed
Threshold singles (L^S_I)	\$4264	\$4264	\$4264
Threshold couples (L^C_I)	\$7592	\$7592	\$7592
Rate of reduction (ϖ^d_I)	\$0.5	\$0.5	\$0.5
Deeming threshold singles (κ^S)	-	\$49,200	\$49,200
Deeming threshold couples (κ^C)	-	\$81,600	\$81,600
Deeming rate below κ^d (ς_-)	-	1.75%	1.75%
Deeming rate above κ^d (ς_+)	-	3.25%	3.25%
Asset-Test			
Threshold homeowners singles ($L_A^{S,h=1}$)	\$209,000	\$209,000	\$250,000
Threshold homeowners couples ($L_A^{C,h=1}$)	\$296,500	\$296,500	\$375,000
Threshold non-homeowners singles ($L_A^{S,h=0}$)	\$360,500	\$360,500	\$450,000
Threshold non-homeowners couples ($L_A^{C,h=0}$)	\$448,000	\$448,000	\$575,000
Rate of reduction (ϖ^d_A)	\$0.039	\$0.039	\$0.078

2.3. Age Pension

The Age Pension rules state that the entitlement age is 65 for both males and females[9], with the current means-test thresholds and taper rates for January 2017 presented in Table 1 (column 'POST2017')

9 As of 1 July 2017, this increased to 65.5 years for people born after 1 July 1952, but for our dataset, the entitlement age was 65. Already retired Australians might have had earlier entitlement ages.

and discussed in detail later in this section. All retirees entitled to Age Pension can receive at most the full Age Pension, which decreases as assets or income increases and is determined by the income- and asset-test. All income streams of Allocated Pension accounts opened after 1 January 2015 are now based on deemed income, while accounts opened prior to this are 'grandfathered'; hence, they will continue to be assessed under the old rules (Department of Social Services 2017). The newer rules have also introduced a 'work bonus' deduction for the income-test, but as the model assumes the retiree is no longer in the workforce, this has been left out.

2.3.1. Deemed Income

Deemed income refers to the assumed returns from financial assets, without reference to the actual returns on the assets held. The deemed income only applies to financial assets and account-based income streams and is calculated as a progressive rate of assets. Therefore, the income-test can depend on both labour income (if any), deemed income from financial investments not held in the Allocated Pension account, drawdown from Allocated Pension accounts if opened prior to 2015 or deemed income on such accounts if opened after 1 January 2015.

The deeming rates are subject to change in relation to interest rates and stock market performance[10]. Two different deeming rates may apply based on the value of the account: a lower rate ς_- for assets under the deeming threshold κ_d and a higher rate ς_+ for assets exceeding the threshold, as shown in Table 1.

2.3.2. Age Pension Function

The Age Pension received is modelled with respect to the current liquid assets, where the account value is used for the asset-test. Since the model assumption states that no labour income is possible, all income for the income-test comes from either deemed income (POST2015, POST2017) or generated from withdrawals of liquid assets (PRE2015). The Age Pension function can thus be defined as:

$$P_t := f(W_t) = \max\left[0, \min\left[P^d_{\max}, \min\left[P_A, P_I\right]\right]\right], \tag{10}$$

where $P^d_{\max}$ is the full Age Pension, P_A is the asset-test and P_I is the income-test functions. The P_A function is the same for rules prior and post 2015 and is defined as:

$$P_A := P^d_{\max} - (W_t - L^{d,h}_A)\varpi^d_A, \tag{11}$$

where $L^{d,h}_A$ is the threshold for the asset-test and ϖ^d_A the taper rate for assets exceeding the thresholds. Superscript d is a categorical index indicating couple or single household status as defined in Equation (7). The variables are subject to whether it is a single or couple household, and the threshold for the asset-test is also subject to whether the household is a homeowner or not ($h = \{0,1\}$). Although the P_A function is the same for both the old and new policies, the P_I function is different. For the deeming rate-based policies, it can be written as:

$$P_I := P^d_{\max} - (P_D(W_t) - L^d_I)\varpi^d_I, \tag{12}$$

$$P_D(W_t) = \varsigma_- \min\left[W_t, \kappa^d\right] + \varsigma_+ \max\left[0, W_t - \kappa^d\right], \tag{13}$$

---

10 The current rates are at a historical low. In 2008, the deeming rates ς_-/ς_+ were as high as 4%/6%, but in March 2013, they were set to 2.5%/4% due to decreasing interest rates, then in November 2013 to 2%/3.5% and to the current levels of 1.75%/3.25% in March 2015. Note that despite the model being defined in real terms, it can be shown with simple algebra that the deeming rates shall not be adjusted to 'real' deeming rates.

where L_{I}^{d} is the threshold for the income-test and ϖ_{I}^{d} the taper rate for income exceeding the threshold. Function $P_{\mathrm{D}}(W_t)$ calculates the deemed income, where κ_d is the deeming threshold, and ς_- and ς_+ are the deeming rates that apply to assets below and above the deeming threshold, respectively.

To model the Age Pension prior to 2015, when the actual withdrawals from Allocated Pension accounts were used for the income-test instead of deeming rates, the P_I function is defined as:

$$P_{\mathrm{I}} := P_{\max}^{d} - (\alpha_t W_t - M(t) - L_{\mathrm{I}}^{d})\varpi_{\mathrm{I}}^{d}, \tag{14}$$

$$M(t) = \frac{W_{t_0}}{e_{t_0}}(1+\widetilde{r})^{t_0-t}, \tag{15}$$

where the function $M(t)$ represents the income-test deduction that was available for accounts opened prior to 2015, e_{t_0} is the lifetime expected at age t_0 and $\widetilde{r}$ the inflation. As the model is defined in real terms, the future income-test deductions must discount inflation. Function parameters are given in Table 1.

2.4. Parameters

The model parameters are taken from Andreasson et al. (2017), where calibration was performed on empirical data from Australian Bureau of Statistics (2011). However, the consumption floor $\bar{c}_d$ and the threshold for luxury bequest a must be adjusted as they represent monetary values. Since the previous model was defined in real terms, we need to set a new base year for the comparison. Therefore, we adjust these parameters based on the Age Pension adjustments from 2010–2016. Currently, the Age Pension payments are adjusted to the higher of the Consumer Price Index (CPI) and Male Average Weekly Total Earnings (MTAWE). The increase in full Age Pension payments from 2010–2016 equals an approximately 4.5% increase per year. We assume that the utility parameters representing monetary values have increased in the same manner. All utility model parameter values are shown in Table 2.

Table 2. Model parameters where monetary values have been adjusted for 2016.

	γ_d	γ_{H}	θ	a	$\bar{c}_d$	ψ	λ	ζ_d
Single household	−1.98	−1.87	0.96	\$27,200	\$13,284	1.18	0.044	1.0
Couples household	−1.78	−1.87	0.96	\$27,200	\$20,607	1.18	0.044	1.3

On 1 January 2017, the thresholds of the asset-test were 'rebalanced', hence changed significantly (Australian Government Department of Veterans' Affairs 2017). The thresholds for the asset-test were increased, and the taper rate ϖ_{A}^{d} doubled. Age Pension parameters do not have to be adjusted other than updating the asset-test thresholds and taper rate according to the changes, as Age Pension payments remained the same. The parameters for the Age Pension for all policies are shown in Table 1. The model will be solved for two different cases of expected returns: a lower real risky return that follows $Z_t \sim \mathcal{N}(0.0325, 0.133)$, which corresponds to an overall portfolio return less than the deeming rate, and a higher real risky return that follows $Z_t \sim \mathcal{N}(0.06, 0.133)$ to generate a portfolio return equal to or above the deeming rate. We are using the standard deviation from yearly returns in S&P/ASX200 Total Return and the deposit rate, both estimated in Andreasson et al. (2017). The real risk-free rate is set to $r_t = 0.005$. While a lower mean return often has lower variance, we are using one variance for both return cases as the comparative results between the policies remains the same. In addition to this, we set the following.

- A retiree is eligible for Age Pension at age $t = 65$ and lives no longer than $T = 100$.
- The lower threshold for housing is set to \$30,000. That is, a retiree with wealth below this level cannot be a homeowner, hence $H \in \{0, [30{,}000, W]\}$.
- A unisex survival probability is used to avoid separating the sexes, as it would add an extra state variable. The survival probabilities for a couple are assumed to be mutually exclusive, based on

the oldest partner in the couple. The actual mortality probabilities are taken from Life Tables published by Australian Bureau of Statistics (2014).

- The subjective discount rate β is set in relation to the real interest rate so that $\beta = e^{-\sum_{i=t}^{t'} r_i}$.

Minimum withdrawal rates for Allocated Pension accounts are shown in Table 3 (Australian Taxation Office 2016). The rates impose a lower bound on optimal consumption; therefore, withdrawals from liquid wealth must be larger or equal to these rates.

Table 3. Minimum regulatory withdrawal rates for Allocated Pension accounts for the year 2017 and onwards (https://www.ato.gov.au/rates/key-superannuation-rates-and-thresholds/?page=10, accessed June 5, 2017).

Age	≤64	65–74	75–79	80–84	85–89	90–94	≤95
Min. drawdown	4%	5%	6%	7%	9%	11%	14%

2.5. Numerical Implementation

The model is solved numerically. By discretising the wealth and house state on a grid of k log-equidistant grid points $W_0, ..., W_k$ and $H_0, ..., H_k$ for each year $t = t_0, ..., T$ and by writing Equation (6) as a Bellman equation, the problem is solved recursively with backward induction. The lower bound of the grid is set to $1; the upper bound H_k is chosen to equal total wealth W; and the upper bound W_k is chosen large enough so that values close to the upper bound have no material effect on the range of wealth in the analysis. Extrapolation is therefore less important when integrating risky returns, and the interpolation between grid points is done with the shape-preserving Piecewise Cubic Hermite Interpolation Polynomial (PCHIP) method, which preserves the monotonicity and concavity of the value function (Kahaner et al. 1988). The expectation with respect to the stochastic return is calculated with the Gauss–Hermite quadrature using five nodes. For each grid point in the wealth and house state, optimal drawdown proportions α_t and risky asset allocation δ_t are found using a two-dimensional optimisation. For a more detailed description of the numerical solution, see Andreasson et al. (2017).

3. Results

The model is solved each year, with respect to optimal decisions for each policy and expected return and for each combination of single/couple and homeowners/non-homeowner households. The income-test changes in POST2015 lead to some interesting implications for the retirees in all three decision variables (housing, consumption and risky asset allocation), due to the assets now being included twice in the means-test.

3.1. Optimal Consumption

The optimal consumption consists of the drawdown from liquid wealth and the Age Pension received and exemplifies a behaviour consistent with traditional utility models. Figure 1 shows the optimal consumption and drawdown for a given liquid wealth under each of the three policies. The grey areas in the background indicate whether any means-test is binding. As can be seen, only PRE2015 is subject to the size of the drawdown in the income test, while the other policies depend on liquid wealth only. The curve is generally a smooth, concave and monotone function of wealth. The curve becomes flatter as the retiree ages, which is the desired effect from the model's "health" proxy as to reflect the lower consumption resulting from decreasing health. However, this general behaviour starts to deviate as the retiree ages due to the minimum withdrawal rates. For a retiree aged 65 with an account of $500,000, the optimal consumption for a non-homeowner couple under the current (POST2017) policy is roughly 13%, which is more than the minimum withdrawal rate of 5% (Table 3). As the retiree ages, his/her consumption tends to decrease, but around age 85, the minimum withdrawal rates cross over the optimal consumption; hence, the drawdown curve becomes proportional to wealth. This is in line with Bateman et al. (2007), which finds that welfare decreases slightly when minimum withdrawal rules are enforced over unconstrained optimal withdrawals, especially for higher levels of risk aversion. This deviation occurs at an even earlier age for singles and wealthier retirees.

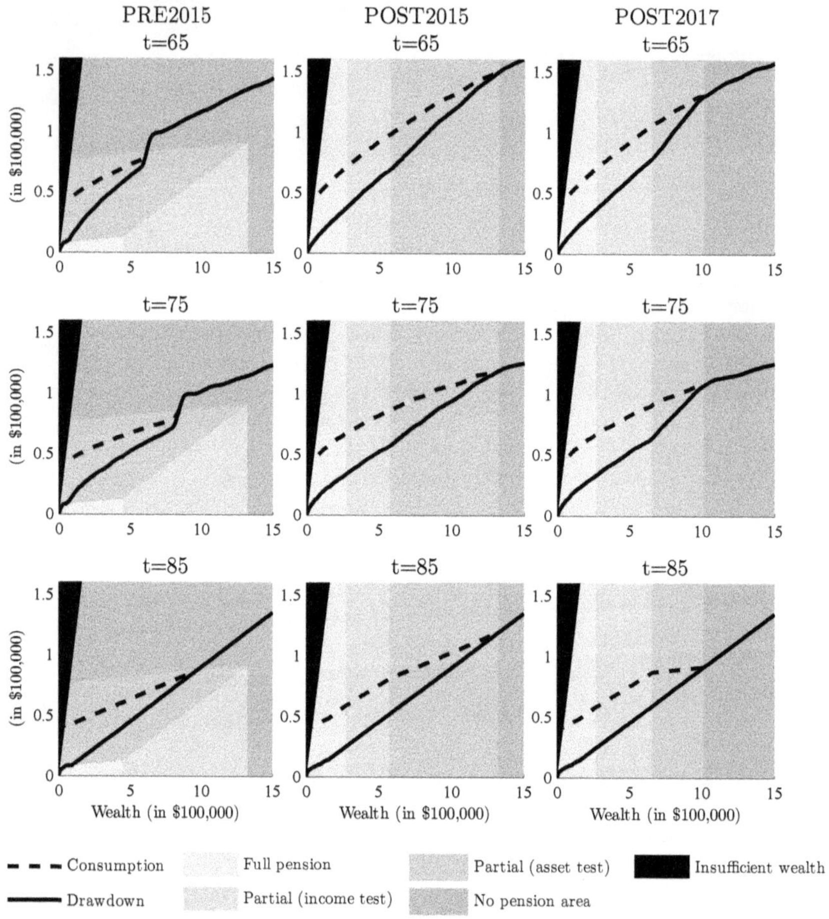

Figure 1. Optimal drawdown and consumption for non-homeowner couple households for a given liquid wealth at the age t, under the three different policy scenarios in the case of low returns ($\mu = 0.0325$).

There are a couple of distinct differences in drawdown behaviour between the policies; however, no apparent differences were identified between homeowner or non-owners or between low and high expected return. Single and couple households had the same behaviour with respect to the means-test thresholds, although at different dollar values. For an illustration of the differences, we therefore only use the case of a couple non-homeowner household. First, consumption is higher for the policies that base the income-test on deeming rates. For a given level of drawdown, deeming rates tend to pay more Age Pension, even for the harsher POST2017 rules. This is because a certain wealth would attract higher penalties in the means-test when drawdown is used, compared to deemed income for the same wealth. Second, the deeming rate-based policies show low-to-no sensitivity to the means-test thresholds, indicating that the retiree can no longer plan their consumption behaviour to optimise Age Pension payments. This is in contrast to PRE2015, which shows that drawdown was highly sensitive to the means-test and could be utilised in financial planning (Andreasson et al. 2017). There is a marginal effect when the retiree goes from no Age Pension to receiving partial Age Pension, especially for the 2017 asset-test adjustment, shown as a tiny dent where the consumption and drawdown curve intersect (the threshold between no pension and partial pension due to asset-test). This implies that a retiree should consume slightly more when his/her wealth is close to this threshold in order to receive partial Age Pension, but the additional utility would be so small that it is negligible in planning. The same behaviour can be expected to occur when the income-test binds over the asset-test (the threshold between partial pension due to income-test and asset-test), which can be seen as a slight change in the drawdown curve due to different taper rates for the partial Age Pension, but no apparent effect is identified in the consumption.

Although the low and high expected return had no effect on optimal drawdown, it does have a significant effect over the lifespan of a retiree. Figures 2 and 3 show the consumption and wealth paths over time for the low and high expected return respectively, as well as the Age Pension payments. The zigzag pattern in the consumption is due to the minimum withdrawal rates, which increase every five years and start to bind around age 75. The higher return leads to a flatter wealth path initially, irrespective of policy, while it is declining steadily for the lower return. The level of consumption shows a similar shape in both graphs, declining early in retirement, but increasing later on due to minimum withdrawals. The consumption is significantly higher with the higher expected return (due to a higher level of wealth) and even exceeds the initial consumption. As indicated in Figure 1, consumption also tends to be higher for the deeming rate policies, even if the wealth decumulation is in line with PRE2015. These characteristics are all expected in the model, but the interesting part is the effect that the policies and expected return have on Age Pension payments. As wealth paths throughout retirement are almost identical, the difference in consumption is mainly due to additional Age Pension under the newer policies. Even if the pension function for POST2017 seems to results in less Age Pension for higher levels of wealth (see Figure 4), in practice, this is not the case. The PRE2015 policy penalizes drawdown very hard and leads to significantly less Age Pension over all. As the minimum withdrawal rate increases with age, the difference in partial Age Pension increases, as well. The POST2015 policy leads to a larger amount of Age Pension at (almost) all times, and the retiree is still better off with PRE2017 despite having a more aggressive taper rate. If the deeming rates are lower than the return on assets, the retiree will receive more Age Pension towards the end of his.her retirement. Even so, the minimum withdrawal at this point would be high enough that any additional Age Pension received would still not increase the consumption. It is only for less wealthy households that deeming rates have an effect on the Age Pension payments throughout retirement, but even for these households, the minimum withdrawal rates bind around age 75; hence, they will have less additional utility in terms of consumption.

One of the reasons for changing the policy was for the government to generate savings, but the deeming rules will not have the desired outcome on Allocated Pension accounts unless the deeming rates increase. Even in the case where returns are less than the deeming rates, the retiree is better off than before as deemed income in the means-test will be less than actual drawdown early in retirement. As a result, the retiree will receive more Age Pension for a given level of wealth than before. Only when the minimum withdrawals are removed (or at least decreased), which in turn could lead to lower withdrawals for given wealth levels, could current rates lead to Age Pension payments being less under the new policy[11]. Under the PRE2015 policy, the relatively high drawdown for the retiree would most often lead to no Age Pension due to the income-test, while under the deeming rate-based policies, the retiree would receive a significant amount of Age Pension throughout retirement.

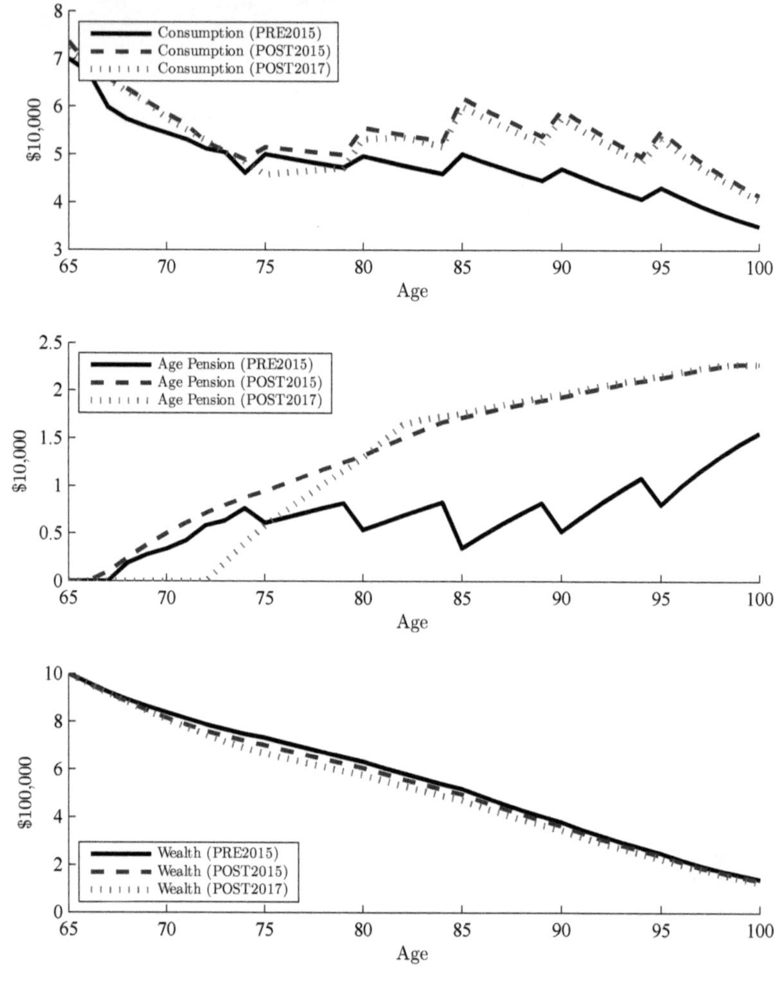

Figure 2. Comparison of consumption, Age Pension and wealth over a retiree's lifetime with the three different policy scenarios. The retiree starts with $1m liquid wealth, which grows with the low expected return each year ($\mu = 0.0325$), and drawdown follows the optimal drawdown paths under each policy.

[11] It should be noted that the findings are for the account-based pension only, as other products that do not enforce the minimum withdrawal rates could incur additional savings for the government under the new rules.

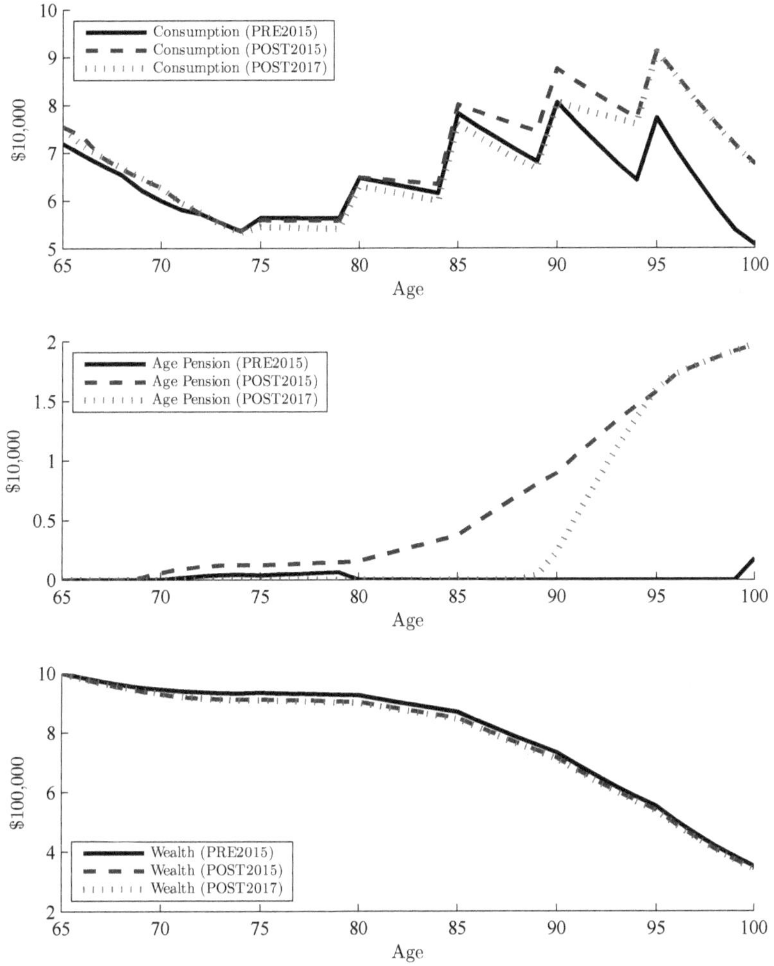

Figure 3. Comparison of consumption, Age Pension and wealth over a retiree's lifetime with the three different policy scenarios. The retiree starts with $1m liquid wealth, which grows with the high expected return each year (μ = 0.06), and drawdown follows the optimal drawdown paths under each policy.

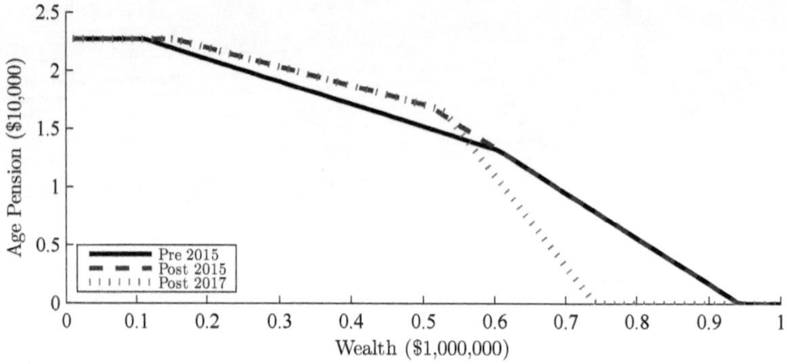

Figure 4. Comparison of the Age Pension function with the three policy scenarios, based on a single household aged 65–74 and where consumption is assumed to be the minimum withdrawal rate of 5%.

3.2. Optimal Risky Asset Allocation

The risky allocation displays similar characteristics in all policies and is essentially the same for homeowners and non-homeowners, but differs between singles and couples. The level of expected returns does not result in any difference in the shape of the risky asset allocation surface, but it does affect the average allocation. Figure 5 shows the optimal risky allocation given age and liquid wealth. A higher expected return leads to a higher overall allocation to risky assets, but the comparatively darker and lighter areas remain the same. High or low deeming rates have no observable effect on risky asset allocation. The exposure to risky assets in the portfolio is however highly dependent on wealth and age, and even more so compared to PRE2015. This is expected since the means-test is now based on wealth in both the asset and the income-test, which means investment returns will have a larger impact on expected utility.

The optimal allocation surface is characterised by the expected marginal utility from the consumption and bequest utility. The black bottom area to the left (Figure 5) suggests 100% allocation to risky assets for low levels of wealth, where the upper bound of the area corresponds to maximum margin utility from the consumption function . The upper bound to the right is the maximum marginal utility from bequest, which occurs at a higher level than for consumption ($\sim$ $450,000). Up to these levels, it is therefore optimal to allocate 100% to risky assets, as the reward is larger than the risk as a result of the 'buffer' effect. This buffer occurs when the decreasing wealth that stems from an investment loss is partially offset via increased Age Pension and can be seen as the comparatively darker area towards the top left (indicating where partial pension becomes no pension) in Figure 5. The buffer effect is, therefore, strongest for a retiree who has no Age Pension, but is close to receiving partial Age Pension. An investment loss, in this instance, would be offset by partial Age Pension, whereas an investment profit would not cause the retiree to miss out on Age Pension that he/she would otherwise receive. The taper rate is steeper for the asset-test than the income-test (especially for POST2017); hence, marginal utility is lower when the asset-test is binding and results in a higher contrast surface. For very low levels of wealth, the buffer effect is the opposite; investment losses can never lead to more than full Age Pension, and investment profits will decrease the amount of partial Age Pension received. Again, this is especially present in POST2017 and can be seen as the comparatively whiter area towards the bottom left.

Another interesting effect occurs as the minimum withdrawal rates cross above unconstrained optimal drawdown. When the retiree is forced to withdraw more from his/her account than is optimal to consume, the marginal utility drops significantly. This occurs approximately at age 75 for both single and couple households, although slightly later for less wealthy households. The marginal utility received from consumption is essentially zero after this age. Thus, the utility consists of an increasingly larger proportion of bequest as the retiree ages (and mortality risk increases). This switch occurs where the bottom black area starts to increase towards the right, as it moves from utility from consumption to utility from bequest. Once the minimum withdrawal rates exceed the non-constrained optimal drawdown, the different policies become nearly identical as minimum withdrawal rates bind. The difference is therefore only for the initial years of retirement, ages 65–80, due to the way the income-test is constructed. In regard to POST2017, the buffer feature is slightly stronger owing to the steeper taper rate, but the characteristics are similar to the other policies.

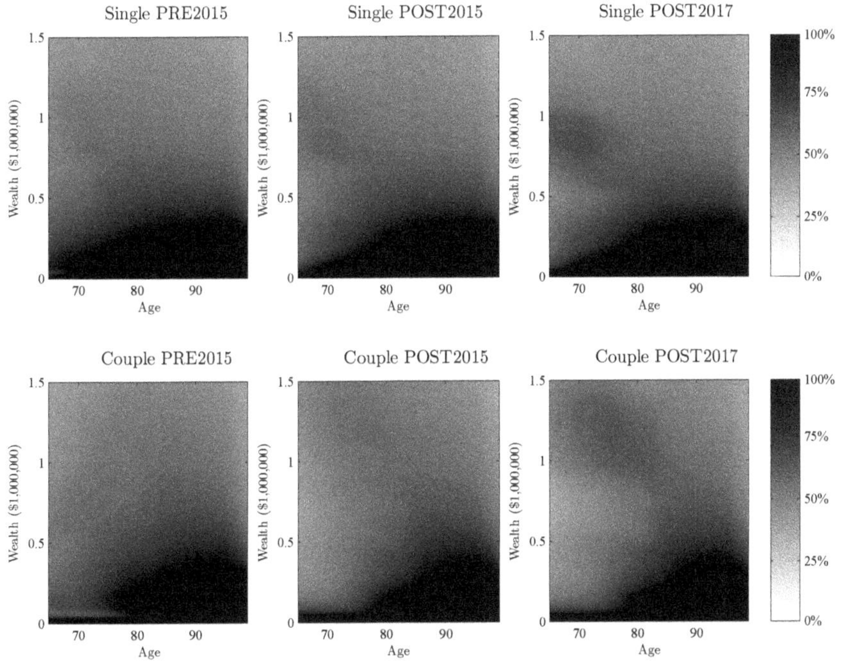

Figure 5. Optimal risky allocation for non-homeowner single and couple household, under each policy, given the low expected return (μ = 0.0325).

3.3. *Optimal Housing Allocation*

The decision variable for the allocation of assets into a family home is expected to change slightly due to the increased focus on assets in the means-test. With respect to expected returns and deeming rate levels, however, the optimal allocation is unchanged. The decision made at the time of retirement shows that under the newer policy rules (POST2015, POST2017), it is optimal to invest marginally less than under PRE2015, up to a total wealth level of approximately $735,000 for single households and $1,155,000 for couple households (see Figure 6). This would leave approximately $144,000 and $247,000 respectively as liquid wealth. Households with total wealth above this level, meanwhile, are recommended to invest slightly more. These allocation decisions leave liquid wealth just below the thresholds for receiving full Age Pension, and the difference in the housing curves can be explained by the income-test changes. For a given wealth, the deeming rate-based policies provide the retiree with more partial pension than with PRE2015. Early in retirement, the optimal consumption is high, which causes the income-test to bind under the PRE2015 policy. The deemed income is much lower than drawdowns, which ultimately results in more partial Age Pension. Since a certain level of liquid wealth under the POST2015 and POST2017 policies will lead to higher expected utility, it is optimal to allocate slightly more to housing (as long as the liquid wealth is not very low) to benefit from receiving additional partial Age Pension. The effects of POST2017 are only marginally larger than POST2015; thus, the steeper taper rates do not impact the housing allocation decision materially.

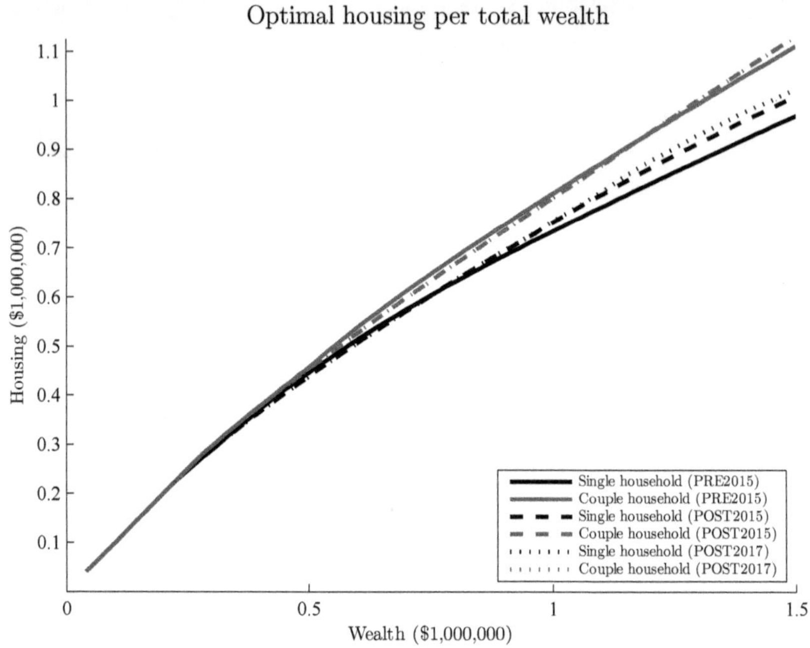

Figure 6. Optimal housing allocation given by total wealth W for single and couple households, under the three policy scenarios with the low return ($\mu = 0.0325$).

3.4. Limitations

The analysis is dependent on the assumptions made in the model. The optimal controls show very low sensitivity to many of the assumptions, such as the choice of process for risky returns and constant house value in real terms. While the overall shape of the risky asset allocation surface (see Figure 5) remains the same given alternative return distributions and volatility, the average level of risky asset allocation increases with risky return and decreases with volatility. The model is more sensitive to the relation between risk aversion parameters than to the absolute vale of any parameter. Most of the main characteristics in the results, such as decreasing sensitivity to the means-test with age and binding minimum withdrawal rates, do not change given slightly different utility parameters or levels of return. The absolute levels are, however, subject to parametrisation and will differ for each individual. Since the calibration of the model in Andreasson et al. (2017) was shown to fit the empirical data for Australian retirees well, we believe that this analysis can reflect the general behaviour of Australian retirees and at least provide important insights into the effects from different Age Pension policies.

We acknowledge that there might be models more suitable to explain the individual behaviour in retirement. By basing the model on the standard utility theory, it is possible that the preferences of the retirees are not properly captured even if the model is well calibrated to data. Risk averse utility functions tend to be concave, but micro economics suggests that the true utility curve is S-shaped.

We use the standard utility theory as we can calibrate this model using the available empirical data. However, the model can benefit from being extended with stochastic dominance theory (Kopa et al. 2016; Levy 2006) or prospect theory (Kahneman and Tversky 1979), in order to avoid the inherent limitations of the standard utility theory. This is the subject of future research.

4. Conclusions

In this paper, we adapt the expected utility life cycle model from Andreasson et al. (2017) to account for the Age Pension policy changes in Australia since 2015, including the new steeper taper rates for the asset-test in force since 2017. These changes apply to all Allocated Pension accounts opened after 1st of January 2015 and affect the treatment of income for the Age Pension income-test, which leads to different optimal decisions for consumption, investments and housing. In addition, we also evaluate the effect of the deeming rate levels in relation to portfolio returns.

We find that optimal consumption only applies early in retirement, as minimum withdrawal rates exceed unconstrained optimal drawdown rates for ages 75–85, depending on wealth level. While it is possible to plan withdrawals for maximum utility prior to this point, these possibilities are almost non-existent under the deeming rate-based policies compared with the previous drawdown-based policy. Optimal drawdown equals minimum withdrawal after age 85 (as it becomes a binding lower constraint for withdrawal); thus, the policies are identical after this age. That said, since the income-test tends to bind for the old rules while the asset-test dominates for the new rules, the retiree will now receive more partial pension throughout retirement. Even with the steeper taper rate introduced January 2017, the retiree can consume more while drawing down less assets, thanks to a more generous Age Pension compared.

Since income (which was considered as drawdown from the Allocated Pension account before 2015) is now replaced by deemed income, the assets are means-tested twice, resulting in the risky asset allocation becoming more sensitive. The changes in optimal risky asset allocation over time and wealth are similar under all policies, but the changes are more aggressive with the steeper 2017 taper rates. This is due to the marginal utility from consumption and bequest, which has increased due to the taper rate, as well as the level of buffering against investment losses the Age Pension provides. This effect is only present in the first part of retirement and dies off as the minimum withdrawal rates bind where the bequest motive becomes more important.

It is optimal to invest slightly more in housing under the deeming rate-based policies, provided that the retiree's remaining liquid wealth is close to (or higher) than the threshold between full and partial Age Pension at the time of retirement. This will allow the retiree to receive more partial Age Pension and to increase his/her expected utility in the long term. If the retiree instead has lower total wealth than the threshold, he/she is alternatively recommended to invest marginally less than before.

With respect to higher and lower expected risky asset returns and high and low deeming rates in relation to the expected returns, optimal decisions tend to be very robust. Neither optimal drawdown, deeming rates nor housing allocating showed sensitivity to the expected return. Risky asset allocation, on the other hand, adjusts the average allocation based on expected return, but does not change in relation to the deeming rates. It is important to put all decisions in context, however, in order to understand how high and low returns and deeming rates affect the retiree. Even if optimal drawdown for a given wealth remains constant, the additional Age Pension received from lower deeming rates can increase the overall consumption. However, this tends to occur later in retirement where higher consumption is not as common; hence, the retiree is only marginally better off.

One surprising finding is that a retiree with an income stream where minimum withdrawal rules are enforced will receive more Age Pension over the course of his/her lifetime with the deeming rate-based policies. Due to the minimum withdrawal requirement, the drawdown tends to be higher than what is optimal for most ages, which under the drawdown-based rules would result in no or low partial Age Pension. The deeming rate-based policies will generate significant Age Pension payments from the same drawdown and wealth levels, irrespective of whether the deeming rates are high or low in relation to returns. This makes the government's goal to reduce the budget difficult to reach. As the retiree is less sensitive to deeming rates than minimum withdrawal rates, our simulations suggest that both the retiree and the government would be better off by lowering the minimum withdrawal rates rather than the deeming rates. However, the goal of reducing incentives for maximising Age Pension payments and focusing on maximising total disposable income is met: the deeming rate based policies are not as sensitive to optimal withdrawal decisions in order to maximise Age Pension payments as the old policy was. The possibility of planning decisions around the means-test has therefore moved from optimal consumption to optimal risky asset allocation, owing to the steeper taper rates.

The analysis can easily be extended to suit the defined-contribution pension system in other countries by adjusting the Age Pension function and necessary constraints and assumptions. This would allow for a comparative analysis between Australia's Age Pension and similar countries or evaluating a specific means-tested pension policy individually. A particularly interesting case would be the comparison with the U.S. pension systems. The assumptions for the Allocated Pension account need to be adjusted to match those of an 'Individual Retirement Account' or 401(k)[12], and the Age Pension needs to be replaced with the Supplemental Security Income and its associated means-test function. Thus, investigating other policies globally will be a subject for future research.

Acknowledgments: This research was supported by the CSIRO -Monash Superannuation Research Cluster, a collaboration among CSIRO, Monash University, Griffith University, the University of Western Australia, the University of Warwick and stakeholders of the retirement system in the interest of better outcomes for all. Pavel Shevchenko acknowledges the support of Australian Research Council's Discovery Projects funding scheme (Project Number DP160103489).

Author Contributions: All authors contributed equally to this research work by providing new ideas, writing the paper, discussing existing results and sharing their knowledge in this field. Numerical calculations were performed by Johan Andreasson.

Conflicts of Interest: The authors declare no conflict of interest.

References

Andreasson, Johan G., Pavel V. Shevchenko, and Alex Novikov. 2017. Optimal Consumption, Investment and Housing with Means-tested Public Pension in Retirement. *Insurance Mathematics and Economics* 75: 32–47.

Australian Bureau of Statistics. 2011. Household Expenditure Survey and Survey of Income and Housing Curf Data. Available online: http://www.abs.gov.au/ausstats/abs@.nsf/mf/6503.0 (accessed on 6 June 2014).

Australian Bureau of Statistics. 2014. 3302.0.55.001 - Life Tables, States, Territories and Australia, 2012–2014. Available online: http://www.abs.gov.au/ausstats/abs@.nsf/mf/3302.0.55.001 (accessed on 4 November 2014).

Australian Government Department of Veterans' Affairs. 2017. Rebalanced Assets Test to Apply from 2017. Available online: http://www.dva.gov.au/rebalanced-assets-test-apply-2017/ (accessed on 19 January 2017).

Australian Taxation Office. 2016. Minimum Annual Payments for Super Income Streams. Available online: https://www.ato.gov.au/rates/key-superannuation-rates-and-thresholds/ (accessed on 27 October 2016).

Bateman, Hazel, Susan Thorp, and Geoffrey Kingston. 2007. Financial engineering for Australian annuitants. In *Retirement Provision in Scary Markets*, 1st ed. Edited by Hazel Bateman. Northampton: Edward Elgar Publishing, pp. 123–44.

Blake, David, Douglas Wright, and Yumeng Zhang. 2014. Age-dependent investing: Optimal funding and investment strategies in defined contribution pension plans when members are rational life cycle financial planners. *Journal of Economic Dynamics and Control* 38: 105–24.

Boender, G. C., P. C. van Aalst, and F. Heemskerk. 1997. *Modelling & Management of Assets & Liabilities of Pension Plans in the Netherlands.* Rotterdam: Erasmus University Rotterdam.

---

[12] A 401(k) is a defined-contribution retirement savings plan sponsored by the employer.

Cocco, João, and Francisco. Gomes. 2012. Longevity risk, retirement savings, and financial innovation. *Journal of Financial Economics* 103: 507–29.

Cocco, João, Francisco Gomes, and Pascal Maenhout. 2005. Consumption and portfolio choice over the life cycle. *Review of Financial Studies* 18: 491–533.

Department of Social Services. 2017. Guides to Social Policy Law. Available online: http://guides.dss.gov.au/guide-social-security-law (accessed on 4 January 2017).

Ding, Jie 2014. Essays on Post-Retirement Financial Planning and Pension Policy Modelling in Australia. Ph.D. Dissertation, Macquarie University, Sydney, Australia.

Ding, Jie, Geoffrey Kingston, and Sachi Purcal. 2014. Dynamic asset allocation when bequests are luxury goods. *Journal of Economic Dynamics and Control* 38: 65–71.

Dupačová, Jitka, and Jan Polívka. 2009. Asset-liability management for Czech pension funds using stochastic programming. *Annals of Operations Research* 165: 5–28.

Fisher, Lance 1930. *The Theory of Interest: As Determined by Impatience to Spend Income and Opportunity to Invest it* (1 ed.). New York: The Macmillan Company.

Henry, Ken 2009. Australia's Future Tax System—Report to the Treasurer (Overview). Technical Report December, Commonwealth of Australia. Available online: http://taxreview.treasury.gov.au/content/downloads/ (accessed on 20 April 2017).

Hilli, Petri, Matti Koivu, Teemu Pennanen, and Antero Ranne. 2007. A stochastic programming model for asset liability management of a Finnish pension company. *Annals of Operations Research* 152: 115–39.

Hulley, Hardy, Rebecca Mckibbin, Andreas Pedersen, and Susan Thorp. 2013. Means-Tested Public Pensions, Portfolio Choice and Decumulation in Retirement. *Economic Record* 89: 31–51.

Iskhakov, Fedor, Susan Thorp, and Hazel Bateman. 2015. Optimal Annuity Purchases for Australian Retirees. *Economic Record* 91: 139–54.

Kahaner, David, Cleve Moler, Stephen Nash, and George Forsythe. 1988. *Numerical Methods and Software*. Upper Saddle River: Prentice Hall.

Kahneman, Daniel, and Amos Tversky. 1979. Prospect Theory: An Analysis of Decision under Risk. *Econometrica* 47: 263–92.

Kopa, Miloš, Vittorio Moriggia, and Sebastino Vitali. 2016. Individual optimal pension allocation under stochastic dominance constraints. *Annals of Operations Research* 14: 1–37.

KPMG. 2010. KPMG Econtech CGE Analysis of the Current Australian Tax System. Technical Report March. Available online: https://www.cpaaustralia.com.au (accessed on 17 September 2016).

Levy, Haim 2006. *Investment Decision Making under Uncertainty*, 2nd ed. Dordrecht: Springer.

Lockwood, Lee 2014. Incidental Bequests: Bequest Motives and the Choice to Self-Insure Late-Life Risks. NBER Working Paper No. 20745. doi:10.3386/w20745.

Merton, Robert 1969. Lifetime Portfolio Selection Under Uncertainty: The Continuous Time Case. *Review of Economics and Statistics* 51: 247–57.

Merton, Robert 1971. Optimum consumption and portfolio rules in a continuous-time model. *Journal of Economic Theory* 3: 373–413.

Modigliani, Franco, and Richard Brumberg. 1954. Utility Analysis and the Consumption Function: An Interpretation of Cross-Section Data. In *Post Keynesian Economics*. Edited by Kenneth K. Kurihara. London: George Allen & Unwin, pp. 388–436.

Plan For Life. 2016. Report on the Australian Reitrement Income Market. Technical Report, Plan For Life. Available online: http://www.pflresearch.com.au (accessed on 3 April 2016).

Rice Warner. 2015. Quo Vadis? Superannuation needs effective policy...not politics. *Submission to Tax White Paper Task Force*. Available online: http://ricewarner.com/wp-content/uploads/2015/07/Tax-White-Paper.pdf (accessed on 20 April 2017).

Samuelson,Paul 1969. Lifetime portfolio selection by dynamic stochastic programming. *The Review of Economics and Statistics* 51: 239–46.

Shevchenko, Pavel V. 2016. *Analysis of Withdrawals From Self-Managed Super Funds Using Australian Taxation Office Data*. CSIRO Technical Report EP164438. Canberra: CSIRO Australia.

Spicer, Alexandra, Olena Stavrunova, and Susan Thorp. 2016. How Portfolios Evolve after Retirement: Evidence from Australia. *Economic Record* 92: 241–67.

The Commonwealth of Australia. 2015. Budget 2015 Overview. Technical Report. Available online: http://www.budget.gov.au (accessed on 1 October 2014).

Vitali, Sebastino, Vittorio Moriggia, and Miloš Kopa. 2017. Optimal pension fund composition for an Italian private pension plan sponsor. *Computational Management Science* 14: 135–60.

Yaari, Menahem 1964. On the consumer's lifetime allocation process. *International Economic Review* 5: 304–17.

Yaari, Menahem 1965. Uncertain Lifetime, Life Insurance, and the Theory of the Consumer. *The Review of Economic Studies* 32: 1–137.

MDPI
St. Alban-Anlage 66
4052 Basel, Switzerland
Tel. +41 61 683 77 34
Fax +41 61 302 89 18
http://www.mdpi.com

Risks Editorial Office
E-mail: risks@mdpi.com
http://www.mdpi.com/journal/risks

www.ingramcontent.com/pod-product-compliance
Lightning Source LLC
Chambersburg PA
CBHW051839210326
41597CB00033B/5704